Books are to be returned on or before
the last date below.

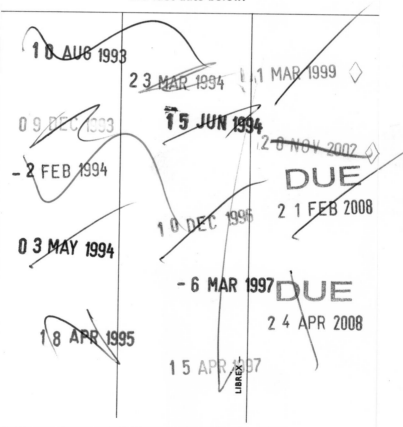

Discontinuity Analysis for Rock Engineering

Discontinuity Analysis for Rock Engineering

STEPHEN D. PRIEST
Professor and Head of Mining Engineering,
University of South Australia

CHAPMAN & HALL
London · Glasgow · New York · Tokyo · Melbourne · Madras

Published by Chapman & Hall, 2–6 Boundary Row, London SE1 8HN

Chapman & Hall, 2–6 Boundary Row, London SE1 8HN, UK

Blackie Academic & Professional, Wester Cleddens Road, Bishopbriggs, Glasgow G64 2NZ, UK

Chapman & Hall Inc., 29 West 35th Street, New York NY10001, USA

Chapman & Hall Japan, Thomson Publishing Japan, Hirakawacho Nemoto Building, 6F, 1-7-11 Hirakawa-cho, Chiyoda-ku, Tokyo 102, Japan

Chapman & Hall Australia, Thomas Nelson Australia, 102 Dodds Street, South Melbourne, Victoria 3205, Australia

Chapman & Hall India, R. Seshadri, 32 Second Main Road, CIT East, Madras 600 035, India

First edition 1993

© 1993 Stephen D. Priest

Typeset in 10/12pt Plantin by Best-set Typesetter Ltd., Hong Kong
Printed in Great Britain by St Edmundsbury Press Ltd, Burg St Edmunds, Suffolk

ISBN 0 412 47600 2

A catalogue record for this book is available from the British Library

Library of Congress Cataloging-in-Publication data

Priest, S. D. (Stephen Donald), 1950–
     Discontinuity analysis for rock engineering/Stephen D. Priest.
1st ed.
     p.   cm.
     Includes bibliographical references (p.   ) and index.
     ISBN 0-412-47600-2 (alk. paper)
     1. Rock mechanics.   2. Strains and stresses — Mathematical models.
I. Title.
TA706.P73   1993
624.1'5132 — dc20
                                                    92-27172
                                                    CIP

For Rosie, Robert and David
and for my brother Peter

Contents

Appendices

Preface and acknowledgements

The idea of writing this book was developed by the Author and Professor John Hudson in 1985 as a culmination of many years of collaborative research and publication in the area of discontinuity analysis. The Author moved to Australia in 1986 and John Hudson took on additional responsibilities associated with the publication of the major work *Comprehensive Rock Engineering*, so progress was delayed for some years. In 1989 pressure of work forced Professor Hudson to withdraw from the project, leaving the Author to write the book alone.

The aim of this book is to open up a relatively new area of rock mechanics by gathering together principles and analytical methods that have previously been distributed between journal papers, conference proceedings and more general text books. The book does not pretend to be the final word on the topic but rather seeks to set out basic ideas that can be built upon by others. The book is directed towards 3rd and 4th year undergraduate students studying civil, mining and geological engineering and to Master's students pursuing postgraduate coursework in rock mechanics, soil mechanics, engineering geology, hydro(geo)logy and related subjects. Most of the analytical sections and examples require only an elementary knowledge of mathematics, statistics and mechanics, to about 1st year undergraduate level. Appendices have been included to help readers with the basic principles of stereographic projection, statistics, probability theory, rock mass classification and the analysis of forces and stresses in three dimensions. In all writing there is personal style and bias. The over-riding desire to make explanations clear and unambiguous has lead, at times, to a somewhat 'clinical' style that may create the false impression that the subject of discontinuity analysis is cut and dried.

The reader can quickly dispel this impression by visiting a fractured rock face and attempting to characterise the three-dimensional rock structure.

A portion of the text is based on original research conducted by Hudson and Priest published in the *International Journal of Rock Mechanics and Mining Sciences*, other journals and conference proceedings between 1976 and 1985. Some of the examples and exercises were developed for a course on Rock Structure given by the author to MSc students at Imperial College between 1977 and 1986. During this time the author benefitted from guidance and encouragement given by Barry Brady, John Bray, Ted Brown, Christine Cooling, John Hudson and John Watson. Research and writing during this period for parts of Chapters 3 to 6 and Chapter 11 was supported by research grants from the Transport and Road Research Laboratory and the Building Research Establishment, Department of the Environment and Transport (UK).

The bulk of the writing and literature research work was done while the Author was a Senior Lecturer in Geotechnical Engineering at The University of Adelaide between 1986 and 1990. A substantial portion of Chapter 3 is based on the author's contribution to Volume 3 of *Comprehensive Rock Engineering* and is used here with the permission of the publishers, Pergamon Press. The Author acknowledges support and advice given by Graeme Dandy, Michael Griffith, Anthony Meyers, Angus Simpson, George Sved and Bob Warner of the Department of Civil Engineering, Keith Preston of BHP, and Peter Warburton of CSIRO during this period. Portions of Chapters 9 and 10 are based on research conducted jointly by the author and Anthony Meyers, with the support of an Australian Research Council research grant, between 1987 and 1991. Research presented in Chapter 6 was undertaken with the support of funds from the Raw Materials Research Group of BHP. The book was completed while the Author was Professor and Head of the Department of Mining Engineering at the University of South Australia from February 1991 onwards. The Author is grateful for assistance given by Peter Cotton, Rhonda Porter, David Stapledon and Bruce Webb of the University of South Australia, Michael Humphreys and Neville Moxon of BHP Raw Materials Research Group, Randolph Klemm of Penrice Quarry Products, and David Walker during this final period. Finally the Author acknowledges the assistance given by Roger Jones during the early stages, Susan Boobis during the copy-edit and by Ruth Cripwell, Helen Heyes and Sharon Donaghy of Chapman & Hall during the later stages of production of the book.

The text was drafted using Microsoft Word on Macintosh SE30, Macintosh IIsi and Macintosh LC computers. The equations were drafted using Prescience Expressionist, spreadsheet calculations were conducted with Microsoft Excel, and software development was undertaken in Think Pascal.

Foreword

Engineers wishing to build structures on or in rock use the discipline known as rock mechanics. This discipline emerged as a subject in its own right about thirty five years ago, and has developed rapidly ever since. However, rock mechanics is still based to a large extent on analytical techniques that were originally formulated for the mechanical design of structures made from man-made materials. The single most important distinction between man-made materials and the natural material rock is that rock contains fractures, of many kinds on many scales; and because the fractures — of whatever kind — represent breaks in the mechanical continuum, they are collectively termed 'discontinuities'.

An understanding of the mechanical influence of these discontinuities is essential to all rock engineers. Most of the world is made of rock, and most of the rock near the surface is fractured. The fractures dominate the rock mass geometry, deformation modulus, strength, failure behaviour, permeability, and even the local magnitudes and directions of the *in situ* stress field. Clearly, an understanding of the presence and mechanics of the discontinuities, both singly and in the rock mass context, is therefore of paramount importance to civil, mining and petroleum engineers. Bearing this in mind, it is surprising that until now there has been no book dedicated specifically to the subject of discontinuity analysis in rock engineering. Naturally, many of the books on rock mechanics and rock engineering do cover different aspects of the influence of discontinuities, but none in such a coherent and comprehensive manner as Professor Priest's latest book.

His earlier monograph, 'Hemispherical Projection Methods in Rock Mechanics', published in 1985 is a model of clarity, demonstrating the ability that Professor Priest has of transferring the lucidity of his logical thinking into 'user-friendly' book form. This new book, covering the much wider subject of discontinuity analysis, is an even more persuasive demonstration of these powers: everything is clearly laid out, presented and explained. Anyone involved with rock engineering — from clients to consultants to contractors to students to researchers to teachers — should be aware of the contents of this book.

Readers of the reference section will note that four papers co-authored by Professor Priest and myself are included. These reflect at least a decade of co-operative research between us; indeed, we both regard these papers as major steps in our own understanding of discontinuity occurrence. Thus, from direct personal experience, I should like to record in this Preface the very significant contribution that Professor Priest has made to discontinuity analysis. There was a possibility at one time that the book might have been written by both of us. I am pleased to discover now that the book is at least as good, if not better, than if I had been a co-author!

For all these reasons, the book has my unqualified recommendation.

J. A. Hudson
Professor of Rock Engineering
Imperial College of Science, Technology & Medicine
University of London
UK

List of tables

1

Introduction to discontinuities

1.1 INTRODUCTION

This book is concerned with the analysis of discontinuities for rock engineering applications. Before proceeding with a discussion of the aims and scope, it is worth taking some time to explain what is meant by a discontinuity and to consider why discontinuity analysis can be of practical value to the rock mechanics engineer.

Rock masses usually contain such features as bedding planes, faults, fissures, fractures, joints and other mechanical defects which, although formed from a wide range of geological processes, possess the common characteristics of low shear strength, negligible tensile strength and high fluid conductivity compared with the surrounding rock material. The rather unwieldy term 'discontinuity' was first adopted about 20 years ago by a number of authors (Fookes and Parrish, 1969; Attewell and Woodman, 1971; Priest, 1975; Goodman, 1976) to cover this whole range of mechanical defects while at the same time avoiding any inferences concerning their geological origins.

In this introductory chapter, section 1.2 sets out some of the definitions and principles that are crucial to the understanding of subsequent chapters. Section 1.3 contains descriptions of the various types of discontinuities that have been observed by geologists, together with some brief comments on how these discontinuities may have been formed. Section 1.4 summarises a number of case histories where discontinuities have played a major role in controlling the design or performance of an excavation or engineering structure.

The discontinuity properties that have the greatest influence at the design stage have been listed by Piteau (1970 and 1973) as follows:

1. orientation,
2. size,
3. frequency,
4. surface geometry,
5. genetic type, and
6. infill material.

All of the currently accepted design methods for foundations, slopes and underground excavations require information on discontinuities in one form or another (Obert and Duvall, 1967; Goodman, 1976; Hoek and Bray, 1981; Priest and Brown, 1983; Brady and Brown, 1985). An unfavourably orientated extensive discontinuity, or group of discontinuities, adjacent to a rock face subject to low stress levels can cause rigid block failures involving sliding, toppling or falling mechanisms, or a combination of these (Warburton, 1981; Priest and Samaniego, 1983; Goodman and Shi, 1985). Discontinuities in zones of high stress adjacent to an underground excavation can provide planes for shear failure and displacement (Hoek and Brown, 1980a; Brady and Brown, 1985). Discontinuity networks can, depending on the orientation and frequency of individual open fractures, provide paths of high permeability through otherwise relatively impermeable rock material (Snow, 1968; Louis, 1974; Long *et al.*, 1985).

This book sets out to bridge the gap between the descriptive methods of the geologist and the analytical methods of the rock mechanics engineer as applied to the measurement and analysis of discontinuity characteristics. The requirement to provide numerical data on discontinuities as input to engineering design calculations has created a need to apply the mathematical methods of probability theory, statistics, vector analysis and mechanics to a topic that has previously been handled in a largely descriptive way. This application of mathematical methods provides the advantages of objectivity and reproducibility but also places limits on the capacity to handle those 'grey' areas that defy quantification even by statistical methods. These grey areas generally arise when a particular characteristic of a rock can be observed but cannot be classified, measured or tested. Up until recently most discontinuity characteristics, including the six listed above, fell into this category to some extent. Advances in testing procedures, sampling methods, rock classification systems and modelling techniques have now reduced the characteristics in this borderline category to such features as discontinuity shape, location, genetic type, mineralogy of infill, weathering and certain aspects of surface geometry.

In the Author's opinion all efforts should be made to analyse discontinuity properties objectively in order to characterise the rock mass mathematically for input to design calculations. It is important that the rock mechanics report contains a description of the sampling methods, sample sizes, the data processing techniques and the assumptions adopted in analysing the particular mechanism or process. Variability and uncertainty can be addressed by adopting appropriate sampling strategies and by applying the principles of statistics and probability. Those properties that cannot be quantified should not interfere with this characterisation process but should be allowed for when discussing and implementing the results of a particular analysis or design exercise. For example, calculations of the stability of a particular wedge failure mechanism may indicate that it has a factor of safety of 1.5, which may be considered acceptable under normal circumstances. Additional qualitative data may indicate, however, that the rock material could be subject to weathering, leading to a reduction in shear strength of the discontinuities over a period of years. In these circumstances a factor of safety of 1.5 may not be regarded as acceptable and modifications in slope geometry may be recommended. In many cases it may be appropriate to adopt a number of different approaches in parallel for analysing a particular problem. For example, support requirements for an underground excavation may be assessed by applying a rock mass strength criterion to the continuum while at the same time analysing the support required to stabilise specific rigid block mechanisms.

The organisation of this book reflects, to a large extent, the list of influential discontinuity properties presented by Piteau (1970). Following a description of discontinuity measurement and data processing techniques in Chapter 2, Chapters 3 to 6 address, in some detail, the topics of discontinuity orientation, frequency, spacing and size. These four chapters present the geometrical, statistical and probabilistic background for the measurement methods discussed in Chapter 2 and also provide background for the applications of discontinuity analysis presented in Chapters 7 to 11. These final chapters apply the theoretical material to five of the major problem areas in discontinuous rock mechanics: the analysis of stresses on discontinuities, the analysis of rigid block mechanisms, and the influence of discontinuities on rock mass deformability, strength and fluid flow. There are five appendices, which support the work in the main part of the book, and which deal with the basic principles of hemispherical projection, statistics, probability density distributions, rock mass classification and the analysis of forces and stresses in three dimensions.

Every effort has been made to present a balanced view of the methods proposed by a wide range of authors up to August 1991. There is, however, an inevitable bias towards work that appears more relevant, that is more widely accepted by others or that is easy to understand and to implement. A conscious effort has been made, as far as possible, to refer only to papers or books that are widely available. This policy has lead to the omission of a number of PhD theses and internal reports that are widely referred to by others but that are difficult to obtain copies of. The following three reference sources have proved to be most valuable for this book: the *International Journal of Rock Mechanics and Mining Sciences and Geomechanics Abstracts*, the *Proceedings of the International Symposium on Rock Joints*, Loen, Norway (1990) and the *Proceedings of the International Conference on Mechanics of Jointed and Faulted*

Rock, Vienna, Austria (1990). Committed readers are urged to refer to copies of these latter two important volumes to obtain an up to date reference source.

A feature of this book is the use of examples within the text to supplement the explanation of principles and analysis techniques. In many cases it has been necessary to quote results to more significant figures than the geological nature of the input data would normally warrant. This practice has been adopted to help readers to check their own solutions without the added complication of round-off errors. These examples are an integral part of the book and should be worked through diligently in order to provide a complete understanding of each subject. A number of exercises are provided at the end of each chapter for those who wish to pursue the subjects further. Most of these exercises are drawn from final year undergraduate examination papers in civil engineering and mining engineering, and from Master's papers in rock mechanics set by the Author over the last 15 years.

All of the important equations have been numbered to assist with reference when the book is used for teaching. No symbol list has been included; instead the meaning of Greek and Roman lettering, and their subscripts, is defined locally and repeatedly within each chapter. Every effort has been made to maintain consistency in symbol use in equations throughout the book and to retain compatibility with published texts. Although several letters such as a, b, i, j, k, *l* and r have been used several times with different meanings, the local definition is always made clear.

The book was written under strict limitations of word count that have made it necessary to curtail many important topics. The book is primarily concerned with discontinuity analysis so minimal attention is paid to the properties of the intact rock material. The chapters dealing with rigid block mechanisms, discontinuity strength, deformability and fluid flow could have been twice the length in order to do justice to these important topics. Geostatistical methods, rock mass classification and the numerical analysis of blocky rock masses have been dealt with relatively cursorily, since these subjects lie beyond the main scope of the book and are dealt with adequately elsewhere. Detailed discussions of dynamic and seismic effects have been omitted, while comments relating to the geological and engineering geological aspects of discontinuities are confined to the last two sections of Chapter 1. Those who wish to pursue these latter topics are advised to consult Blyth and de Freitas (1974) and the book shortly to be published by the Author's colleague, Professor David Stapledon.

Each chapter aims to take the reader from an elementary level to a relatively comprehensive appreciation of a particular topic. Every attempt has been made to strike a balance between explaining first principles for those who are new to the topics and discussing recent developments for more advanced readers. Most sections of the book have been designed to be 'readable' in the sense that a broad appreciation of the topics can be obtained by reading through at a normal technical pace. The more mathematical sections and the examples are rather more demanding and will require a considerable amount of re-reading and cross-referencing, supplemented by notes and additional algebraic derivation.

1.2 DEFINITIONS AND PRINCIPLES

A discontinuity is here defined as **any significant mechanical break or fracture of negligible tensile strength in a rock.** The term discontinuity makes no distinctions concerning the age, geometry or mode of origin of the feature. In many cases it is helpful to distinguish between **natural discontinuities,** which are of geological or geomorphological origin, and **artificial discontinuities** which are created by such activities as drilling, blasting and excavation. The complex three-dimensional structure of discontinuities in a rock is here termed the **discontinuity network** or the **rock structure.** Elements of intact, unfractured rock are referred to as the **rock material,** which, together with the discontinuity network form the *in situ* **rock mass.** The decision as to whether a particular mechanical break is 'significant' must be made subjectively on the basis of specific knowledge of a particular site and in the context of the proposed engineering activity. This requirement generally places a lower limit of between 1 and 100 mm on discontinuity size and excludes such features as pore spaces, micro-cracks and cleavage planes in crystals; such features are here regarded as part of the rock material.

Although discontinuities often have an irregular or curved geometry, there is usually a scale at which the whole surface, or a portion of it, is sufficiently planar to be represented by a single orientation value. Field measurements of orientation are usually taken using a simple compass–clinometer device (Hoek and Bray, 1981). Such a device is designed to take angular measurements, in degrees, of the orientation of a line or plane in three-dimensional space by reference to magnetic north and the horizontal plane. Before proceeding with a discussion of discontinuity characteristics it is necessary to set out some fundamental definitions concerning the orientation of lines and planes in three-dimensional space. Priest (1985) provides a more comprehensive explanation and a diagrammatic illustration of these definitions for those who are new to the subject. In order to facilitate the visualisation of geometrical relationships, angular measurements will be expressed in degrees throughout this and subsequent chapters. In certain circumstances, however, mathematical constraints will require the use of radian measure.

The pair of angles trend and plunge provide a measure of the orientation of a line in three-dimensional space as follows:

Plunge, β ($-90° \leqslant \beta \leqslant 90°$) This is the acute angle measured in a vertical plane between a given line and the horizontal plane. A line directed below the horizontal is here described as having a **downward sense** and is taken to have a **positive plunge**; a line directed upwards is described as having an upward sense and is taken to have a negative plunge. The downward-directed (positive) value of plunge will always be taken for lines, such as the normal to a plane, that can have an upward and a downward directed end.

Trend, α $(0° \leqslant \alpha \leqslant 360°)$ This is the geographical azimuth, measured in clockwise rotation from north $(0°)$, of the vertical plane containing the given line. Any vertical plane possesses two geographical azimuth directions, 180° apart; trend is the azimuth that corresponds to the direction of plunge of the line.

The orientation of any line can be recorded unambiguously in terms of its trend α and plunge β in the form of a three digit and a two digit number separated by a slash, with the 'degree' sign omitted. For example 268/31 refers to a line plunging downwards at an angle of 31° towards 268°, and 156/−63 refers to a line plunging upwards at an angle of 63° towards 156°.

A plane can be regarded as an infinite number of coplanar lines radiating from an arbitrary point. The **line of maximum dip** of a non-horizontal plane is the imaginary line whose plunge exceeds that of all other lines in the plane. The trend α_d and the downward plunge β_d of the line of maximum dip of a plane are here referred to as the **dip direction** and the **dip angle** of the plane. Unless stated otherwise, the **orientation of a plane** will always refer to the dip direction and dip angle of the plane because these are the angles that are generally measured in the field. A line that runs at right-angles to a given plane, the **normal to a plane**, will in general have an upward and a downward directed end. Unless stated otherwise the trend α_n and the plunge β_n will refer to the downward directed end of the normal to a given plane. If the dip direction and dip angle α_d/β_d of a plane are known, the trend and plunge of its normal can be found from the following simple expressions

$$\alpha_n = \alpha_d \pm 180° \quad 0 \leqslant \alpha_n \leqslant 360° \tag{1.1}$$

$$\beta_n = 90° - \beta_d \quad 0 \leqslant \beta_d \leqslant 90° \tag{1.2}$$

The trend direction α_s of a horizontal line in a given plane is referred to as the **strike** of the plane. All planes possess two strike directions, 180° apart. In the absence of other over-riding factors, the strike direction in the range 0 to 180° will be quoted as the strike of the plane. For a given plane the strike α_s will lie 90° from α_d and 90° from α_n.

The **pitch** of a given line is the acute angle measured in some specified plane between the line and the strike of the plane. As with plunge, lines directed downwards from the horizontal are taken to have a positive pitch while lines directed upwards have a negative pitch. It is important to record from which end of the strike line the angle of pitch has been measured. For this purpose it is sufficient to record the geographical quadrant (south-west, north-west etc.) rather than the exact azimuth of the strike line. In most cases we will be working with lines of downward plunge which will have positive angles of pitch.

An extensive plane cutting through a rock mass will divide the rock into two

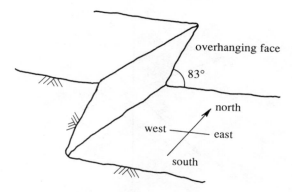

Figure 1.1 Western margin of open pit mine, Example 1.1.

zones or blocks. If the plane is non-vertical, the block that lies directly above the plane will be referred to as the **overhanging block** or the **hangingwall block**; the block that lies directly below the plane will be referred to as the **footwall block**. If the non-vertical plane is a free face, forming the interface between rock and air, then the face is **overhanging** if the rock mass lies above the face and is **non-overhanging** if rock lies below the face.

Example 1.1 (Figure 1.1)

A planar rock face of dip direction/dip angle 261/83 forms the western margin of an open pit mine. Is this face overhanging or non-overhanging?

Solution

If the face forms the western margin of the pit then the rock mass must lie to the west of the face. This face dips steeply towards the west ($261° \approx 270°$) so the rock mass must lie above the face, indicating that the face is overhanging. Figure 1.1 illustrates the geometry of this example.

A valuable graphical technique, referred to as **stereographic** or **hemispherical projection**, for recording and analysing orientation data is described in detail by Priest (1985) and also summarised in Appendix A. This appendix contains a number of simple examples that serve to explain further the definitions and principles presented above. This appendix also explains the determination of angles between coplanar lines and the analysis of intersecting planes.

Many of the operations described later in this book will be conducted by applying the elementary principles of three-dimensional vector algebra, adopting the right-handed Cartesian coordinate system shown in Figure 1.2. In this coordinate system the positive end of the x axis is horizontal to the

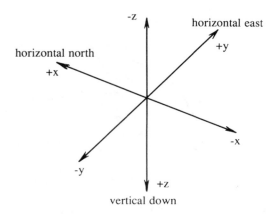

Figure 1.2   Three-dimensional right-handed Cartesian coordinate system, viewed from above.

north (trend 000°), positive y is horizontal to the east (trend 090°) and positive z is vertical down. This coordinate system has been selected to maintain compatibility with the two-dimensional system adopted in Chapter 3 while ensuring that positive z is associated with positive angles of plunge. It is worth noting that this coordinate system is slightly different from the left-handed system adopted by Priest (1985) in which x is east and y is north. Conversion from this left-handed system to the current right-handed system can be achieved simply by swopping x and y on the diagrams and in the associated equations. Any line or vector **u** in three-dimensional space can be represented in the Cartesian system of Figure 1.2 by putting the start point of the line or vector at the origin of the system and then noting the Cartesian coordinates u_x, u_y, u_z of its end point. These coordinates are usually referred to as the Cartesian components of the vector. The length of the line, or the magnitude of the vector, is given by

$$|\mathbf{u}| = \sqrt{u_x^2 + u_y^2 + u_z^2} \tag{1.3}$$

If $|\mathbf{u}| = 1.0$ the vector is referred to as a **unit vector** and u_x, u_y, u_z are its **direction cosines**.

The trend α and plunge β of a line with Cartesian components u_x, u_y and u_z in the system of axes in Figure 1.2 are given by

$$\alpha = \arctan\left(\frac{u_y}{u_x}\right) + Q \tag{1.4}$$

$$\beta = \arctan\left(\frac{u_z}{\sqrt{u_x^2 + u_y^2}}\right) \tag{1.5}$$

Table 1.1 The quadrant parameter Q in equation 1.4

u_x	u_y	Q
$\geqslant 0$	$\geqslant 0$	0
< 0	$\geqslant 0$	180°
< 0	< 0	180°
$\geqslant 0$	< 0	360°

The parameter Q is an angle, in degrees which ensures that α lies in the correct quadrant and in the range 0 to 360°. This parameter, which depends upon the signs of u_x and u_y as listed in Table 1.1, is required because the arc tangent function of most computers and calculators returns a value in the range −90° (corresponding to −ve y) to +90° (corresponding to +ve y). Care must be taken when the denominators in equations 1.4 and 1.5 are zero. In equation 1.4, if $u_x = 0$ and $u_y \geqslant 0$, then α = 90°, while if $u_x = 0$ and $u_y < 0$ then α = 270°. In equation 1.5, a zero denominator means that if $u_z \geqslant 0$ then β = 90°, while if $u_z < 0$ then β = −90°.

The quadrant parameter Q is unnecessary if the arc tangent function ATAN2, found in FORTRAN and Excel, is applied to the parameters u_x and u_y. This function returns a value in the range −180° to +180° so it is necessary to add 360° to the negative results to give α in the range 0 to 360°. Readers are advised to mark the pages containing Table 1.1 and Figure 1.2 since these are referred to several times later in the book.

The inverse forms of equations 1.4 and 1.5 are

$$u_x = |\mathbf{u}| \cos \alpha \cos \beta$$
$$u_y = |\mathbf{u}| \sin \alpha \cos \beta \qquad (1.6)$$
$$u_z = |\mathbf{u}| \sin \beta$$

Equations 1.6 allow discontinuity orientation data to be converted to vectorial form by calculating the Cartesian components of the downward directed unit vector normal to the discontinuity plane. Cartesian components of a unit vector such as this are usually referred to as **direction cosines**. Appendix D outlines how vectorial methods can be applied to the analysis of forces in three dimensions. For this purpose the components u_x, u_y and u_z represent components of the force $\mathbf{u}$, and $|\mathbf{u}|$ is the magnitude of the force.

Example 1.2

Adopt the Cartesian coordinate system in Figure 1.2 to solve the following:

(i) Determine the Cartesian components of the downward directed unit vector that is normal to a plane of dip direction/dip angle 147/69.

(ii) What is the trend/plunge of a line whose end point has x, y and z Cartesian components 3.65, −7.28 and −5.96, respectively?

Solution
(i) The trend and plunge of the downward directed normal to the discontinuity plane are, from equations 1.1 and 1.2, 327/21. Inputting these results to equations 1.6 for a unit vector ($|\mathbf{u}| = 1.0$) gives x, y and z Cartesian components (direction cosines) 0.783, −0.508 and 0.358.

(ii) The x component is +ve and the y component is −ve so, by Table 1.1, Q = 360°. Putting this value into equation 1.4 gives the trend α = 296.6°. Equation 1.5 gives β = −36.2° which indicates that the line is directed upwards. The downward directed end of this line has Cartesian components of opposite sign (−3.65, 7.28 and 5.96) giving a trend/plunge 116.6/36.2

The principles outlined above are elaborated further in Example 3.2 in section 3.3.

1.3   DISCONTINUITIES AND THEIR ORIGINS

Gabrielsen (1990), discussing the characteristics of joints and faults from a geological perspective, concludes that even a single fracture may have a long and complex history of changing stress, temperature, strain rate, mineralisation and recrystallisation. Despite this complexity, geologists have adopted a range of terms to describe discontinuities and also to indicate their dominant mode of formation and geological history as determined by observational studies. The following sections summarise the most widely accepted terms.

1.3.1   Faults

Price (1966) defines a fault as a plane of shear failure that exhibits '. . . obvious signs of differential movement of the rock mass on either side of the plane'. It is assumed that a fault is induced when changing tectonic stresses produce a shear stress that exceeds the shear strength on a particular plane in the rock mass (Kersten, 1990). Ragan (1985) presents a simple but convincing discussion of the origins of faults based on the Coulomb yield criterion and on postulated states of stress that could lead to planes of shear failure of various orientations. Evidence of shear displacement includes the offset of identifiable features such as bedding planes or veins, or the creation of slickensides and fault gouge by the scraping and grinding action associated with slip. Although shear displacements can range from just a few millimetres to several hundred metres, the term 'fault' is usually reserved for the more extensive features on which there has been significant displacement. Whitten and Brooks (1972) emphasise that faults rarely occur as single planar features but are usually grouped together in sub-parallel sets, or fault zones. Each element in a fault zone may exhibit shear displacement to some degree.

Faults that have experienced very large shear displacements often accumulate a significant thickness of powdered rock, called fault gouge, or generate a zone of broken rock, called fault breccia, extending several metres on each side of the shear plane. Shear displacements of a few millimeters can, in theory, be accommodated as elastic displacements of the surrounding rock. Larger displacements can be accommodated by subsidiary structures such as folds, hinge lines or secondary faults at each end of the primary fault (Hobbs et al., 1976; Petit and Barquins, 1990). Very large shear displacements must inevitably lead to an extension of the fault in the plane of shear. This process leads to the development of major faults, such as the San Andreas Fault in California, the Great Glen Fault in Scotland and the Alpine Fault in New Zealand (Spencer, 1969) which extend for many kilometres through the Earth's crust. Large faults such as these are usually linked to the movement of tectonic plates and may also be responsible for deep-seated seismic activity (Kalkani, 1990). Major faults are often associated with current (or past) volcanic activity, though it is generally difficult to tell whether it was the fault or the volcano which first ruptured the Earth's crust. Deep-seated faults can provide pathways for migrating hot fluids carrying dissolved minerals. This hydrothermal activity can lead to the formation of extensive zones of mineralisation within, and adjacent to, faults.

A number of terms have been coined by geologists to classify faults on the basis of the direction of shear displacement in the plane of the fault (Price, 1966; Ragan, 1985). If the displacement is generally along the strike of the fault it is classified as **strike-slip**; faults with displacement along the line of maximum dip are **dip-slip**, while those with displacement along a line of general pitch are **oblique-slip**. Dip-slip faults produced by downward movement of the overhanging block are called **normal faults**. Dip-slip faults produced by upward movement of the overhanging block are called **thrust faults** if the fault has an angle of dip of less than 45° and are called **reverse faults** if the angle of dip is more than 45°. Strike-slip faults, which are usually subvertical, are often called **wrench** or **transcurrent** faults and are classified as having a clockwise or anti-clockwise sense of shear depending on the sense of rotation when viewed from above.

Almost without exception, faults create major problems for the rock mechanics engineer. At the small scale, fault breccia can create a zone of weak, broken rock extending across the full width of a tunnel, stope or foundation. It is often the case that the fault will either provide a pathway for groundwater flow or, if filled with clay gouge, will create a barrier to flow and produce dangerously high water pressures on the upstream side. Large faults can create slip surfaces of low shear strength, or form release surfaces for major slope failure mechanisms. Faults are at their weakest when geological shear displacements are reactivated by engineering activity. Faults are particularly problematical when associated with dams since they not only weaken foundations but also provide pathways for leakage which can become progressively more serious as the fault gouge or fault breccia is flushed out.

The identification and mapping of major faults is a job that is best tackled by a geologist or geotechnical engineer who is familiar with the geology and structure of a particular site. Although many of the analytical techniques in this book can be applied to isolated major features such as faults, their three-dimensional characterisation is essentially a large-scale mapping problem, utilising aerial photographs and drawing on the skills of the structural geologist.

1.3.2 Joints

Price (1966) defines joints as '. . . cracks and fractures in rock along which there has been extremely little or no movement'. Most authors who have addressed the issue, including Goodman (1976), Makiyama (1979) and Ragan (1985), concur with this definition. Joints are found in all competent rocks within about 1 km of the Earth's surface, at all orientations and at sizes ranging from a few millimetres to several hundred metres. Joints are many thousands of times more frequent than faults; indeed it is rare to find a cubic metre of rock that does not contain any joints. Many geologists believe that studying joints and their origins can provide valuable clues to the history of tectonic processes in near-surface rocks. It is, however, worth considering the following factors when debating the mechanisms that may have created joints:

(i)   Joints can form in materials ranging from relatively fresh partly-consolidated sediments to rocks that have lain intact for thousands of millions of years.
(ii) Mechanisms such as thermal metamorphism and pressure solution, which can lead to the healing or removal of joints, are rare in near-surface rocks encountered in rock engineering.
(iii) The formation of a joint will lead to a complex redistribution of the local stress field in a rock mass (Cundall, 1987).

The origins of certain types of joints are clearly related to relatively simple mechanisms such as the columnar jointing formed by stresses induced during the cooling of basalts, and the slabbing joints caused by diurnal temperature changes on exposed rock faces. The ubiquitous nature of other joints suggests that their formation is related to some other, more common, geological process. In discussing a range of hypotheses for the formation of joints, Price (1966) suggested that joints in horizontally bedded rocks may be generated by stress changes induced by geological uplift. He argued that during uplift the total lateral stresses decrease more rapidly than the vertical gravitational stresses, leading to the development of horizontal tensile stresses and near-vertical tension joints close to the surface. Although it is difficult to see how simple stress relief can lead to the development of brittle fracture in homogeneous rocks, it is possible that differences in mechanical properties between adjacent horizons in sedimentary rocks could lead to the development of extensile strains sufficient to cause fracturing. Consider, for example, two adjacent horizons that have different Young's moduli and different tensile strengths, but that are maintained in contact by cementing and by compressive stresses normal to the horizons. Assuming that there is strain compatibility between the horizons, the elastic extensile strains produced by the release of compressive stresses in one horizon could produce extensile strains in the adjacent horizon that take the material beyond its tensile fracture limit. These ideas are supported by observations that joint occurrence and joint frequency are often controlled by lithology and bed thickness. Another plausible mechanism for the creation and extension of joints is the pattern of cyclic stresses developed by semi-diurnal tides in near-surface rocks, caused by the gravitational attraction of the Sun and Moon. The Earth's crust is extremely thin and brittle, and plate tectonics has carried large slabs of this crust for many hundreds of kilometres; it is not surprising that most rocks have become heavily fractured.

Observational studies and measurements reveal that fractures often occur in planar, sub-parallel groups or **sets**; such joints are said to be **systematic**. Non-parallel joints of irregular geometry, termed **non-systematic** joints, are of minor interest to the geologist since they cannot be tied in with any clear geological processes. Systematic joints often display spatial and orientational relations with folds, anticlines, synclines and faults formed during the same period of tectonic activity (Price, 1966; Ramsay, 1967; Whitten, 1966). Figure 1.3 (after Price, 1966) is a block diagram illustrating typical orientations of joints on the limbs of an asymmetrical anticline. Both systematic and non-systematic joints create discontinuities that must be considered by the rock mechanics engineer. Joints have been classified qualitatively on the basis of their size, ranging from master joints through major and minor joints down to micro-joints, and on the basis of their frequency, ranging from the most frequent primary joints through secondary joints and so on. These qualitative classifications are of little use to the rock mechanics engineer, who requires numbers on which to base analysis and design. It is this need to provide rational, quantitative information on complex geological structures that provides the impetus, and the major challenge, for this book.

1.3.3 Bedding

Bedding is a surface created by a change in such factors as grain size, grain orientation, mineralogy or chemistry during the deposition of a sedimentary rock. Bedding does not always create discontinuities; in many cases it forms only a slight change in colour or texture in an otherwise intact rock material. In most sedimentary rocks, some of the bedding planes find expression as

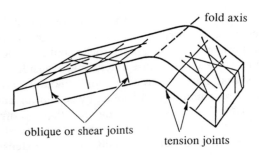

Figure 1.3 Block diagram illustrating the orientation of joints in the limbs of an asymmetrical anticline (after Price, 1966).

discontinuities. In fine grained sedimentary rocks such as shales, bedding planes can form discontinuities that are only a few millimetres apart, dominating the discontinuous structure of the mass.

Although initially horizontal and generally planar, bedding can be tilted, folded and even inverted to a complex range of orientations. Bedding features can be recognised by the fact that they generally run parallel to each other, even when tilted or folded as shown in Figure 1.3. The fact that bedding planes almost never intersect each other makes them unique amongst discontinuities and necessitates the application of special statistical methods when studying their spacing and orientation. Bedding planes generally form some of the most extensive discontinuities in a sedimentary rock mass, sometimes extending for many kilometres across the deposit. The surface geometry of bedding discontinuities is controlled by local factors such as water currents, grain size and the activities of plants and animals at the time of deposition. Temporary changes in the mineralogy of the sediments can produce thin bands of soft clayey material between strong sandstone beds, creating features that present similar engineering problems to clay-filled faults and joints. The cyclic nature of deposition often produces bedding discontinuities that are relatively evenly spaced when compared with discontinuities produced by rock fracture.

1.3.4 Cleavage

Spencer (1969) and Whitten and Brooks (1972) identify two broad types of rock cleavage: fracture cleavage and flow cleavage. **Fracture cleavage** (also known as false cleavage and strain slip cleavage) is a term describing incipient, cemented or welded parallel discontinuities that are independent of any parallel alignment of minerals. Spencer (1969) lists six possible mechanisms for the formation of fracture cleavage. In each mechanism, lithology and stress conditions are assumed to have produced shearing, extension or compression, giving rise to numerous closely-spaced discontinuities separated by thin slivers of intact rock. Fracture cleavage is generally associated with other structural features such as faults, folds and kink bands. **Flow cleavage**, which can occur as slaty cleavage or schistosity, is dependent upon the recrystallisation and parallel alignment of platy minerals such as mica, producing an inter-leaving or **foliation** structure. It is generally accepted that flow cleavage is produced by the high temperatures and/or pressures associated with metamorphism in fine grained rocks. Spencer (1969) suggests that mechanisms such as the rotation and flattening of existing minerals, and the recrystallisation and growth of new minerals, produce the parallel alignment of crystals and the associated cleavage observed in rocks such as slates, phyllites and schists.

Although cleavage is usually clearly visible in slates, phyllites and schists, most cleavage planes possess significant tensile strength and do not, therefore, contribute to the discontinuity network. Cleavage can, however, create significant anisotropy in the deformability and strength of such rocks. Geological processes, such as folding and faulting, subsequent to the formation of the cleavage can exploit these planes of weakness and generate discontinuities along a proportion of the better developed cleavage planes. The decision as to whether a particular cleavage plane is a discontinuity presents one of the more challenging problems to those undertaking discontinuity surveys in cleaved rocks.

1.3.5 Fractures, fissures and other features

Bridges (1975) defines a **fracture** as '. . . a discrete break in a rock which is not parallel with a visible fabric'. In coining this term he presumably excludes discontinuities that have been produced by the exploitation of cleavage, and, in so doing, concurs with one of the definitions given by Whitten and Brooks (1972). Bridges specifically avoids the term 'joint' to prevent confusion arising from the range of different definitions. The terms 'fracture' and 'crack' have been adopted, but not explicitly defined, by most of the authors cited in this section for describing joints and other discontinuities that have arisen from brittle fracture mechanisms. Rock mechanics engineers also use these terms to describe the cracks generated during rock material testing, blasting and brittle rock failure. It must also be recognised that these terms are widely used in general speech so it is inappropriate and unwise to claim specific meanings for them. The terms fracture and crack will be used in this book as synonyms for 'discontinuity' when it is felt that a more concise or a more colloquial emphasis is appropriate.

Fookes and Denness (1969) and Fourmaintraux (1975) have accepted the term 'discontinuity' as defined earlier but go on to define the term 'fissure' as follows: 'discontinuity dividing an otherwise continuous material without separation of units' (Fookes and Denness, 1969), and, according to Fourmaintraux (1975) in translation from the french '. . . planar discontinuities that are extensive in two directions but restricted in the third, which corresponds to the thickness or aperture of the discontinuity'. Fookes and Denness go on to define the terms 'true fissure' and 'apparent fissure' for the relatively weak Cretaceous sediments of south east England, and have proposed a size classification ranging from 'very large' ($\geq 100\,m^2$) to 'very small' ($\leq 1\,cm^2$). Unfortunately the term 'fissure' also has a range of other, less formally defined meanings. Goodman (1976) distinguishes fissures as the small fractures that can be found in specimens of rock material that can be tested in the laboratory. Price (1966) refers to 'gashes' or 'fissures' as fractures that '...are open or, more usually, filled with quartz or some carbonate material'. In concurring with this general definition Whitten and Brooks (1972) point out that fissures and other discontinuities that have become filled with extraneous material are also referred to as 'veins', 'lodes', 'dykes' and 'sills' depending on their geometry, composition and mode of formation. In the Author's opinion, the term 'fissure' is somewhat ambiguous and should not be used to describe any specific types of discontinuities unless the meaning has been defined locally.

1.4 DISCONTINUITIES IN ROCK ENGINEERING

The aim of this section is to outline a number of case histories that serve to illustrate the impact that discontinuities can have on the engineering performance of a rock mass.

1.4.1 Ground movements caused by tunnelling in chalk (Priest, 1976)

In 1973 the Author was fortunate enough to be involved in the Transport and Road Research Laboratory (TRRL) mechanised tunnelling trials in Lower Chalk at Chinnor in Oxfordshire, UK. A site investigation revealed that the chalk had a uniaxial compressive strength in the order of 7 MPa and a secant Young's modulus between 1 and 3 GPa measured to stress levels between 0.1 and 2.0 MPa. Scanline surveys (see Chapter 2) on freshly exposed rock faces indicated a complex pattern of discontinuity orientation (see Figure 3.7) with mean spacings between 0.11 and 0.13 m. The 5 m diameter experimental tunnel was driven from a quarry face with the crown at a depth of approximately 6 to 8 m below ground level and the invert between 0.5 and 3 m above the water table.

A comprehensive programme of ground displacement monitoring was instituted by the TRRL, involving inclinometers and extensometers installed in boreholes and also precise surveying in a 3 m diameter shaft adjacent to the tunnel. The author also installed 140 Demec gauge spans in the walls of a smooth-sided trench excavated across the tunnel line, to monitor displacements along discontinuities. Figure 1.4 shows horizontal strain profiles recorded on 48 × 400 mm spans across the tunnel line, measured at six stages during tunnel advance. The highly discontinuous nature of this profile reflects the development of local strains induced by slip along discontinuities.

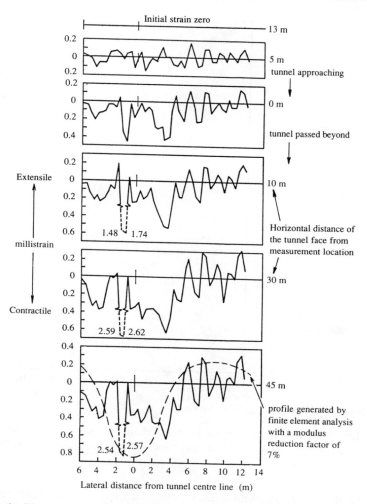

Figure 1.4 Horizontal strain profiles at six stages during tunnel advance, Chinnor UK (after Priest, 1976).

Figure 1.5 shows vertical ground movements induced by tunnel excavation, observed in vertical boreholes 3 m from the tunnel centre line. An attempt was made to model the observed ground displacements by means of plane strain finite element analysis. The dashed line in Figure 1.5 shows the best fit, obtained by inputting a Young's modulus that was only 7% of that obtained from tests on intact, unfractured rock. The final profile in Figure 1.4 contains a horizontal strain profile generated by finite element analysis with this same reduced Young's modulus. It appears that discontinuities have dramatically

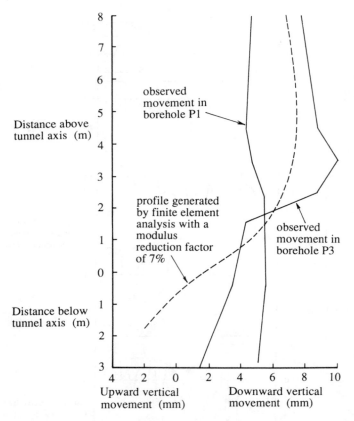

Figure 1.5 Vertical ground movements induced by tunnel excavation, observed in vertical boreholes 3 m from the tunnel centreline, Chinnor UK (after Priest, 1976).

decreased the deformation modulus of the rock mass by something exceeding an order of magnitude. The mechanisms for modulus reduction effects such as this are discussed in Chapter 9.

1.4.2 Sugarloaf Reservoir Project (Regan and Read, 1980)

The Sugarloaf Reservoir Project, located 35 km north-east of Melbourne, Australia, consists of a 95 Gl storage reservoir fed from the Maroondah Aqueduct and the Yarra River to serve the needs of the Melbourne Metropolitan District. Regan and Read (1980) describe the design and construction in 1977–78 of two large excavations within the reservoir basin: a 350 m long, 35 m deep tapered inlet channel, and a 400 m long, 65 m deep draw-off channel. The rocks are folded and deeply weathered siltstones and

(a)

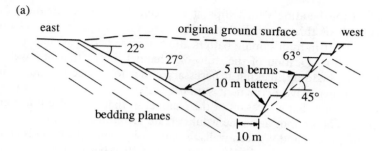

(b)

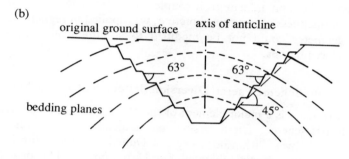

Figure 1.6 Cross-sections through Sugarloaf Reservoir Project, Australia: (a) inlet channel, (b) relocation of draw-off channel to coincide with axis of anticline (after Regan and Read, 1980).

sandstones of Silurian age with distinct beds of medium grained sandstone 100 to 1000 mm thick. The main regional structure is a broad syncline, plunging gently to the north, cut by numerous minor folds. The principal discontinuities are 'faults' developed during flexural slip folding and orientated parallel to the bedding (Casinader and Stapledon, 1979). There are also two additional orthogonal discontinuity sets normal to the bedding. Sheared and crushed seams up to 20 mm thick, containing mixtures of rock fragments, silt and clay, are orientated parallel to the bedding and also to certain joint sets. Clay-filled seams up to 30 mm thick occur parallel to bedding and to joints in highly weathered zones. Direct shear tests on material from these clay-filled seams indicated residual and peak friction angles between 10 and 20°.

The rock mass at the Sugarloaf Reservoir Project presented a significant challenge for the design and construction of the inlet and draw-off channels. This challenge was met by collecting data on the discontinuities at all stages of the project, by adopting appropriate designs that recognised the controlling aspects of these discontinuities, and by maintaining flexibility in these designs throughout the project. The eastern wall of the inlet channel was excavated parallel to the bedding which dips at between 22° and 30° to the west; the western wall of this channel was cut at an overall angle of 45° by pre-split blasting with 10 m high sloping batters and 5 m wide berms as shown in Figure 1.6a. The initial location of the draw-off channel meant that one wall would undercut the bedding, making it necessary either to reduce the slope angle or to install an extensive permanent support system. Further geological investigations indicated that relocation of the channel so that its centre line coincided with the axis of a minor anticline would create favourable bedding orientations in both the eastern and western walls, as shown in Figure 1.6b. This change in design was implemented, with 10 m batters and 10 m berms achieving a largely unsupported, stable overall slope angle of 45°. Reinforcement, comprising 5 m fully grouted anchors on a 2.5 m grid, coupled with drainage holes, wire mesh and a 100 mm thickness of wet-mix shotcrete, was applied in regions where the excavation geometry could not be modified to accommodate unfavourable discontinuity orientations.

1.4.3 Maniototo Scheme Paerau Diversion (Paterson *et al.*, 1988)

The Paerau diversion is a major element of the Maniototo combined irrigation and hydroelectric scheme. The diversion runs generally north–south across a loop in the Taieri River, 70 km north-west of Dunedin on the South Island of New Zealand, in two canals separated a 1.4 km tunnel . The bed-rock in the region consists of a blocky, competent pelitic schist with well-developed schistosity dipping at between 10 and 20° to the east, together with steeply-dipping joints striking approximately east–west. Borehole investigations revealed that the schist alternates with blocky, quartz-rich, highly micaceous foliated lithologies. Numerous clayey fault zones of limited lateral extent were also found, distributed throughout the schist. Triaxial tests on core samples revealed peak friction angles of between 11 and 23° with zero cohesion for pre-existing partings, and peak friction angles of between 22 and 33° with an apparent cohesion of 2 MPa for intact specimens.

At an early stage during canal excavation at the northern end of the tunnel the entire western batter, which had been constructed at a slope angle of 76°, failed by sliding along foliation shear planes which were subsequently found to be coated with a 10 mm thick highly plastic, weak gouge. As a direct result of this failure the batter had to be flattened to 20° over a length of several hundred metres to conform to the orientation of the schistosity. Although the eastern batter was generally stable, joint intersections created localised wedge failures and associated toppling instability, which limited stable slope angles to 45°. The western batters of the southern canal also had to be flattened from 45° to 20° as a direct result of sliding failures on weak schistosity planes and along localised foliation shear zones. Lateral release of unstable blocks was provided by steeply dipping joints striking across the canal line, as illustrated in Figure 1.7. These changes in excavation geometry necessitated a significant increase

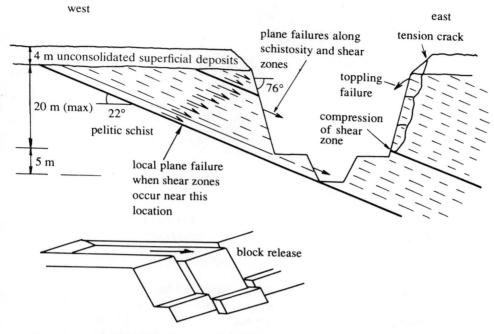

west

east

plane failures along
schistosity and shear
zones

tension crack

4 m unconsolidated superficial deposits

toppling
failure

76°

20 m (max)   22°

pelitic schist

compression
of shear
zone

5 m

local plane failure
when shear zones
occur near this
location

block release

Figure 1.7 Lateral release of unstable blocks by steeply dipping joints, Paerau Diversion, New Zealand (after Paterson *et al.*, 1988).

in excavation volumes. The weak nature of the rock, however, made it possible to remove this extra volume without significantly detracting from the economic viability of the scheme.

The Sugarloaf and Paerau case studies are classic examples of how a single set of discontinuities can control excavation design and stability. It is often the case that a major feature, such as the schistosity encountered in the Paerau Diversion, dictates a flat slope angle on one side of an excavation while permitting a much steeper angle on the opposite side.

1.4.4 Varahi Underground Power House (Eshwaraiah and Upadhyaya, 1990)

This case study concerns the Varahi Underground Power House constructed for the Karnataka Power Corporation at a depth of approximately 230 m in the Peninsular granitic gneiss in the foothills of the Western Ghats in northern India. Eshwaraiah and Upadhyaya (1990) describe a complex pattern of discontinuities including foliation joints with dip directions/dip angles of approximately 060/50 and 235/75, sub-horizontal joints dipping gently towards the south, vertical joints with an east–west strike, and joints with dip directions/

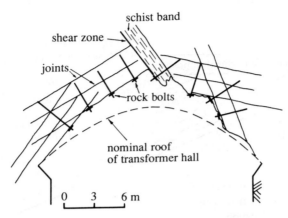

Figure 1.8 Instability in the roof of the transformer hall Varahi Underground Power House, Karnataka, India (after Eshwaraiah and Upadhyaya, 1990).

dip angles of approximately 180/45, giving an overall mean spacing of between 2 and 2.5 m. The valve house, machine hall and transformer hall were excavated with their long axes running north-east. The largest of these excavations was the machine hall which is 157 m long, 48.8 m high and has a span of 28.3 m; the transformer hall has a length of 151.3 m, a height of 14.5 m and a span of 18.8 m.

No problems were encountered when excavating the small diameter approach adits and tail race tunnels. Roof falls were experienced, however, during excavation of the transformer hall in rock that contained the same joint pattern as that observed in the smaller excavations. Intersections between schist bands and joints in the roof of the transformer hall created unstable blocks, which extended up to a height of 3 m. This instability, which was exacerbated by blasting operations and by joint dilation induced in zones of local tensile stress, necessitated rock bolting, as shown in the sketch in Figure 1.8, together with concrete backfill supported by reinforced concrete beams. The problem was alleviated when excavating the larger machine hall by taking out staggered slices and installing reinforced concrete support before widening to the full span.

This example shows how discontinuities can intersect to form blocky instability, despite extensive support measures. Experience in the transformer hall also demonstrates that discontinuities only provide a potential for instability. Whether this instability actually occurs or not depends on several important factors, including the size and orientation of the excavation, the initial and induced stress fields, the excavation sequence and techniques, and the timing and nature of support measures.

EXERCISES FOR CHAPTER 1 AND APPENDIX A

Notes:

1. A number of exercises in this and subsequent chapters draw on material presented in several chapters and appendices.
2. Although the data in these exercises are hypothetical, they are realistic.

1.1

A discontinuity plane has a dip direction/dip angle of 157/62. Calculate the trend/plunge of the normal and the strike of the plane.

1.2

Adopting the Cartesian coordinate system in Figure 1.2, calculate the magnitude, trend and plunge of lines that have the following x, y, z Cartesian components: (i) −0.085, 0.262, 0.961 (ii) −0.565, −1.471, −1.231.

1.3

Adopting the Cartesian coordinate system in Figure 1.2, calculate the x, y, z direction cosines for lines with the following trends/plunges: (i) 074/−34 (ii) 344/59.

1.4

Two lines of trend/plunge 135/48 and 209/75 are known to pass through the same point. Determine the acute angle between these lines.

1.5

Two discontinuities with dip directions/dip angles 237/55 and 318/66 are known to intersect. Determine the trend/plunge of their line of intersection.

Answers to these exercises are given on page 460.

2

Measurement of discontinuity characteristics

2.1 INTRODUCTION

In order to understand and to quantify the influence that discontinuities have on rock mass behaviour it is first necessary to measure and to represent quantitatively the relevant characteristics of the discontinuities that form the complex three-dimensional fabric of mechanical breaks, termed the **discontinuity network** or the **rock structure**, in the mass. Although this chapter occurs early in the book, the recommended measurement methods presented here cannot be appreciated fully nor implemented properly until the theoretical aspects of discontinuity geometry, presented in Chapters 3 to 6 have been studied in some detail. Readers are also advised to consult Appendix B which contains an introduction to statistics and probability density.

Before embarking on discontinuity measurement of any form it is important to consider the purpose(s) for which the measurements are being taken; these may include:

(i)   investigation of geological structure,
(ii) rock mass classification,
(iii) generating input data for specific analytical, numerical or empirical models of rock mass stability, rock deformation, fluid flow, blasting, rock cutting or support design.

The data required for each of these purposes will vary considerably, necessitating different sampling and measurement strategies. It is worth also considering two conflicting principles in discontinuity measurement: there is little point in collecting and processing data that cannot be used as input for one of the specific purposes listed above; on the other hand it is generally easier to measure all relevant properties and subsequently to discard any superfluous data, rather than return to a site and take additional measurements. It is also often the case that discontinuity data are used for a number of different purposes, some of which may not be apparent at the time of taking the measurements. It is the aim of this chapter to describe discontinuity sampling strategies that can satisfy the basic needs of each of the above applications, but which can be extended or modified to suite specific requirements.

The suggested methods for the quantitative description of discontinuities in rock masses, prepared by ISRM (1978) provide a good general introduction to the qualitative aspects of discontinuity measurement. The suggested methods are, however, limited by the fact that they do not incorporate data processing techniques, developed in the 1980s for the elimination of sampling bias and the quantification of discontinuity characteristics. It is hoped that the work in this book goes some way towards addressing this deficiency. An irregular, highly fractured rock face in a mine, quarry or natural exposure presents a daunting challenge to anyone who wishes to quantify the discontinuity network in an unbiased way. The rock mass contains an enormous amount of geometrical information which at some stage must be filtered and interpreted by an engineer or geologist who is familiar with the site and the lithology. Automatic data collection systems have not yet been developed that can replace the human ability to view and interpret the rock mass in colour, in three dimensions, from a range of distances, locations and angles. Nor can automatic systems replace the human capacity to touch and to probe the rock face, to make instantaneous comparisons with features observed elsewhere, and to discuss observations with other experts. Despite these impressive advantages it is necessary also to acknowledge that humans are susceptible to personal bias and subjectivity. They may have varying degrees of experience and motivation, they work relatively slowly and can get bored or tired, particularly when working under adverse environmental conditions.

The measurement techniques presented in this chapter have been designed to take advantage of the many benefits of on site personal sampling while minimising the disadvantages. The measurement systems are based upon objective but flexible sampling strategies linked to rigorous data analysis based upon the principles of geometrical probability and statistics. Experience has shown that between 1000 and 2000 discontinuities must be sampled to provide an adequate characterisation of a typical site (Priest and Hudson, 1976). This number might typically be made up from samples of between 150 and 350 discontinuities taken at between 5 and 15 sample locations chosen to represent the main zones of geological structure and lithology. Additional measurements may be required where a site exhibits many different lithologies, highly variable discontinuity characteristics, or where a higher degree of confidence in the engineering design is required.

Discontinuity characteristics such as orientation, size, frequency and surface geometry are essentially geometrical properties, which must be measured physically in some way. The two broad sampling strategies that can be adopted involve either the logging of borehole core or the examination of an exposed rock face. These strategies are described in sections 2.2 and 2.3. Techniques for preliminary data processing are described in section 2.4 which links with background theory presented in Chapters 3 to 6 and in Chapter 10. Section 2.5 is concerned with the analysis of spatial variability by the application of geostatistical methods. The chapter concludes with some brief comments about rock mass classification.

2.2 BOREHOLE SAMPLING

The recovery, examination and testing of high quality drill core obtained by diamond drilling has been used for many years to probe rock conditions at depth. A wide range of drilling rigs, core barrels and drill bits are available to provide drill core at diameters between 20 and 150 mm from depths of several hundred metres in a wide range of rock types. Hoek and Brown (1980a) and Brady and Brown (1985) describe the principal types of drill rigs, core barrels and drill bits that have been used in diamond drilling. By far the most common application of diamond drilling is for probing the extent of orebodies and associated strata in the region of existing or proposed mining operations. The primary purpose here is to identify the various rock types and their mineral compositions, to build up a three-dimensional picture of mine geology. Borehole core can, however, also provide a relatively undisturbed sample of rock material containing discontinuities from deep within the rock close to an area of proposed excavation or potential instability, making it a valuable source of information for geotechnical design. In addition, mechanical and fluid flow tests can be carried out on the recovered rock material and on the walls of the borehole (Snow, 1970). The borehole walls can also be inspected by remote visual techniques (Kamewada et al., 1990), and the surrounding rock can be probed by geophysical devices.

One significant problem with borehole sampling is that the core can rotate during extraction, so special sampling and analysis techniques are needed to determine the true orientation of the sampled discontinuities within the rock mass (see Chapter 4 of Priest, 1985). A second difficulty is that the core is usually of small diameter (<100 mm), making it virtually impossible to measure discontinuity size, and rendering the core susceptible to breakage during coring and recovery. A further problem is that infill material may be washed out from discontinuities, or extraneous matter can be deposited from the drilling mud, making it difficult to investigate this particular discontinuity characteristic with any confidence. High equipment hire charges, the costs of skilled operatives and the desirability of professional supervision can make borehole sampling a relatively expensive operation.

The Geological Society (1970) and Rosengren (1970) present valuable guidelines on the logging of rock core for engineering purposes. They identify two sources of information: the driller's report and the core itself. A lot can be learned from the driller's report, which should contain details of drilling progress, loss of core, bit replacements, colour of drilling fluid, loss of drilling fluid, standing water levels and other factors relating to the drilling operation recorded on a standard form. Drill core is usually recovered in runs of between 1 and 4 m, depending on the barrel length, and then placed in wooden or plastic core boxes prior to logging. For the purposes of discontinuity logging it is imperative that the core is handled with extreme care to minimise the disruption of existing fractures and the creation of new ones. The logging process should be carried out in the following sequence: (i) remove any protective covering from the core, (ii) label the core by borehole number and depth, then photograph it in colour, (iii) log the core, (iv) remove, label and seal samples for laboratory testing, (v) conduct point load testing or other destructive on-site tests, (vi) split the core for further photography if required, and (vii) reassemble and re-seal the core as far as possible for future reference.

The borehole log itself is recorded on site using standard forms, such as those reproduced by the Geological Society (1970) and Rosengren (1970). Although specific requirements may vary, so that the exact layout of the form may need to be tailored for each site, it is usual to record the following details in symbolic, graphic or numerical form as a function of depth on the site log: rock type, core size, discontinuity characteristics, Rock Quality Designation and on-site test results. The final borehole log is a neat amalgamation of the driller's report and the site log, containing details of the project name, dates, ground level, drill type, personnel, borehole number, collar coordinates and borehole orientation recorded as headers and footers on each form. A record of drilling progress, core loss, water recovery, water levels, a symbolic representation of rock type, together with the information listed above for the site log, are plotted by depth on each page of the core log. A blank core logging form designed for site use and as a final neat log is reproduced in Figure 2.1. This form, which has been specifically designed to satisfy the requirements for logging discontinuities, may need modification or extension to suite specific site conditions.

It is beyond the scope of this book to discuss all aspects of core logging. Readers who wish to pursue this matter further are advised to consult the texts by the Geological Society (1970), Rosengren (1970) and Attewell and Farmer (1976). Interesting papers by Andersson et al. (1984) and by Karzulovic and Goodman (1985) have addressed some of the problems of sampling discontinuity characteristics from boreholes.

It is, however, appropriate to make some additional comments about the logging of discontinuities in borehole core. In the Author's experience, the easiest way to record discontinuity characteristics is to fix a thin measuring tape to form a scanline down the surface of the core. The tape can be run out

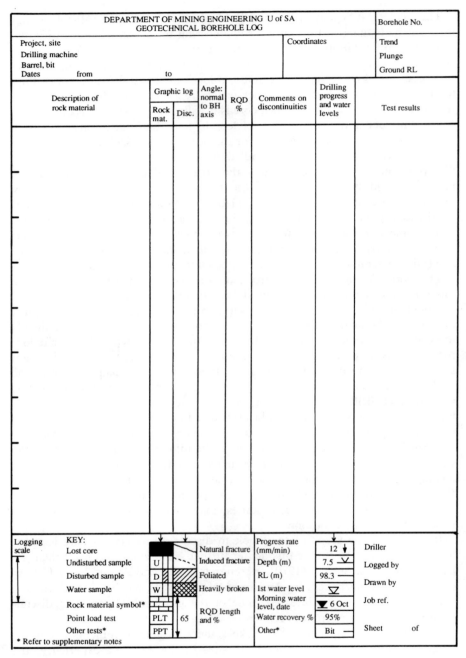

Figure 2.1 Blank geotechnical borehole logging form.

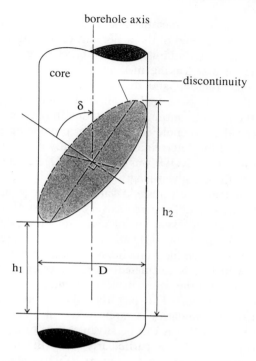

Figure 2.2 Intersection geometry for a discontinuity and borehole core (after Priest, 1985).

so that its distance markings correspond directly with depth in the borehole. The precise depth d of the intersection between the borehole scanline and each discontinuity is then recorded graphically and/or numerically on the site log. The orientation of each discontinuity can also be indicated approximately on a graphic log, as indicated in Figure 2.1. Zones of closely spaced discontinuities, severely broken rock or lost core can be recorded by means of appropriate symbols. As an alternative, or a supplement to the graphic discontinuity log, and if time and resources permit, a suitably scaled colour photograph of the undisturbed core can be glued as a strip in the final log and treated in the same way as the graphic record.

The angle δ in degrees between each discontinuity normal and the borehole axis can be measured by means of a protractor and recorded where the discontinuity appears on the graphic log. Alternatively, δ can be found from the following expression

$$\delta = \arctan\left(\frac{h_2 - h_1}{D}\right)$$

(2.1)

where $h_1 \leq h_2$ are the distances measured parallel to the borehole axis from an arbitrary datum level to each end of the major axis of the ellipse created by the intersection between the discontinuity and the borehole core of diameter D, as illustrated in Figure 2.2. Taking measurements in this way may, unfortunately, involve some rotation and disturbance of the core. Priest (1985) presents details of the analysis of angles collected from borehole core in this way, to determine the true discontinuity orientation in the rock mass. It must, however, be accepted that borehole core does not provide an efficient nor an entirely effective method for determining discontinuity orientation.

Rock Quality Designation (RQD) was devised by Deere (1964) and defined as the percentage length of a given length of core consisting of intact, sound pieces that are longer than the threshold value of 0.1 m (4 inches). RQD is sometimes referred to as a modified core recovery since loss of core, weathering or fracturing can lead to the exclusion of core from the RQD summation. Some of the theoretical aspects of RQD and its interpretation are discussed in section 5.3. If RQD is determined on site, it is necessary to decide upon a length of core over which it is calculated. For convenience RQD is usually calculated for each run from the core barrel, which may correspond to lengths ranging from about 1 to 4 m. The fact that these core runs often cross lithological or structural boundaries is rarely taken into account. Priest and Hudson (1976) have shown that it can be advantageous to calculate RQD for larger threshold values than 0.1 m, particularly when the fracture spacing is high. It is a relatively tedious matter to convert RQD values recorded at one threshold value to RQDs for another threshold. These criticisms indicate that it is preferable simply to make a record of discontinuity intersection distances d along the borehole scanline, together with the associated angles δ, and to process these data at a later stage to calculate such values as mean discontinuity spacing and RQD over lengths of core that reflect geological rather than operational factors. These calculations are particularly easy if the site log has been transferred to a computer file. Discontinuities that appear to have been introduced by the drilling and recovery process, or that mark the boundaries of zones of closely spaced fractures, severely broken rock or lost core can be tagged with an appropriate index number in such a file, to facilitate special treatment during processing. Details of techniques for the processing of discontinuity data to analyse spacing and frequency are introduced in section 2.4 and discussed further in Chapters 4 and 5.

For many applications it is desirable to make a record of discontinuity surface geometry and the properties of any infill material in discontinuities intersected by the borehole. This information should be determined by following the methods recommended in the next section, and then recorded on the borehole log. In many rock types it can be difficult to differentiate between natural discontinuities and fractures introduced during the drilling and recovery process, particularly where the drilling mud has contaminated the fracture surface. Some guidelines to help in identifying induced fractures are presented in the next section. A particular advantage of borehole core is that it is relatively easy to take samples of discontinuities and the adjacent rock material for deformability and strength testing. Procedures and data processing techniques for such tests are described in Chapter 9.

2.3 MEASUREMENT AT EXPOSED ROCK FACES

Taking measurements at exposed rock faces, either above or below ground, has the advantage of utilising a relatively large area of rock, which enables the direct measurement of discontinuity orientation, size and other large-scale geometrical features. The geological relations between the various discontinuity groups can also be observed. One disadvantage of this approach is that the rock face is often remote from the zone of interest and may suffer from blasting damage or degradation by weathering and vegetation cover. Although skilled personnel are needed to take the measurements, equipment and labour costs are negligible compared with borehole sampling costs. Until recently, measurements at exposed faces were taken in an arbitrary, subjective way derived from geological mapping techniques; this yielded little quantitative data of value for engineering design. Recently more rigorous statistical sampling and data processing methods have been adopted. The most widely used of these methods are the scanline and window sampling techniques. These techniques have been described and discussed by a number of authors including Fookes and Denness (1969), Attewell and Farmer (1976), Baecher and Lanney (1978), ISRM (1978) and Priest and Hudson (1981). The relative simplicity of the measurement process at exposed faces, and the statistical rigour of these techniques, make them ideally suited to the determination of discontinuity orientation, and other large-scale geometrical properties of the rock structure. Rouleau and Gale (1985) and Kulatilake et al. (1990a) present instructive recent case studies of the use of these techniques in conjunction with borehole sampling for the characterisation, modelling and verification of discontinuity orientation, spacing, frequency and size for a granitic rock mass in Stripa, Sweden. The following sections contain descriptions of the principal practical features of the scanline and window sampling techniques. Data processing techniques are described in Chapters 3 to 6.

2.3.1 Scanline sampling

It is important to recognise that there is no universally accepted standard for scanline sampling. Indeed it is desirable to modify the details of the technique to suit local rock conditions and to provide specific data that may be required for a particular design exercise. The methods summarised below are based on a review of the literature and upon the Author's experience of some 20 years of discontinuity sampling, involving the measurement of many thousands of discontinuities.

A clean, approximately planar rock face is selected that is large relative to the size and spacing of the discontinuities exposed. As a rough guide the sample zone should contain between 150 and 350 discontinuities, of which about 50% should have at least one end visible. Such exposures can be found on beach cliffs, in gorges, road cuttings, quarries, open pit mines and unsupported adits. Care should be exercised when selecting the face, to ensure that the rock material and discontinuities are representative of those across the site and also to ensure that the face is safe to work at. Falling blocks and mine vehicles present particular hazards which should be guarded against at all times. Many natural and excavated rock faces are formed from major joints or faults; if such faces are selected for sampling it is important to set up additional scanlines on other faces, and at different orientations, to provide a three-dimensional sample of the discontinuity network.

Intersections between discontinuities and the rock face will produce linear traces which provide an essentially two-dimensional sample of the discontinuity network. The scanlines themselves are simply measuring tapes, between 2 and 30 m long, pinned with masonry nails and wire to the rock face along its strike and line of maximum dip. Further scanlines should be set up on a second rock face, approximately at right angles to the first, to minimise the orientation sampling bias (Chapter 3). The aim is to impose a rigorous linear sampling regime that is similar to that of a borehole but which does not suffer from the small sample width. It is desirable, but not essential, to position the start of each scanline at a discontinuity. The location, orientation and condition of the rock face are recorded at the top of the first logging sheet together with the trend and plunge of each scanline (Figure 2.3). Rock faces are often irregular, so it is usually necessary to pin the scanline back, to conform to the face geometry. Deviations in the scanline of less than about 20° from a straight line have a negligible influence on the sampling regime and can be ignored. Larger deviations can be accommodated simply by splitting the scanline into sub-scanlines and measuring the trend and plunge of each.

It is desirable to take colour photographs of the rock face and scanline, including a scale and appropriate label, before commencing the sampling process (Hudson and Priest, 1979). It may be necessary to take photographs from several view points in order to record all areas of an irregular face, and also to retake the photographs after logging if the scanline has been moved during the measurement process. A simple way to provide a scale is to attach clearly visible markers at 1 m intervals along each scanline, as shown in Figure 2.4. These markers also make it easier to locate specific discontinuities for the purpose of scaling off their trace lengths. It is rarely possible to position the camera at the mid-height of the rock face with its lens axis normal to the face. It is usually necessary to shoot upwards from the bottom of the face, which may be tilted back from the vertical by as much as 30°. This geometry, illustrated in Figure 2.5, can introduce a significant distortion in the resulting photograph, since features at the top of the face are further away from the

SCANLINE SURVEY LOGGING FORM

Page	Of

Details of scanline:

Label ....

Trend ....

Plunge ....

Trimming level ....m

Logged by ....

Date logged ....

Details of rock face:

Location ....

Dip direction ....

Dip angle ....

Non-overhanging / Overhanging

Height ....m

Width ....m

Rock type ....

Excavation method ....

Condition of exposure

Comments

Intersection distance d (m)	Dip Direction (Degrees)	Dip Angle (Degrees)	Semi-trace length *l* (m) above or left of scan	Semi-trace length *l* (m) below or right of scan	Termination I=1, A=2, O=3	Rough-ness JRC 1-20	Curv-ature 1-5	Comments (Refer to table of abbreviations and codes)

Figure 2.3 Blank scanline survey logging form.

Figure 2.4   Scanline set up on a rock face in Penrice Quarry, South Australia.

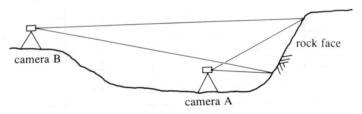

Figure 2.5   Photographing a non-overhanging rock face.

camera and will therefore produce smaller images than features of a similar size at the bottom of the face. There are a number of ways to minimise this distortion. The simplest of these is to use a long focal length lens mounted on a tripod some distance back from the face, and preferably on elevated ground, to reduce the ratio of camera distances for features at different locations on the face (location B in Figure 2.5). Specialised tilt-shift lenses, which can remove modest amounts of distortion, have been developed by Canon Inc and other companies, for architectural photography. Lenses such as these can be valuable for work underground and in other confined areas, where it may be impossible to move any distance back from the rock face. If it is possible to place scales at the corner points of the field of view it is a relatively easy matter to remove small amounts of distortion during film processing, by reversing the angle of tilt.

Each scanline tape is scanned, starting from the zero end, until a discontinuity trace is intersected. The following properties of only those discontinuities intersected by the tape are measured and recorded in a systematic tabular form on a logging sheet such as the one illustrated in Figure 2.3:

Intersection distance d   This is the distance in metres, rounded to the nearest centimetre, along the scanline to the intersection point with the discontinuity. If the face is not planar it may be necessary to extrapolate some of the discontinuities to obtain this point. This extrapolation process can sometimes produce an intersection distance that is out of sequence, back down the scanline. Such intersections can be re-ordered either manually or by computer prior to processing. The intersection distance on a given scanline provides a simple and unambiguous identification for any particular discontinuity in the sample.

In some cases it may be difficult to decide whether a given feature is a natural geological discontinuity or a fracture introduced during blasting and excavation. For most applications only those features that form true mechanical breaks of geological origin should be measured. Familiarity with a particular site generally makes it easier to recognise natural discontinuities, which tend to be extensive, relatively smooth, gently curved, and often exhibit some evidence of weathering, surface staining or in-filling. Fractures induced by blasting are usually small, rough, irregular, clean, randomly orientated and associated with blast holes (Figure 2.6). Many inexperienced workers waste a lot of time deciding whether a particular feature should be measured or not. If there is any doubt it is generally easier to take the measurements and to record any uncertainty about the origin of a particular feature in the comments column.

There is little point in trying to measure discontinuities in broken or heavily fractured rock, or across areas of the face that have been obscured by features such as vegetation and scree. It is better simply to record the extent of the broken or obscured zone in terms of distance along the scanline and to describe the nature of the zone in the comments column. Sub-parallel discontinuities with a spacing less than 1 cm can be produced by bedding, slaty cleavage or schistosity (section 1.3). It is rarely necessary, or feasible, to measure each closely-spaced feature separately. It is better to take representative measurements, as described below, and then to count the number of such features occuring in each 0.1 m increment of the scanline.

Figure 2.6 Photographs of (a) natural discontinuities and (b) induced discontinuities.

(a)

Orientation This is expressed in degrees as the dip direction (3 digits) and dip angle (2 digits) of the discontinuity measured at the point of intersection with the scanline. If the discontinuity is poorly exposed at this point it may be necessary to measure the orientation at an exposed surface on the discontinuity

(b)

some distance from the scanline. The orientation is usually measured by means of a magnetic compass and clinometer device fitted with a spirit level (ISRM, 1978; Ragan, 1985).

Figure 2.7 illustrates the use of a simple Silva compass (type 15T) to measure dip direction and dip angle. In order to measure the dip direction, the hinged back plate is maintained in contact with the discontinuity surface while the hinge angle and the compass orientation are adjusted until the spirit level bubble is in the centre of the bull's-eye. With the compass in this position, the graduated outer ring is rotated until the black arrow is in exact alignment with the red end of the compass needle. The dip direction is given by the reading on the outer ring, indicated by one of the diametrically opposing markings on the base plate of the compass. The marking closer to the hinge is used when the measurement has been taken from the overhanging block of a discontinuity; the other mark is used for measurements on non-overhanging discontinuities. It is always a good idea to maintain a clear sense of the northerly azimuth while taking orientation measurements to minimise the risk of gross

(b)

errors. Many compasses, including the one shown in Figure 2.7, have the capacity to correct for differences between magnetic north and true north. It is recommended that this adjustment is always set at zero; corrections can be made later during processing or plotting. It should also be noted that compass

(a)

Figure 2.7   Use of the Silva compass for measuring (a) dip direction and (b) dip angle.

needles balanced for magnetic inclination in the northern hemisphere will be severely out of balance in the southern hemisphere.

The dip angle is measured with the Silva compass by first rotating the graduated outer ring until the 360° mark lies exactly adjacent to one of the

(b)

diametrically opposing marks on the base plate. The mark closer to the hinge is used for measurements on an overhanging block; the other mark is used for measurements on non-overhanging discontinuities. With the neck cord removed, the edge of the base plate opposite to the hinge is placed on the discontinuity along its line of maximum dip. While maintaining contact, the compass is rotated slightly until the small pendulum registers its maximum reading on the inner red scale; this reading is the angle of dip. Although the above explanation may sound somewhat involved, with practice it is possible to take a reading of dip direction and dip angle on a readily accessible discontinuity in less than 30 seconds. Ewan and West (1981) conclude that different operators measuring the orientation of the same feature have a maximum error of $\pm 10°$ for dip direction and $\pm 5°$ for dip angle.

It should be noted that the scanline will tend to intersect preferentially those discontinuity traces that make a large angle with it, and in the limit, the scanline will fail to intersect traces that lie parallel to it. This effect, which is discussed in detail in Chapter 3, can be allowed for by applying simple trigonometrical correction factors to the data before plotting and analysis. A practical implication of this orientation sampling bias occurs where a number of relatively short discontinuities run almost parallel to a scanline that is located some distance from the rock face. Parallax effects can make it difficult to decide whether a given discontinuity actually intersects the scanline or not. This problem can be overcome by positioning a light at the same level as the scanline so that its shadow is cast on to the rock face. The line of this shadow can be traced off with chalk or spray paint to delineate a fixed sampling line.

Semi-trace length l   This is the distance from the intersection point on the scanline to the end of the discontinuity trace. This distance can either be measured directly if the face is accessible, estimated by eye or scaled from the photograph of the rock face, when it becomes available. There will be two semi-trace lengths associated with each discontinuity: one above and one below a horizontal scanline; one to the left and one to the right of a scanline along the line of maximum dip of the face, as indicated on the log sheet in Figure 2.3. In many cases the scanline will have been set up close to the edge of the exposure so it will only be possible to measure semi-trace lengths on one side of it. The semi-trace length sampling system presents no problem because the intersection point will be at a random location along each discontinuity trace, permitting the use of the statistical techniques described in Chapter 6 to estimate the properties of the complete trace length distribution.

Some operators choose not to measure semi-traces that are smaller than a given threshold value t; this process is here referred to as **trimming**. If no record is kept of the number of traces that are ignored, this practice has the effect of **truncating** the semi-trace length sample for values less than t. If, on the other hand, a record is kept of the *number* of traces that are not measured, the semi-trace length sample is said to be **censored** for values less than t (Cheeney, 1983). All rock faces are of finite extent, so, for a given discontinuity orientation and scanline position, there will always be some maximum observable discontinuity semi-trace length c that can be observed. This effect is here referred to as **curtailment**. Again, If no record is kept of the number of traces that exceed c, this practice has the effect of truncating the semi-trace length sample for values greater than c. If, on the other hand, a record is kept of the number of traces that exceed c, the semi-trace length sample is said to be censored for values greater than c.

In the Author's opinion it is a wise policy to collect all available data; trimming and truncation should be avoided wherever possible during the sampling process. In theory there will be a number of small discontinuities, with trace lengths of the order of 1 cm or less, that intersect the scanline and that are consciously, or unconsciously, trimmed during sampling. In practice such very small discontinuities, by virtue of their size, are rarely intersected by a scanline, so it is worth taking the trouble to measure those that do. Measurements should be taken on all visible discontinuities that intersect the scanline, including those that are curtailed by extending beyond the edge of the exposure. Trimming, curtailment, truncation and censoring can, however, be imposed artificially to assist with data processing and analysis, as discussed in Chapter 6.

During statistical processing, allowance can also be made for the fact that the scanline will tend to have intersected preferentially discontinuities with longer traces. Although it can be argued that these longer traces are more significant from an engineering point of view and should, therefore, feature more prominently in the sample, it is not satisfactory to replace engineering judgement by this arbitrary sampling bias. In the Author's opinion it is preferable to remove all sampling bias and then to examine the true discontinuity network data, taking into account not only discontinuity size but other properties such as orientation, frequency and strength. A number of techniques for removing sampling bias, and for determining the distributional form and the distribution parameters of discontinuity size measurements taken at planar rock faces of limited extent are discussed in Chapter 6.

Termination   It can be helpful to keep a record of the nature of the termination of each semi-trace. The following recording scheme has proved to be adequate: 'I' or 1: discontinuity trace terminates in intact rock material, 'A' or 2: terminates at another discontinuity, 'O' or 3: termination is obscured. A trace can be obscured by blocks of rock, scree, soil, vegetation or by extending beyond the limits of the exposure. Obscuring in this way has the effect of curtailing the sample of semi-trace lengths for values larger than a variable length that depends upon the geometry of the rock face, the location of the discontinuity within the face and the orientation of the discontinuity. This complex problem is discussed in Chapter 6. ISRM (1978) have proposed a termination index T_i as follows

$$T_i = \frac{100 \, N_i}{N_i + N_a + N_o} \%$$ (2.2)

where N_i, N_a and N_o are, respectively, the total number of discontinuities whose semi-trace terminations are in intact rock, at other discontinuities or are obscured, calculated for the complete scanline sample or for a specified discontinuity set. A large value of T_i indicates that a large proportion of discontinuities terminate in intact rock, suggesting that the rock mass contains many intact rock bridges rather than being separated into discrete blocks. It might be expected, therefore, that a rock with a high termination index would be relatively stiffer and stronger than a mass with a lower index, that it would not be susceptible to rigid block failures and would have a lower mass permeability. The nature of the discontinuity termination does not, however, provide complete information about the discontinuity network. The number of discontinuities intersected by a given discontinuity also has a major influence on these rock mass properties. The number of such intersections depends upon a complex interaction between discontinuity orientation, frequency and size, as discussed in Chapters 3, 4 and 6. The influence of discontinuity geometry on rock mass permeability is investigated further in Chapter 11.

Roughness   Surface irregularities with a wavelength less than about 100 mm are here referred to as roughness and can be expressed in terms of Barton's Joint Roughness Coefficient (*JRC*) described in Chapter 9. Roughness can be measured by taking an impression or profile of the surface then digitising and quantifying the result in the form of a *JRC* value (Clerici *et al.*, 1990; Maerz *et al.*, 1990). For most practical purposes, however, it is sufficient to assess *JRC* visually by reference to the example profiles presented in Figure 9.4. Before embarking on the assessment of discontinuity roughness on a particular site it can be advantageous to obtain specimens of discontinuities with a wide range of roughnesses, and to conduct the simple block sliding test described in Chapter 9, to determine the respective *JRC* values. The specimens can then be retained to provide examples to assist with the visual assessment of roughness. The resulting *JRC* values provide a basis for predicting the strength and deformability of the discontinuities, by applying the methods explained in Chapters 9 and 10.

Curvature   Surface irregularities with a wavelength greater than about 100 mm are here referred to as curvature. Curvature can be determined by measuring offsets at 100 mm intervals along a straight base line, then digitising and quantifying the resulting profile (ISRM, 1978). As with roughness, it is often sufficient to assess curvature visually. A five point scale ranging from 1 = planar to 5 = very curved is satisfactory for most purposes. Alternatively, initial letters of descriptive terms that are appropriate for a particular site, such as 'Stepped', 'Undulating' and 'Planar', can be adopted to provide a direct link with rock mass classification systems. It should also be recognised that variability in discontinuity orientation measurements is often simply a reflection of irregular discontinuity geometry. Indeed, ISRM (1978) have proposed a method for assessing large scale irregularities by taking orientation measurements using a compass fitted with back-plates ranging in diameter between 50 and 400 mm. Although it is likely that highly curved discontinuities will offer greater resistance to shear failure, there are at present no simple techniques for incorporating readings of curvature into a rigorous analysis of discontinuity deformability and shear strength, in the manner developed by Barton and his co-workers for smaller scale roughness features.

Undulations, corrugations, slickensides and other orientated features can impart anisotropy to the measured roughness and curvature. The orientations of such features, expressed in terms of their pitch in the plane of the discontinuity, should be measured and recorded in the comments column.

Comments The comments column is used to provide additional qualitative information about each discontinuity in abbreviated form. There is little point in recording this information on an *ad hoc* basis; it is preferable to decide what additional information is required on a particular site, bearing in mind the use to which the discontinuity data will be put. Quite specific qualitative information is required for the rock mass classification schemes discussed in section 2.6 and Appendix C. The following information may be recorded:

- Type of discontinuity. Size, orientation, surface geometry and other clues may together indicate whether the discontinuity is a fault, joint, bedding plane, cleavage, blasting crack or other feature (Chapter 1).
- Broken or obscured rock. Zones of broken or heavily fractured rock, or areas of the rock face that are obscured, should be described and recorded in terms of their extent along the scanline.
- Nature of infill. Close inspection will reveal whether the discontinuity is clean or is in-filled with clay or mineral deposits. Familiarity with a particular site will facilitate the recognition of infill minerals such as calcite, chlorite, ilmenite, iron oxide and quartz.
- Aperture. The aperture, or opening, of a discontinuity can be estimated with feeler gauges or measured by other more sophisticated techniques (Chapter 11). It should be noted, however, that discontinuity apertures exposed at rock faces are highly sensitive to blast vibrations, block movements and local weathering effects.
- Water flow. It can be helpful to note those discontinuities that show signs of water flow or seepage and to estimate the quantity and the position on the face where the water is emerging.
- Slickensides. These scratch marks on the surface of discontinuities indicate the direction of previous shear displacement. If they are present their orientation should be recorded in terms of their pitch.
- Sample locations. The scanline distance of samples of discontinuities and rock material should be recorded.

A wide range of descriptive terms can be adopted in the comments column to describe various discontinuity and rock material properties. It is useful to define terms such as 'polished', 'irregular', 'broken', 'sheared' and 'softened' for a particular site and to devise unambiguous abbreviations for the commonly used terms. When computer analysis methods are to be employed it is necessary to abbreviate comments and descriptions by the use of specified reference letters and/or numbers. Physical specimens exhibiting these characteristics should be kept on display to provide a consistent basis for the use of these terms. It should also be made clear whether the absence of a particular term, or the omission of a comment should be taken to imply the absence or the converse of a particular property. For example, whether the absence of any indication of aperture should be taken to indicate that the discontinuity is closed, or whether the absence of any comments about infill or surface staining should be taken to indicate that the discontinuity has a clean surface.

If comments on specific characteristics are judged to be of major importance, it may be desirable to create specific additional columns to accommodate a range of accepted abbreviations. For example a column on discontinuity type may contain the abbreviations Fa (fault), J1, J2, J3 etc. (joint set 1, 2, 3 etc.), Be (bedding plane), Cl (cleavage), Bl (blasting crack) and so on. A column on discontinuity aperture may contain an estimate of the aperture range in millimetres. The exhaustive completion of such additional columns can, however, significantly slow down the sampling process and can reduce the amount of quantitative data collected over a given period. It should also be recognised that it can be extremely difficult to draw together extensive descriptive comments for a sample containing several hundred discontinuities, to provide a meaningful overall picture of the rock mass.

2.3.2   Window sampling

Alternative discontinuity measurement techniques have adopted window sampling, to provide an area-based sample of discontinuities exposed at a given rock face (Pahl, 1981). The preliminaries and measurement techniques are essentially the same as for scanline sampling except that **all** discontinuities that have a portion of their trace length within a defined area of the rock face are measured, rather than only those that intersect the scanline. Although this approach reduces the sampling biases for orientation and size created by linear sampling, problems of discontinuity curtailment remain where the rock face is of limited extent.

The sampling window can be defined by setting up a rectangle of measuring tapes pinned to the rock face. The window should be as large as possible in order to minimise sampling bias effects, with each side of a length such that it intersects between about 30 and 100 discontinuities. Where possible at least two windows of similar dimensions should be set up on adjacent rock faces of different, and preferably orthogonal, orientations.

The method proposed by Pahl (1981), summarised in section 6.4, requires that three classes of discontinuities are measured:

(i)   Discontinuities that intersect the window and have **both** ends visible in the window are said to be **contained** within the window.
(ii)   Discontinuities that intersect the window and have **only one** end visible in the window are said to **dissect** the window. The other end is obscured by extending beyond the limits of the window.
(iii)   Discontinuities that intersect the window and have **neither** end visible in the window are said to **transect** the window. Both ends are obscured by extending beyond the limits of the window.

For the purposes of estimating mean trace length it is only necessary to count the numbers of discontinuities in each of the three classes and then to apply the methods in section 6.4. The method is best implemented by taking a colour photograph of the face and then producing a large print. An appropriate window can then be drawn on a transparent overlay and the discontinuity traces for each observed set can be traced off, using a different coloured pen for each set. It is then a relatively simple matter to count the numbers of contained, dissecting and transecting discontinuities for each set. Although relatively straightforward, this photographic window sampling method suffers from a number of disadvantages. Its primary shortcoming is that it does not provide any information on discontinuity orientation, frequency, surface geometry or the qualitative characteristics discussed in the previous section; these properties must be sampled physically at the rock face. Areal sampling provides a poor framework within which to collect these data: the window will contain a large number of relatively small discontinuities making it difficult to keep track of which discontinuities have been measured and rendering the process even more laborious than scanline sampling. A second difficulty is that the method can be inaccurate if significant areas of the face are inaccessible or are obscured by loose rock or vegetation cover. The idea of classifying discontinuities according to whether both, one or neither end is visible is, however, valuable and has been adopted by Laslett (1982) and more recently by Villaescusa (1991) in methods that are essentially line sampling within a window.

Before leaving this section it is worth commenting on some of the more promising novel techniques for sampling and measuring discontinuity characteristics. Ord and Cheung (1991) describe an automatic system for measuring the three-dimensional geometry of a rock face. Their system is based on a planar laser, which is aligned at 45° to the rock face so that it draws a stripe across the face, as shown in Figure 2.8. This stripe is distorted by surface relief on the face created by discontinuities, irregular rock breakage and other features. As the laser scans across the face the distorted stripe is monitored by a solid-state video camera linked to a frame grabber. The image is analysed by a PC to generate three-dimensional coordinates of the face on a 512 by 512 grid. Interpretation of the resulting face profile data to obtain information on discontinuity orientations is relatively straightforward; estimation of discontinuity frequency, size, surface geometry, and qualitative characteristics such as infill, presents a more challenging prospect.

Tsoutrelis et al. (1990) have extended the application of photographic techniques to provide a partly automated method for estimating discontinuity orientation, size, spacing, surface geometry and RQD. Photographs of the rock face are first digitised and then interrogated by computerised sampling along horizontal and vertical scanlines. Discontinuity characteristics obtained in this way were found to agree well with values obtained using standard manual procedures. Although photogrammetric methods such as this can

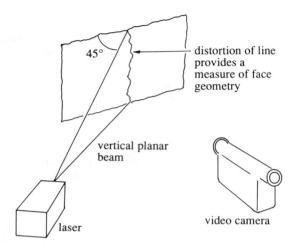

Figure 2.8 Determining the surface geometry of a rock face by laser profiling.

provide only limited information on discontinuity orientation, they are potentially valuable for measuring discontinuity surface geometry both at the small and the large scale.

Other remote techniques such as ground probing radar and seismo-acoustic holography (Sattarov *et al.*, 1990) have not yet proved to be sensitive enough to provide accurate data on discontinuity characteristics. There is no doubt, however, that automated data collection systems such as these will increasingly provide a valuable supplement to manual techniques in the future.

2.4 PRELIMINARY DATA PROCESSING

Readers are advised to consult Appendix B, which contains an introduction to statistical methods, before embarking upon data processing. Discontinuity spacings can be obtained by subtracting consecutive intersection distances for a specified group of discontinuities. Mean discontinuity spacing is usually calculated separately for each identifiable set and then processed to obtain the mean spacing along the normal to each set, following the methods explained in Chapter 5. The concepts of total spacing, set spacing, normal set spacing, the relation between mean spacing, discontinuity repetition and frequency, and the statistical distribution properties of discontinuity spacing are also discussed in Chapter 5.

Field measurements of discontinuity orientation are usually recorded in terms of the dip direction and dip angle of a plane that lies parallel to a portion of the discontinuity. For the purpose of discontinuity orientation analysis, however, it is generally preferable to refer instead to the trend α_n and the plunge β_n of the normal to the plane. Unlike vectors such as force and displacement, the lines referred to above do not necessarily require a prescribed direction. For example, an upward directed normal with a trend/plunge 308/−35 refers to the same plane as a downward directed normal of trend/plunge 128/35. In view of this, it is convenient to work consistently with only the downward directed end of a given orientated line. This approach ensures that all angles of plunge are positive and makes it possible to apply equations 1.1 and 1.2 to calculate α_n and β_n for each discontinuity in a particular sample.

An increasing amount of data plotting and processing can now be conducted by computer using programs such as CANDO for the analysis of discontinuity orientation (discussed in Chapter 3), and CANDIS for the analysis of discontinuity size (discussed in Chapter 6). In view of this, it is desirable to type the relevant data into an appropriate file by means of a convenient word processor system, for subsequent access by the data analysis programs. The intersection distances should be re-ordered manually at this stage to ensure that they increase sequentially. Qualitative data can be included in such a file by adopting an agreed coding system to represent the various properties listed in section 2.3.1. It is recommended that the general format of the scanline logging sheet in Figure 2.3 is adopted for this data file. It is important that scanline orientation and rock face orientation values are also recorded in this file as headers. These orientations can be included as negative values to indicate the start of a new group of scanline data, with the end of the scanline being indicated by a negative intersection distance. This system avoids the need to count the number of data lines. The first four and final two lines of such a data file may appear as follows:

```
Scanline 7, Linwood Quarry, location 25
−7   −25   −165   −05   −253   −63
0.05   146   75   3.5   1   1.4   3   9   2   7   2   16
0.17   283   36   4.5   2   2.5   1   5   4   0   3   8
     .
     .
     .
16.8   132   63   5.0   1   1.6   3   9   1   7   1   16
−1.0
```

These data refer to scanline number 7 at location 25 of trend/plunge 165/05 set up on a face of dip direction/dip angle 253/63. The first discontinuity occurs at an intersection distance of 0.05 m, has a dip direction/dip angle 146/75, a trace length above the scanline of 3.5 m terminating in intact rock (termination code 1) and a trace length of 1.4 m below the scanline obscured in some way (termination code 3). The discontinuity has a Joint Roughness Coefficient of 9 and a curvature index of 2 (in the range 1 to 5). Additional qualitative data are represented by the numbers 7, 2 and 16. The second discontinuity does not exhibit the first qualitative property, so a zero has been entered in the appropriate field. The end of the data for this scanline is indicated by the negative intersection distance -1.0. The accidental omission of a data field can be detected prior to processing by checking that the intersection distances increase sequentially. An alpha-numeric header has been included to make the data file more readable. The above data file structure has been designed specifically to allow the rapid input of large volumes of scanline data. Those who have sufficient confidence in their portable PCs can, of course, input the data directly on site. In such cases it is desirable to generate a hard copy at regular intervals to minimise the risk of losing data as a result of battery failure or computer malfunction.

2.5 GEOSTATISTICAL METHODS

2.5.1 Introduction

It is assumed throughout this book that the mean values of discontinuity properties such as orientation, frequency and size do not vary significantly across the zone of interest. This assumption makes it possible to undertake a sampling and data processing exercise within the zone to establish these mean values and then to apply the results to rock mass classification, stability analysis, rock mass modelling, support design and other applications of rock engineering. Although discontinuity characteristics are sampled along a scan-line, the spatial distribution of the properties measured are not considered explicitly in the analysis described in this book. Discontinuity characteristics, like other rock properties, must, of course, vary with distance to some degree. This spatial variability only becomes a problem, however, when the zone of interest is sufficiently large, or when the rate of change is rapid enough, to create a significant change in properties. For most practical purposes, significant spatial variability can be accommodated by dividing the zone of interest into smaller domains within which the rock properties are assumed to be constant. The boundaries of such domains are usually dictated by major structural features such as folds, faults, volcanic vents and mineralised zones, by changes in lithology or by weathering effects. Kulatilake *et al.* (1990b), examining structural homogeneity in the Stripa mine, identified 10 m wide statistically homogeneous regions in order to build a stochastic model for discontinuity orientation. If spatial variability is significant, however, it becomes desirable to incorporate the physical location of, as well as the values observed at, sample points in any statistical analysis.

The problem of spatial variability is of particular relevance to the estimation of the grade of an orebody; the following hypothetical example will serve to introduce the concept. The process of diamond drilling, sampling and assay for a particular newly-discovered gold-bearing orebody might yield values of ore grade, expressed as grammes of gold per tonne of rock, at 0.5 m intervals along vertical boreholes sunk on a 15 m grid. It is the nature of most mineral-

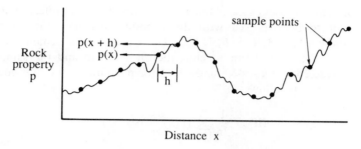

Figure 2.9 Sampling rock properties along a line.

isation processes that ore grades vary significantly with distance. The aim is, therefore, to delineate zones of the orebody that offer an economic prospect for mining under the prevailing commodity prices. It would, of course, be possible to sink further boreholes on a 5 m grid to provide more information, but this exercise could prove to be too expensive and time-consuming at this preliminary phase. An alternative approach is to try and estimate ore grades between and beyond the boreholes. The process of mineralisation often creates a pattern of ore grades that vary in a highly complex but smooth manner across the orebody. This pattern makes it reasonable to assume that the best estimate of unknown grade at a particular location is strongly influenced by the known grade at the geometrically closest sample point. Known grades that are further away are likely to give a poorer indication of the unknown grade, while known grades beyond a certain critical distance are unlikely to be of any predictive value at all.

2.5.2 The semi-variogram

The intuitive ideas presented above form the basis of the branch of mathematics and statistics known as geostatistics; the prefix 'geo-' emphasises the geometrical and not the geological nature of the statistical analysis. Clark (1979) provides a highly readable practical introduction to the subject; Journel and Huijbregts (1978) provide a more comprehensive mathematical text. It is the aim of this short section to investigate whether the methods of geostatistics, which have found wide application in the mining industry, could be of any value in studying the spatial variability of discontinuity characteristics. It is first necessary to review some of the fundamental principles of geostatistics.

Figure 2.9 shows a graph of how a particular rock property might be expected to vary in a continuous way with distance x along a particular line. The dots indicate samples of the property, taken at intervals along the line. Let $p(x)$ be the value of the property measured at a certain distance x along the line, and $p(x + h)$ be the value measured at distance $x + h$. Consider a total of n pairs of sampled values each taken a distance h apart, referred to as the spacing (not to be confused with discontinuity spacing). For example, if sample numbers 1, 2, 3, 4, 5, 6, 7, 8 . . . etc. were taken at distances of 0, 0.5, 1.0, 1.5, 2.0, 2.5, 3.0, 3.5 m . . . etc., then h = 0.5 m and the sample pairs would be 1&2, 2&3, 3&4, 4&5 and so on for n sample pairs. We now define the quantity $\gamma(h)$ as follows

$$\gamma(h) = \frac{1}{2n} \sum_{i=1}^{n} [p(x) - p(x + h)]^2 \tag{2.3}$$

where the index i points to the n sample pairs. The term inside the summation is, in some respects, like the experimental variance of a sample, discussed in Appendix B and defined in equation B.2. To acknowledge this similarity, and to emphasise the factor of 2 in the denominator, the quantity $\gamma(h)$ is referred to as the experimental semi-variogram. It is possible to repeat the calculation in equation 2.3 for other values of h from the same sample. For example we could choose h = 1.0 m and take sample pairs 1&3, 2&4, 3&5 etc., then h = 1.5 m with sample pairs 1&4, 2&5, 3&6 and so on. Each different value of h is likely to give a different value of the quantity $\gamma(h)$. It is instructive to plot a graph of $\gamma(h)$ versus h to give a visual indication of the properties of the semi-variogram over a range of spacing values. As in conventional statistics, where probability density functions have been formulated to model observed histograms, in geostatistics theoretical semi-variograms have been formulated to model experimental semi-variograms.

Four examples of theoretical semi-variograms that have found practical application are shown in Figure 2.10. The theoretical semi-variogram in Figure 2.10a is the spherical model, given by

$$\gamma(h) = C\left(\frac{3h}{2a} - \frac{h^3}{2a^3}\right) \qquad \text{for } h \leqslant a$$
$$\gamma(h) = C \qquad \text{for } h > a \tag{2.4}$$

The semi-variogram $\gamma(h)$ is less than C when h is less than a. This property implies that there is some spatial correlation between values when h is relatively small. This correlation decreases as h increases and is lost when h exceeds a. The parameter a is called the **range of influence** of the model; the constant C in this and other models is usually referred to as the **sill** and is equal to the sample variance. Figure 2.10b shows the so-called nugget effect model. This second model is, in effect, a spherical model for which the range is very small. The nugget effect is produced where the grade, or other property being investigated, is distributed randomly through the rock mass. The third semi-variogram, in Figure 2.10c, is the exponential model given by

$$\gamma(h) = C\left(1 - \exp\left(\frac{-h}{a}\right)\right) \tag{2.5}$$

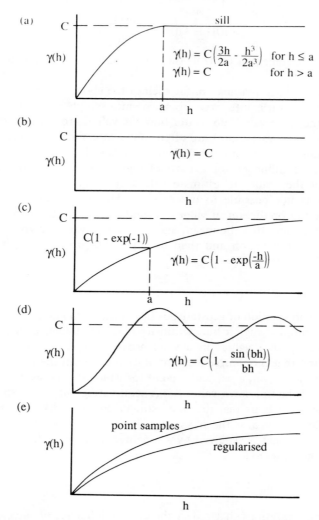

Figure 2.10 Examples of semi-variograms: (a) spherical; (b) nugget effect; (c) exponential; (d) hole-effect; (e) regularisation.

The semi-variogram for this model asymptotes to C for large values of h, so the effective range of influence is theoretically infinite. The semi-variogram when h = a is $\gamma(a) = C(1 - \exp(-1))$. Figure 2.10d shows a semi-variogram that displays a non-monotonic characteristic, referred to as the hole-effect model. This behaviour, which may reflect an underlying periodic characteristic in the spatial variation, can be modelled by an expression of the following form

$$\gamma(h) = C\left(1 - \frac{\sin(bh)}{bh}\right) \tag{2.6}$$

where b is a constant that controls the wavelength of oscillation about the sill value C.

The theoretical semi-variogram for each of the above models when h = 0 is $\gamma(0) = 0$. This result is intuitively obvious, since sample points at zero spacing must yield the same value, no matter how the values are spatially distributed. Experimental semi-variograms are often found to conform to one of these, or to combinations of these and other theoretical models.

The range of influence for a particular group of values provides a good indication of the ability to estimate values at locations that have not been sampled. It is not possible to use existing data and to apply geostatistical methods for the prediction of values beyond the range. In such regions it is necessary to assume that the mean, and the sample variance given by the sill, are relevant in the region and then to apply the principles of conventional statistics.

2.5.3 Kriging

The valuable application of geostatistics lies in the estimation of values that are beyond the sampled region but within its range of influence. Suppose that a particular group of l values in a sequence of sampled values are X_1, X_2, $X_3 \ldots X_l$, and that the sample location of each is within the range of, but at a different distance from, a particular point for which it is necessary to obtain an estimate X_e of the unknown value X_v. A semi-variogram with a shape like the spherical model tells us that the best estimate for X_e is likely to be closer in value to that observed at the physically closer sample points. This principle leads to the idea that X_e is given by a weighted average of the l values that lie within the range, as follows

$$X_e = \sum_{i=1}^{l} w_i X_i$$

where w_i are weightings that reflect the greater influence of the closer sample points. This principle is implemented in geostatistics through a process known as **kriging**, named after its inventor D. G. Krige. In essence, the aim of kriging is to establish an optimum set of values for the l weights w_i according to the following criteria:

(i)   The estimate is unbiased; i.e. the sum of the l weights w_i must be unity, and

(ii) the variance of the estimate or 'kriging variance' $E\{[X_v - X_e]\}^2$ must be a minimum.

The first criterion imposes a relatively straightforward constraint. Satisfaction of the second criterion is not, however, simple because X_v is unknown.

Kriging systems involving the application of Lagrangian multipliers and the solution of $l + 1$ simultaneous equations to determine the optimal weights, are described by Journel and Huijbregts (1978). The resulting group of optimal weights depends only upon the nature of the experimental or theoretical semi-variogram and upon the geometrical disposition of the sample points and the unknown value. Kriging can be applied equally well to non-monotonic semi-variograms, such as the hole-effect model in Figure 2.10d, where the semi-variogram for closely spaced points can be more than that for more widely spaced points. A semi-variogram model such as this would lead to a spatial variation in optimal weights that reflects the underlying periodic characteristic.

2.5.4 Application of geostatistics to discontinuity analysis

In order to determine any property of a rock mass, whether it is ore grade, specific gravity or mean discontinuity spacing, it is necessary to sample and test a finite volume of rock. It so happens that the sample volume required to determine properties such as ore grade is of the order of a few cubic centimetres, while the sample volume required to determine discontinuity characteristics such as mean discontinuity spacing depends on the spacing values themselves and would generally be of the order of several cubic metres. Although the necessity to sample over large volumes such as this may increase the scale of the geostatistical analysis of discontinuity characteristics, it does not necessarily diminish its effectiveness. It is important to appreciate, however, that averaging any property over a specified volume involves taking an implicit or explicit mean of a number of values. The central limit theorem, discussed in section 5.4.2, tells us that the observed variance of the sample is inversely proportional to the number of values in the sample, so larger sample volumes will yield lower variances. This effect, which is referred to as regularisation in geostatistical texts, reduces the sill level for the particular semi-variogram by an amount that depends on the sample size at each location, as illustrated in Figure 2.10e.

Miller (1979) was one of the first to apply geostatistical methods to discontinuity analysis. Depending on the purpose of the exercise, it is generally desirable only to consider discontinuities that lie within a specified orientation range, or that belong to a particular set when calculating the semi-variogram. Taking all discontinuities whatever their orientation and size provides an indication of the overall fracturing pattern. Miller considered three alternative methods for obtaining a sample of discontinuity spacing at each location. These methods are best illustrated by a simple example. Table 2.1 lists the intersection distances for the first 20 discontinuity traces intersected by a long hypothetical scanline.

(i) *Discontinuity spacing by sequence*. In this method each discontinuity spacing is calculated and assigned a sequence number. The sequence numbers

Table 2.1 Hypothetical discontinuity intersection distances

Discontinuity	Intersection distance (m)	Discontinuity	Intersection distance (m)
1	0.0	11	2.18
2	0.19	12	2.22
3	0.26	13	2.26
4	0.41	14	2.31
5	0.70	15	2.38
6	0.89	16	2.59
7	1.03	17	2.74
8	1.32	18	2.90
9	1.66	19	2.92
10	1.94	20	3.19

and discontinuity spacings for the above data would be (1, 0.19), (2, 0.07), (3, 0.15) and so on. The semi-variogram for data presented in this way is based only upon sequence. The concept of sample spacing h is replaced by sample sequence, so that parameters such as the range of influence a would be interpreted as 'number of discontinuity spacings'.

(ii) *Discontinuity spacing by distance*. This approach assumes that each discontinuity spacing occurs at the discontinuity intersection point. The intersection points and associated spacings for the above data would be (0.19, 0.19), (0.26, 0.07), (0.41, 0.15) and so on. It is not possible to select a single sample spacing *h* for discontinuity data processed in this way because the sample locations are a direct function of the varying sample values.

(iii) *Mean discontinuity spacing by distance*. The difficulties created by considering each discontinuity spacing as a separate sample value can be overcome by calculating mean spacing over a specified range of scanline distance. The resulting mean is assumed to occur at the mid-point of the associated scanline range. For example, if we select a scanline range of 1.0 m for the above data, the numbers of discontinuities encountered in the 1st, 2nd and 3rd metres are 6, 4 and 9, respectively, giving sample distances and mean spacings of (0.5, 0.167), (1.5, 0.25), (2.5, 0.111) and so on. This last approach involves a degree of regularisation and an associated reduction in the sill value. In practice it may be preferable to retain the original frequency values, rather than compute the mean spacing over a short length of scanline, giving sample distances and frequencies for the above example of (0.5, 6), (1.5, 4), (2.5, 9) and so on.

Villaescusa and Brown (1990) applied the three methods outlined above to investigate whether there was any spatial correlation in joint spacing and joint locations for the most prominent sets at a number of sites. They found that a semi-variogram based on joint spacing by sequence for the Brisbane ignimbrites resembled the nugget effect model, but was not perfectly flat and

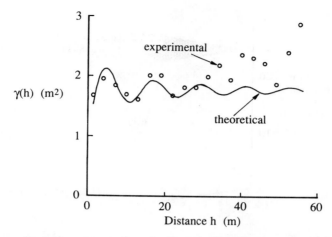

Figure 2.11   Semi-variogram of joint frequency with respect to distance, Elura mine (after Villaescusa and Brown, 1990).

had a sill that was too low for a pure nugget effect. They found that semi-variograms based on discontinuity spacing by distance for the Brisbane ignimbrites could be described by a spherical model with a range of 32 m, but that those for the Panguna andesite conformed to a modified hole-effect model with ranges of influence between 8 and 30 m. Figure 2.11, after Villaescusa and Brown (1990), is a semi-variogram of joint frequency with respect to distance for measurements at the Elura mine. Villaescusa and Brown concluded that the periodic characteristics in these data, and also the data for the Panguna andesite, could be represented by a modified hole-effect model with ranges between 15 and 30 m. They found that joint frequency by distance semi-variograms for the Brisbane ignimbrites conformed to a spherical model with a range of 25 m.

La Pointe and Hudson (1985) applied geostatistical methods to the analysis of jointing patterns in the Niagra dolomite, Wisconsin. Figure 2.12 is a two-dimensional fracture frequency semi-variogram based on 3 m scanline segments for an area dominated by two sub-vertical joint sets. The darker plateau area indicates the sill for these data, with ranges of approximately 18 m along trend 019°, 28 m along 071° and 22 m along 111°.

There are powerful arguments that support the application of geostatistical methods to discontinuity analysis. In particular it seems logical to process the spatial data that have been collected along a scanline or borehole rather than to discard them. The resulting semi-variograms give a clear indication of any spatial correlations and provide a basis for extrapolating the data and for planning further investigations. It must be acknowledged, however, that semi-variograms based on discontinuity spacing or frequency generally indicate a fairly weak spatial correlation. It is not clear at this stage whether it is possible

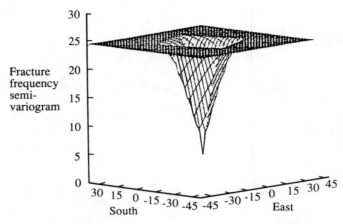

Figure 2.12 Two-dimensional fracture frequency semi-variogram, Niagra dolomite (after La Pointe and Hudson, 1985).

effectively to apply geostatistical techniques to the investigation of other discontinuity characteristics, such as size and orientation.

2.6 ROCK MASS CLASSIFICATION

The aim of rock mass classification is to process information on rock material properties, discontinuity characteristics and excavation geometry to obtain representative values that provide a rational basis for rock engineering decisions. The most widely used classification systems are the Rock Mass Rating (RMR) System proposed by Bieniawski (1973) and the Q-system developed by Barton *et al.* (1974). Bieniawski (1989) provides a comprehensive description of these and other rock mass classification systems. He goes on to discuss applications of these classifications for excavation and support design in tunnelling and mining, for the estimation of rock mass strength and rock mass deformability and for the assessment of slope stability. He summarises 351 case histories where the RMR and Q-systems have been applied and concludes with a listing of a BASIC program for the calculation of RMR on a PC.

Tables and figures in Appendix C summarise the main features of the RMR and the Q-system rock mass classification schemes. Readers are urged to consult the text by Bieniawski (1989) if they wish to learn more about these schemes and their applications in rock engineering. It is appropriate, however, to make some brief observations on how the fundamental principles of discontinuity analysis discussed in this book interface with the empirical principles of rock mass classification.

The development of rock mass classification schemes has proceeded largely independently of research on discontinuity sampling and analysis over the last 20 years. As a consequence, rock classification schemes have not been designed to accept statistical information about the discontinuity network and rely to a large extent upon personal judgement. There are a number of areas of difficulty that merit discussion:

RQD   The Rock Quality Designation, discussed in sections 2.2 and 5.3, is one of the most important parameters in both the RMR and the Q-systems. It is shown in Chapter 4 that discontinuity frequency, and therefore RQD, can vary significantly with borehole orientation in a given rock mass. Vertical boreholes in a rock mass with well-developed vertical jointing would present a grossly optimistic impression of RQD. It is shown in Chapter 5 that the conventional RQD is relatively insensitive to changes in mean discontinuity spacing above about 0.3 m. These issues, together with the fact that RQD also depends upon practical factors such as borehole diameter and drilling methods, make it necessary to question the adoption of RQD in its present form as a primary component in rock mass classification.

Discontinuity orientation   In the RMR scheme the rating for discontinuity orientation is based on an essentially qualitative assessment of how favourable the orientation of the 'dominant' discontinuity set is for the particular tunnel, mine, foundation or slope. If there is no dominant set the ratings for each set are averaged to obtain the overall orientation rating. This averaging procedure is also applied when estimating the rating for discontinuity condition where there are several sets. Presumably a form of weighted average should be taken that reflects the relative frequencies of the various sets. The Q-system takes account of discontinuity orientation simply on the basis of the number of sets. Those who refer to Chapter 3 will see that the highly variable nature of discontinuities makes it necessary to describe their orientation in a statistical way that recognises sampling bias and that provides an objective basis for the identification and analysis of preferred orientation. Depending on which clustering algorithm and parameters are adopted it is generally possible to identify anything between 1 and 10 sets for a given group of orientation readings. Discontinuity orientation data should, therefore, be incorporated in a way that reflects the mean orientation, the degree of clustering and the normal frequency for each set together with the frequency of the background randomly orientated component. The interaction between a given pattern of discontinuity orientations and a particular rock face is a complex problem that should be tackled by applying methods such as those discussed in Chapters 8 to 10 and not purely by subjective assessment.

Discontinuity spacing   Although this property is reflected in the RQD, discontinuity spacing provides a separate rating in the RMR system. It is not clear which of the definitions of spacing in section 5.1 is applicable nor is it specified whether the mean, mode, median or maximum spacing should be adopted. Where there are several sets, presumably the relevant spacing is the mean spacing along the mean normal for each set, with the ratings for the sets being combined in the form of a weighted average. Laubscher (1977 and 1984) went some way towards addressing these criticisms with a modified spacing rating system for hard rock masses containing up to three discontinuity sets, as shown in Figure C.1.

Discontinuity size   The above comments about discontinuity spacing are also applicable to discontinuity size. Reference to Chapter 6 will show that discontinuity size is one of the most difficult discontinuity characteristics to quantify. This property is incorporated in the RMR scheme through the 'condition of discontinuities' rating but does not appear explicitly in the Q-system. Again it is not clear which of the measures of discontinuity size, such as trace length and diameter, discussed in Chapter 6 is applicable nor is it specified whether the mean, mode, median or maximum size should be adopted. There is a link between linear discontinuity frequency, volumetric density and size (section 6.6) so some measure of discontinuity size is incorporated in the classification schemes through such parameters as RQD and discontinuity spacing.

Qualitative parameters   Rock mass classification schemes are particularly valuable for taking account of those discontinuity characteristics that are difficult to measure and/or quantify on a statistical basis. These characteristics, which include the nature of infill, degree of weathering, water condition and to some extent aperture, surface geometry and stress reduction effects, can be assessed visually by an experienced geologist or engineer and then assigned an appropriate rating.

It is acknowledged that rock mass classification schemes have been adopted widely not only for preliminary excavation and support design but also to provide input parameters for rock mass strength criteria (section 9.4). A large group of engineers and geologists with expertise in the use of the classification schemes has developed over the years while an impressive inventory of published experience of the applications and limitations of the schemes has been built up. The value of these schemes lies in their relative simplicity and the fact that they force engineers and geologists to work through the complete check-list of classification parameters for the rock material and discontinuity network.

Many of the comments in this section are critical of existing rock mass classification schemes, so it is appropriate to outline an alternative approach. It is suggested that the rock mass should be classified on the basis of the following parameters determined from rigorous borehole sampling, scanline sampling and laboratory testing:

1. strength parameters for the intact rock material (not considered here),
2. number of sets, mean orientation and Fisher's constant for each set (Chapter 3),
3. mean normal frequency for each set plus isotropic frequency (Chapters 4 and 5),

4. mean size (trace length or disc diameter) for each set plus isotropic size (Chapter 6),
5. mean shear strength characteristics for each set (Chapter 9),
6. mean normal and shear stiffness characteristics for each set (Chapter 10), and
7. mean physical or effective hydraulic aperture for each set (Chapter 11).

The relative importance of these parameters in controlling the stability, support requirements or general performance of a given excavation will depend on the orientation and geometry of the excavation, excavation methods, support systems, stress conditions, water conditions and over-riding qualitative factors such as geological uncertainty concerning the possible occurrence of a single major fault, a zone of weak material or the like. The impact of these factors can be assessed through rock mass modelling procedures described in Chapters 7 to 11. The discontinuity network can be input to these models either in the form of a simplified idealisation (sections 7.4, 8.2 to 8.5, 9.3 and 10.5) or as a random realisation (sections 6.7, 8.6, 8.7, 11.5 and 11.8). The predictions of these models should be interpreted in the context of additional qualitative properties and uncertainty factors that were not input to the models.

It is hoped that as the reader works through this book he or she will begin to appreciate how rigorous discontinuity analysis can supplement and extend existing rock mass classification schemes.

EXERCISES FOR CHAPTER 2 AND APPENDICES B AND C

2.1

The data listed below are the intersection distances for 100 discontinuities sampled by a scanline 10.04 m long and measured in metres from the zero end of the scanline. By taking a class interval of 0.05 m, construct a histogram to demonstrate that the discontinuity spacings accord reasonably well with the negative exponential distribution.

0.20	1.85	4.18	6.98	8.96
0.25	2.11	4.26	7.07	8.99
0.32	2.13	4.30	7.08	9.01
0.42	2.23	4.39	7.17	9.15
0.47	2.59	4.40	7.19	9.19
0.51	2.64	4.47	7.22	9.26
0.54	2.76	4.48	7.54	9.28
0.60	2.84	4.99	7.64	9.32
1.10	3.00	5.27	7.84	9.36
1.15	3.17	5.65	7.85	9.49
1.18	3.18	5.80	8.01	9.56
1.20	3.23	5.88	8.05	9.57
1.26	3.45	5.90	8.06	9.58
1.33	3.53	6.04	8.13	9.66

continued overleaf

1.40	3.66	6.10	8.34	9.79
1.43	3.71	6.33	8.45	9.89
1.62	3.72	6.46	8.67	9.92
1.73	3.77	6.59	8.71	9.97
1.81	3.97	6.68	8.80	10.03
1.82	3.98	6.89	8.81	10.04

2.2

In a total scanline sample of 147 semi-traces from a particular discontinuity set, 67 were observed to terminate at other discontinuities, 41 terminated in intact rock, 15 extended beyond the edge of the rock face and the terminations of the remainder were obscured by scree. Calculate the termination index for this sample.

2.3

Taking the observed discontinuity frequency over each 1 m range of the scanline data listed in Exercise 2.1, calculate the experimental semi-variograms for scanline distances h = 1 m and h = 2 m.

2.4

A site investigation for a proposed 4 m diameter tunnel to be driven horizontally in the direction 245° at a depth of 60 m in an undisturbed, slightly weathered, fractured, water bearing sandstone revealed the following data:

Mean uniaxial compressive
strength of the rock material   55 MPa
Rock Quality Designation   70%

Discontinuity set	Mean spacing along normal to set (m)	Mean dip direction for set (Degrees)	Mean dip angle for set (Degrees)	Mean discontinuity length (m)
1	0.4	160	40	5
2	0.4	325	35	5
3	0.8	060	65	2

The geologist described discontinuity sets 1 and 2 as 'curved on the large scale, with a generally smooth surface geometry and a localised 1 mm thick surface coating of fine-grained soft material'. Set 3 was described as 'generally planar with a smooth, slickensided surface and no infilling, with apertures generally less than 1 mm'. Estimate the Rock Mass Rating for the rock adjacent to the tunnel.

Answers to these exercises are given on pages 460–1.

3

Discontinuity orientation

3.1 INTRODUCTION

The previous chapter described techniques for sampling and conducting preliminary processing of discontinuity data. One of the most important characteristics of discontinuities is their orientation, relative both to each other and to any engineering structure or excavation face. Discontinuity orientation data can be presented and utilised in design by two different methods: if the rock face at the design site is readily accessible the locations and orientations of actual discontinuities can be measured and used explicitly in the design calculations. If, however, the rock face is not accessible it is necessary to measure discontinuity orientation at other rock faces, or from boreholes, and build up a statistical model that represents the discontinuity orientation characteristics of the rock mass. In most cases the statistical model is based on the fact that geological processes usually generate one or more clusters (or **sets**) of nearly parallel discontinuities in a given rock mass.

This chapter is primarily concerned with the latter of the above methods. The first part of the chapter deals with aspects of sampling discontinuity orientation data, and the graphical and vectorial representation of these data. A method for eliminating sampling bias will be presented and incorporated into an algorithm for identifying clusters of preferred orientation. A vectorial method for determining representative orientations for sets will be introduced and linked to a statistical analysis of set data based on the Fisher distribution. Finally, a Pascal computer program CANDO, based on the methods explained in this chapter, for rapid analysis of large volumes of discontinuity orientation data will be outlined. One of the main features of this chapter is the use of examples to illustrate the data processing methods. The aim of these examples

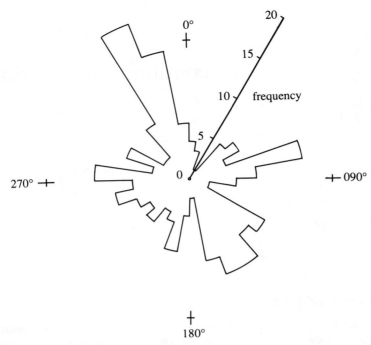

Figure 3.1 Rose diagram for discontinuity dip direction, Chinnor UK, Location 2, 226 values.

is to illustrate principles rather than to simulate an actual data processing exercise. For this reason, and to save space, data volumes have been kept to an absolute minimum. Numerical results in these examples are presented to more significant figures than are warranted by the nature of the data and the precision of the measurement techniques. These extra significant figures are provided to allow the reader to work through the calculations by hand and to check intermediate results without being troubled by accumulated round-off errors.

3.2 GRAPHICAL REPRESENTATION OF ORIENTATION DATA

One of the simplest forms of graphical representation is the rose diagram (Attewell and Farmer, 1976; Cawsey, 1977). This approach is particularly suited to cases where most of the discontinuities have angles of dip in excess of about 60°. In such cases the dip direction data are of primary significance and can be plotted on a simple circular histogram. The 0 to 360° circle is divided into convenient class intervals, usually of 5, 10 or 15° depending upon the sample size, and the number of dip direction values in each class interval is

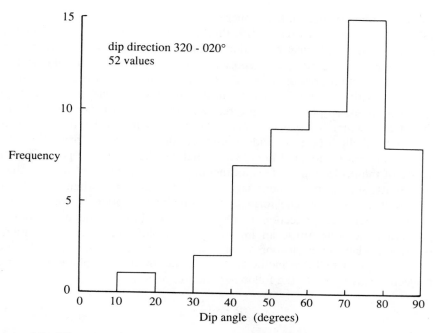

dip direction 320 - 020°
52 values

Figure 3.2 Histogram for discontinuity dip angle, Chinnor UK, Location 2, dip direction range 320 to 020°.

counted. The results are plotted as wedges which have a radial extent that is proportional to the frequency in each class interval. This frequency can be expressed either as a raw number, as a proportion or as a percentage of the total sample size. The rose diagram in Figure 3.1 based upon a sample of 226 discontinuities obtained by Priest (1975), shows how the orientation and the relative significance of clusters of preferred dip direction are clearly visible. In the Author's opinion, there is little point in plotting rose diagrams based upon strike direction, since this produces a duplication of information across the rose diagram and an associated loss of dip direction data.

The disadvantage of rose diagrams is that they contain no information on dip angle. This disadvantage can be overcome to some extent by selecting data from the more significant class intervals and then plotting a histogram of dip angles. The histogram in Figure 3.2, based upon 52 values from Figure 3.1 with a dip direction in the range 320 to 020°, shows that 33 of the discontinuities in this range have an angle of dip greater than 60°; only one discontinuity has an angle of dip less than 30°. In this case, then, the rose diagram provides a reasonable representation of discontinuity orientation.

The difficulties of representing three-dimensional orientation data in two dimensions on a sheet of paper can be overcome by adopting the technique known as stereographic, or hemispherical, projection (Duncan, 1981; Goodman, 1976; Kalkani and von Frese, 1979; Phillips, 1971 and Priest, 1985). The basic principle of hemispherical projection is that the orientation of a line in three-dimensional space is uniquely represented by the position of a point within a circular projection area of radius R. The perimeter of this projection area is associated with the circle of geographical azimuth directions so that the radius on which the point plots is given directly by the trend direction, α, of the line that it represents. It is usual to mark the north (azimuth 0°) direction with a small line labelled 'N' to provide a reference direction on the projection. This convention will be adopted here. The radial distance, r, of the point from the centre of the projection circle is a function of the plunge, β, of the line that it represents, subject to the boundary conditions that $r = 0$ when $\beta = 90°$ and $r = R$ when $\beta = 0$. The form of the functional relation between r and β depends upon the projection method adopted. Two of the most common projection methods utilise an imaginary hemisphere of radius R positioned below the plane of projection so that its circular face forms the projection circle. The first of these methods, termed the lower hemisphere equal angle projection, gives rise to the following relation between r and β

$$r = R \tan\left(\frac{90° - \beta}{2}\right) \qquad (3.1)$$

The second method, termed the lower hemisphere equal area projection, gives the following relation

$$r = R \sqrt{2} \cos\left(\frac{90° + \beta}{2}\right) \qquad (3.2)$$

A full discussion of the properties and the relative merits of these two methods of projection is given by Priest (1985). An explanation of the main techniques involved in plotting and analysing orientation data is given in Appendix A together with a series of simple examples.

Example 3.1 (Figure 3.3)

Plot on a lower hemisphere equal angle projection of 90 mm diameter, points representing the line of maximum dip and the normal to a plane of dip direction/dip angle 146/57.

Solution
The trend and plunge of the line of maximum dip α_d, β_d are given directly by the dip direction and dip angle of the plane. Hence $\alpha_d = 146°$ and $\beta_d = 57°$. The trend and plunge of the normal α_n, β_n are, by equations 1.1 and 1.2, respectively, 326° and 33°. The point D, representing the line of maximum dip, and the point N, representing the normal, plot along radii of azimuths

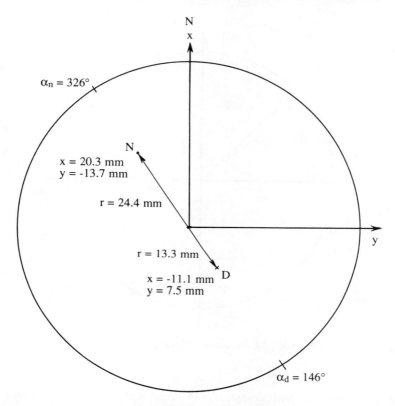

Figure 3.3   Lower hemisphere equal angle projection of the line of maximum dip, D, and the normal, N, of a plane of dip direction/dip angle 146/57, Example 3.1.

146° and 326°, respectively, on the '90 mm diameter' projection circle in Figure 3.3. (The actual printed diameter may not be exactly 90 mm.) Setting $R = 45$ mm in equation 3.1 puts the point D 13.3 mm from the centre, and the point N 24.4 mm from the centre of the projection. It is worth pointing out that the point N, representing the normal to the plane, should not be confused with the label 'N', denoting the north point on the perimeter of the projection.

If a large number of data points are to be plotted it is usually quicker to adopt computer graphics in preference to manual plotting methods. Figure 3.4 shows a circular projection area of radius R related to the x,y Cartesian coordinate system of Figure 1.2 in which positive x is horizontal to the north (trend 000°) and positive y is horizontal to the east (trend 090°). The x,y Cartesian coordinates of a point on the projection representing a line of trend/plunge α/β are given in Table 3.1 for equal angle and equal area projections. The x,y coordinates for the points D and N in Example 3.1,

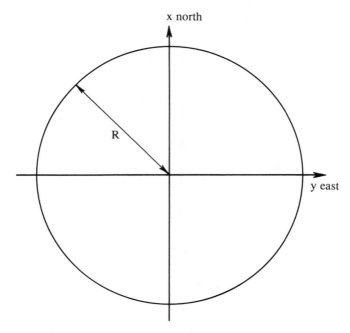

Figure 3.4   Two-dimensional Cartesian coordinate system.

Table 3.1   The x,y Cartesian coordinates of a point representing a line of trend/plunge α/β on a lower hemisphere projection of radius R

	x coordinate (north 000°)	*y coordinate (east 090°)*
Equal angle	$R \cos \alpha \tan\left(\dfrac{90° - \beta}{2}\right)$	$R \sin \alpha \tan\left(\dfrac{90° - \beta}{2}\right)$
Equal area	$R \sqrt{2} \cos \alpha \cos\left(\dfrac{90° + \beta}{2}\right)$	$R \sqrt{2} \sin \alpha \cos\left(\dfrac{90° + \beta}{2}\right)$

determined from the top row of Table 3.1, are given in Figure 3.3. It is a relatively straightforward matter to write a computer program that utilises the expressions in Table 3.1 to enable automatic plotting of data.

   Large numbers of discontinuity orientation values can be plotted on a lower hemisphere projection to give a graphical representation of the orientation properties of the rock structure. The best approach is to plot only the points representing the normals to each discontinuity plane. It is often feasible to use symbols of different shapes to represent different types of discontinuities

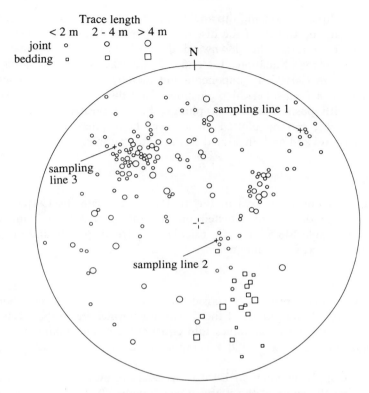

Figure 3.5   Lower hemisphere, equal angle plot of discontinuity normals (after Priest, 1985).

(joints, bedding planes, faults etc.) and to use symbols of different sizes to represent a range of discontinuity sizes. An example of such a plot, from Priest (1985) is reproduced in Figure 3.5. Plots of this type permit the identification of groups of sub-parallel discontinuities, or **sets**, that have been produced by a single geological process (Price, 1966). The orientation of these sets, and the degree of clustering within each set, can have a major influence on the engineering performance of the rock mass. It can be beneficial, therefore, to apply quantitative methods in the analysis of discontinuity orientation data, to provide an objective assessment of any preferred orientation.

3.3 VECTORIAL REPRESENTATION OF ORIENTATION DATA

Vectorial methods provide a powerful tool for the representation and analysis of discontinuity orientation data. Adopting the Cartesian coordinate system of Figure 1.2, equations 1.1, 1.2 and 1.6 allow discontinuity orientation data measured as dip direction and dip angle α_d/β_d to be converted to the Cartesian components u_x, u_y and u_z of the discontinuity normal. For this purpose it is convenient to consider the downward directed unit vector normal to the discontinuity plane. Equations 1.4 and 1.5 give the trend and plunge of a vector of known Cartesian components and thereby permit its graphical representation on a hemispherical projection. Only downward directed vectors, associated with positive values of plunge, β, and positive values of the z components, u_z, can be plotted on a lower hemisphere projection. These principles are revised and illustrated in the next example.

Example 3.2

Utilising the co-ordinate axes in Figure 1.2 (i) calculate the Cartesian components of the downward directed unit vector normal to a plane of dip direction/dip angle 146/57, and (ii) calculate the trend, plunge and magnitude of a vector with x, y, z components 1.36, -2.85, -1.93.

Solution
(i) This is the plane previously considered in Example 3.1. By equations 1.1 and 1.2 the trend and plunge of the downward normal are, respectively, 326° and 33°. Substituting these values into equations 1.6, and taking a vector of unit magnitude, gives x, y and z components of 0.695, -0.469 and 0.545, respectively.

(ii) Before applying equation 1.4 it is necessary to evaluate the parameter Q by examining the signs of the x and y components. In this case, since the x component is positive and the y component is negative, Table 1.1 gives $Q = 360°$. Equation 1.4 gives $\alpha = 295.5°$; equation 1.5 gives $\beta = -31.4°$. By equation 1.3 the vector has a magnitude of 3.70. It is important to note that the vector has a negative plunge; this means that it has an upward sense and cannot be plotted directly on to a lower hemisphere projection. The line of action of the vector can, however, be represented on a lower hemisphere projection by taking its reverse or downward directed end. The Cartesian components of this reverse vector, found by multiplying the original components by -1.0, are -1.36, 2.85 and 1.93. The parameter Q in equation 1.4 for this reverse vector is 180°, giving $\alpha = 115.5°$. Equation 1.5 gives $\beta = 31.4°$ for this reverse vector. When this reverse vector is plotted as a point on a lower hemisphere projection it is necessary to annotate it to record its magnitude and also the fact that the original vector has an upward sense.

3.4 ORIENTATION SAMPLING BIAS DUE TO A LINEAR SURVEY

Although the linear sampling regime of the scanline survey produces an objective sampling strategy it does introduce an orientation sampling bias. One of the first to analyse this bias was Terzaghi (1965), who advocated the application of a geometrical correction factor based on the observed angle between the sampling line and the normal to a particular discontinuity. Others who have considered this problem include Baecher (1983), Kulatilake and Wu (1984b) and Priest (1985). Before proceeding with the use of a correction factor it is first necessary to understand the exact nature of the orientation sampling bias introduced by a linear survey.

Consider a single planar discontinuity with a normal of trend/plunge α_n/β_n and surface area A. The probability, P_s, that a randomly located long scanline of trend/plunge α_s/β_s will intersect, and thereby sample, this discontinuity is directly proportional to the area, A_s of the discontinuity projected on to a plane normal to the scanline direction. Hence

$$P_s \propto A_s$$

But
$$A_s = A \cos \delta \qquad (3.3)$$

where δ is the **acute angle** between the discontinuity normal and the sampling line.

So
$$P_s \propto A \cos \delta \qquad (3.4)$$

The angle δ can be determined either graphically from a hemispherical projection, by vector algebra methods or from the following expression

$$\cos \delta = |\cos(\alpha_n - \alpha_s) \cos \beta_n \cos \beta_s + \sin \beta_n \sin \beta_s| \qquad (3.5)$$

The absolute value function in equation 3.5 ensures that the angle δ is always acute; this property is important in subsequent analysis. The highest probability of intersection, P_{sm}, occurs when $\delta = 0$ and $A_s = A$. The lowest probability of intersection is zero; this occurs when $\delta = 90°$ and $A_s = 0$. Any scanline sample will, therefore, be biased to contain a lower proportion of those discontinuities that happen to have a higher value of δ. This reduced proportion can be expressed by the ratio

$$\frac{P_s}{P_{sm}} = \cos \delta$$

This reduced sample size at the higher values of δ can be compensated for by assigning a higher weighting to those discontinuities that *are* sampled. A discontinuity with a normal of trend/plunge α_n/β_n sampled by a scanline of trend/plunge α_s/β_s is assigned a weighting w given by

$$w = \frac{1}{\cos \delta} \qquad \delta < 90° \qquad (3.6)$$

where cos δ is given by equation 3.5. For a large sample size this weighting will serve to balance the orientation sampling bias introduced by linear sampling. When δ approaches 90°, w becomes very large, to the extent that a single data point could dominate the distribution pattern, as shown in the next example. To avoid this it may be desirable to set a maximum allowable weighting. A maximum value of 10 has been adopted in the program CANDO presented later in this chapter, corresponding to δ = 84.3°. This means that all discontinuities whose normals make an angle of more than 84.3° with the sampling line will have their maximum weighting arbitrarily limited to 10. Although it is desirable to keep analyses of size and orientation separate, it would be a relatively simple matter to provide an additional weighting that is proportional to the area (or trace length) of each discontinuity in the sample, thereby giving greater emphasis to the larger features. If such a weighting were used it should also take account of the size sampling bias imposed by a linear survey, as discussed by Priest and Hudson (1981) and also in Chapter 6. This bias is caused by the fact that a sampling line will already have tended to sample preferentially those discontinuities of a larger area, as shown by equation 3.4.

If each discontinuity normal is represented by a downward directed vector, the weighting w can be regarded as the **magnitude** of this vector. Utilising the Cartesian system in Figure 1.2 the components of this weighted normal vector are, from equation 1.6, given by

$$n_x = w \cos \alpha_n \cos \beta_n$$
$$n_y = w \sin \alpha_n \cos \beta_n \qquad (3.7)$$
$$n_z = w \sin \beta_n$$

Example 3.3

Part of a sample obtained from a scanline of trend/plunge 128/15 contains discontinuities of dip direction/dip angle (i) 297/73 (ii) 162/49 and (iii) 133/18. Calculate the weighting factor for each discontinuity required to compensate for the orientation sampling bias, and hence determine the components of the respective weighted normal vectors.

Solution
It is first necessary to apply equations 1.1 and 1.2 to find the trend and plunge of the normal to each discontinuity. The weighting factor for each is found by applying equations 3.5 and 3.6, noting that in this case $\alpha_s = 128°$ and $\beta_s = 15°$. The results are listed in Table 3.2. The Cartesian components of the weighted normal vectors, found from equations 3.7, are listed in Table 3.3.

It is interesting to note that in the above example the theoretical weighting factor of 19.531 for discontinuity (iii) is considerably higher than those for the

Table 3.2 Weighting factors for Example 3.3

Discontinuity	a_d/β_d	a_n/β_n	δ Degrees	Weighting factor w
(i)	297/73	117/17	10.8	1.018
(ii)	162/49	342/41	64.2	2.301
(iii)	133/18	313/72	87.1	19.531

Table 3.3 Cartesian components for weighted normal vectors in Example 3.3

Discontinuity	Cartesian components of the weighted normal vector		
	n_x	n_y	n_z
(i)	−0.442	0.867	0.298
(ii)	1.652	−0.537	1.510
(iii)	4.116	−4.414	18.575

other two. This is because the discontinuity plane lies almost parallel to the scanline and so the angle δ is close to 90°. The assumption is that this single discontinuity represents 18 or so other discontinuities of similar orientation that were not intersected by the scanline due to their lying almost parallel to the sampling line. Without further sampling it is impossible to tell whether these other discontinuities actually exist or not. Great care must be exercised when interpreting data that contain high weighting values such as this. The approach adopted here, that of limiting the maximum weighting to 10, provides a reasonable compromise for most applications. Yow (1987) approached this problem by considering the error ε associated with taking orientation measurements. Yow then linked this error with the angle δ between the discontinuity normal and the sampling line, to produce an expression for the normalised maximum weighting factor error $w_{\varepsilon,\max}$. He showed that for an orientation measurement error ε (degrees), this maximum weighting factor error is given by

$$w_{\varepsilon,\max} = \left(\frac{\cos \delta}{\sin(90° - \delta - \varepsilon)} - 1 \right) \times 100\%$$

For example, if the random error in orientation measurements is expected to be 1°, and a maximum allowable error $w_{\varepsilon,\max}$ of 20% is permitted, then solving the above expression indicates that δ is approximately 84°. This result indicates that a maximum weighting factor of $1/\cos 84° = 9.6$ would be appropriate in these circumstances.

The bias compensation methods described above will result in a list of orientation values, each of which is associated with a weighting factor. If the data are presented graphically on a hemispherical projection, each data point must be annotated to record the associated weighting factor. Since visual interpretation of the resulting matrix of numbers could be difficult, it is recommended that alternative approaches to orientation data analysis are adopted. One of these alternatives, which involves contouring the weighted data points, is described in detail by Priest (1985) and also by Ragan (1985), and will be mentioned only briefly here. Computerised plotting and contouring methods have been discussed by Attewell and Woodman (1971), Kalkani and von Frese (1979), Beasley (1981) and by Bridges (1990).

Essentially the process of contouring involves setting up a small moving sample-window on the lower hemisphere projection. This sample-window is usually circular with a radius r_w that is 1/10th of that of the projection, thereby giving a window area that is 1% of the area of the projection circle. The window, drawn on a transparent plastic film, is moved systematically so that its centre is positioned at the intersection points of a square grid that has a grid dimension r_w and is positioned beneath the projection. The weighted sample size within the circular window is counted for each grid intersection point and then recorded on a blank transparent sheet superimposed on the projection. As the circular window is moved from grid point to grid point a matrix of numbers is generated which provides a moving average of weighted sample size per 1% area of the projection. These values can be converted to a percentage of the total weighted sample size for all of the data on the projection and then contoured by hand. A typical result from Priest (1985), presented in Figure 3.6, illustrates how a contoured projection provides an easily interpreted picture of the major clusters of discontinuity orientation in a given rock structure. The major disadvantages of contouring are that the process is largely subjective and provides no quantitative information about the mean orientation and degree of clustering within each set. An alternative approach to the analysis of discontinuity orientation data, which involves the statistical analysis of the orientation data expressed in vectorial form, is presented in sections 3.4 to 3.6.

Before proceeding with the vectorial analysis of weighted orientation data, it is worth commenting on a simple practical step that can be taken to minimise the orientation sampling bias. If the geometry of the rock face permits, it may be possible to conduct two, or ideally three, mutually orthogonal scanline surveys of approximately the same length at a given location, adopting the methods explained in Chapter 2. This sampling scheme, adopted by authors such as Bridges (1990), will ensure that any discontinuities which, by virtue of a large angle δ, tend to be ignored by one scanline will be sampled prefer-

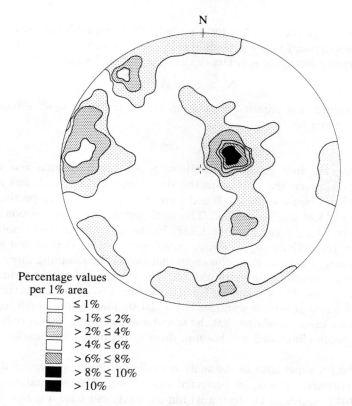

Figure 3.6 Contoured lower hemisphere projection (after Priest, 1985).

entially along another. The aggregated values from the orthogonal scanlines
will, therefore, produce a relatively unbiased sample of the discontinuity
orientation data. Although the bias is reduced, it is not in fact completely
eliminated, as the following example will show.

Example 3.4

A set of parallel planar discontinuities of dip direction/dip angle 135/55 is to be
sampled by two groups of three mutually orthogonal scanlines of equal length.
In the first group the scanlines have trends/plunges of (a) 000/00, (b) 090/00
and (c) 000/90. The second group of scanlines have trends/plunges of (a)
045/00, (b) 135/55 and (c) 315/35. Determine the ratio of the expected sample
sizes of the discontinuity set for the two groups of scanlines.

Solution
The expected sample size, N_s, for a particular set of parallel discontinuities is directly proportional to the probability, P_s, that a given scanline will intersect a discontinuity from that set. Hence, using equation 3.4

$$N_s \propto P_s \propto A \cos \delta$$

If it is assumed that scanline orientation has no influence upon discontinuity area, for a given set

$$N_s \propto \cos \delta$$

Considering the first group of scanlines, which are horizontal and vertical, the angles between the normal to the discontinuity set, which has a trend/plunge 315/35, and scanlines a, b and c are, by equation 3.5, respectively $\delta_a = 54.6°$, $\delta_b = 54.6°$ and $\delta_c = 55.0°$. The total sample size is proportional to $\cos 54.6° + \cos 54.6° + \cos 55.0° = 1.732$. In the second group of scanlines the angles are, respectively, $\delta_a = 90°$, $\delta_b = 90°$ and $\delta_c = 0$. This second group of scanlines has, of course, been chosen so that two of the sampling directions are parallel to the specified discontinuity set. The total sample size is proportional to $\cos 90° + \cos 90° + \cos 0 = 1.0$. Hence the ratio of the expected sample sizes for the two groups of scanlines is 1.732:1.0. This result, which represents two extreme cases, confirms that the orientation sampling bias is reduced but not completely eliminated by choosing three orthogonal scanlines.

One of the principal aims in the analysis of discontinuity orientation data is to identify clusters, or sets, of preferred orientation. The orientation of these sets, and the degree of clustering within each set, can have a major influence on the engineering properties of the rock mass. The final three sections in this chapter are devoted to identifying and delimiting the orientation boundaries of sets, determining a representative orientation for a set, and the statistical analysis of data within a given set by means of the Fisher distribution model.

3.5 IDENTIFYING AND DELIMITING SETS

Hemispherical projection methods were introduced earlier as a graphical approach to the analysis of orientation data. Clusters, or sets, of preferred orientation, such as those in Figures 3.5 and 3.6, can be identified by eye. The orientation limits for each set can then be specified either in terms of a range of trend and plunge angles, as an angular range from an axis near the centre of the cluster or by the manual delineation of a range of orientations. This method has the advantage of allowing an individual's expertise and familiarity with a particular site to play a part in the identification of clusters. In advocating this subjective approach, Bridges (1990) emphasises the value of human capabilities in pattern recognition where there are complex and overlapping clusters of discontinuity orientation. The approach has the disadvantage of being almost entirely subjective and therefore susceptible to personal bias and inconsistency, particularly when weighting factors have been applied. The human eye can also become distracted by the perimeter of the hemi-spherical projection, which presents an arbitrary boundary to the orientation pattern.

A rigorous and less subjective approach to the analysis of clusters in orien-tation data was presented by Shanley and Mahtab (1976) and later modified by Mahtab and Yegulalp (1982). Their clustering algorithm is based upon the assumption that a discontinuity set will exhibit a significantly greater degree of clustering than a totally random distribution of orientations. The probabilities associated with random events can be expressed in terms of the Poisson process, where the probability, $P(t,v)$, of exactly t events occurring in an interval of size v is given by

$$P(t,v) = \frac{e^{-\lambda v}(\lambda v)^t}{t!} \tag{3.8}$$

where t is an integer and λ is the event frequency per unit dimension (time, distance, angle etc.). In the present context the interval v can be regarded as a range of orientations for the discontinuity normals. This range can be specified in terms of a cone angle ψ about some specified axis of trend/plunge α_a/β_a. Such a cone angle will contain a proportion c of all possible uniformly dis-tributed orientations on the hemisphere, given by

$$c = 1 - \cos \psi \tag{3.9}$$

If the sample space of all possible orientations on the hemisphere is con-sidered to be of unit size, then the interval $v = c$. For a total sample size of n discontinuity normals the event frequency λ will, therefore, be equal to n. Substituting for v and λ in equation 3.8 gives

$$P(t,c) = \frac{e^{-nc}(nc)^t}{t!} \tag{3.10}$$

where c is given by equation 3.9. Equation 3.10 gives the probability that exactly t discontinuity normals occur within an angle ψ of a specified axis set up in a group of n randomly orientated normals. The probability, $P(>t,c)$, of more than t randomly orientated discontinuity normals occurring within a cone angle ψ is given by simple summation as follows

$$P(>t,c) = 1 - \sum_{j=0}^{t} \frac{e^{-nc}(nc)^j}{j!} \tag{3.11}$$

where, as before, c is given by equation 3.9 and j is an integer pointer.

For given values of n and c, as t is increased the probability $P(>t,c)$ decreases. For the analysis of orientation data, Mahtab and Yegulalp identified a critical value of t, here termed the critical frequency t_{crit} and defined it as the smallest value of t for which $P(>t,c) \leqslant s$, where s is a limiting probability. Shanley and Mahtab (1976) took s to be 0.05. Mahtab and Yegulalp (1982), taking the limiting probability $s = c$, provided a slightly more discriminating algorithm which will be adopted here.

A suitable cone angle ψ is selected and then the search cone is constructed about the first discontinuity normal in a given sample, utilising equation 3.5. This equation ensures that the smallest (i.e. acute) angle between a pair of normals is always taken. For computer applications it is necessary to inspect all normals in the particular sample to identify, and count, those that make an acute angle of less than ψ with the normal that is currently at the centre of the cone. This process is repeated as the search cone is centred on each discontinuity normal in the sample in turn. Any normal that has t_{crit} or more other discontinuity normals within its search cone angle is said to be **dense** at the angle ψ. It is here suggested that each normal within the cone angle should be counted according to its **weighted** value, to provide compensation for orientation sampling bias, and normalised to preserve the sample size, as explained in the next section. The use of weighted orientation values in this way makes it theoretically feasible to adopt a real, rather than an integer, value for t_{crit}. This option, which would require numerical interpolation for the determination of t_{crit}, has not been adopted here but could be implemented relatively easily.

A discontinuity is considered to be dense because its normal is within an angle ψ of significantly more normals than would be expected from purely random orientations. All pairs of dense points are inspected; if the acute angle between any pair is less than ψ they are deemed to belong to the same cluster. A cluster is allowed to grow or 'chain', linking together dense points of widely different orientations. Any non-dense data points that lie within an angle ψ of a dense point are assigned to the same cluster as the dense point. In many cases discontinuities assigned to one set may become reassigned subsequently to another set. This process, here referred to as 'overlaying', can easily be prevented if desired by modifying the set assignment algorithm. A certain number of non-dense data points may remain unassigned to any cluster. The modified clustering algorithm explained above has been implemented in the Pascal program CANDO. The method for determining the critical frequency t_{crit} is illustrated in the following example.

Example 3.5

A cluster analysis of 162 discontinuity normals is to be conducted by the methods outlined above. Calculate the critical frequency, t_{crit}, for cone angles ψ of (i) 10° and (ii) 20°

Solution
(i) Putting $\psi = 10°$ into equation 3.9 gives $c = 0.0152$. Inputting this value to equation 3.11 for a sample size of $n = 162$ gives the following results:

1st table for Example 3.5

t	$P(>t,c)$
0	0.915
1	0.705
2	0.446
3	0.234
4	0.104
5	0.039
6	0.013

The smallest value of t for which $P(>t, c) \leq 0.0152$ is 6, hence $t_{crit} = 6$.

(ii) Putting $\psi = 20°$ into equation 3.9 gives c = 0.0603. This time equation 3.11 gives the following results:

2nd table for Example 3.5

t	$P(>t,c)$
0	0.999
1	0.999
2	0.997
.	.
.	.
.	.
13	0.119
14	0.072
15	0.041

In this case $t_{crit} = 15$. This higher value for t_{crit} is a direct reflection of the larger cone angle specified in the second part of this example.

It is interesting to note that in the above example the criterion proposed by Shanley and Mahtab (1976) would have given t_{crit} values of 5 and 15 for cone angles of 10° and 20°, respectively. In order to illustrate the clustering algorithm more fully, and to demonstrate the capabilities of the program CANDO, a case study based upon real discontinuity measurements will be pursued during the remainder of this chapter.

Figure 3.7 is a computer-generated equal angle lower hemisphere projection of 407 discontinuity normals, sampled along three scanlines in a chalk quarry in Oxfordshire, UK. These data, from Priest (1975), are labelled according to the scanline along which they were sampled. The scanline orientations are given by the large circles on the projection. Clustering these data at angles

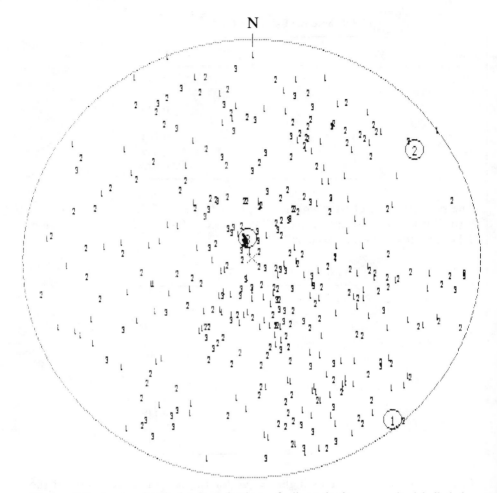

Figure 3.7 Lower hemisphere projection of discontinuity normals labelled by scanline, Chinnor UK, three scanlines, location 7, total of 407 values.

of ψ equal to 5, 10, 15 and 20° gives t_{crit} = 6, 12, 21 and 32, respectively. Clustering at an angle of 18.2° would be equivalent to adopting a limiting probability s = 0.05 and taking c = s in equation 3.11.

The program CANDO was employed to analyse and to plot the data in Figure 3.7. Figure 3.8 is a lower hemisphere projection of the discontinuity normals from Figure 3.7, unweighted for orientation sampling bias, clustered at a cone angle of 15° and labelled according to the set to which they have been assigned. Figure 3.9 shows the same data, weighted for orientation sampling bias and clustered at 15°. The fact that the sets are numbered differently in

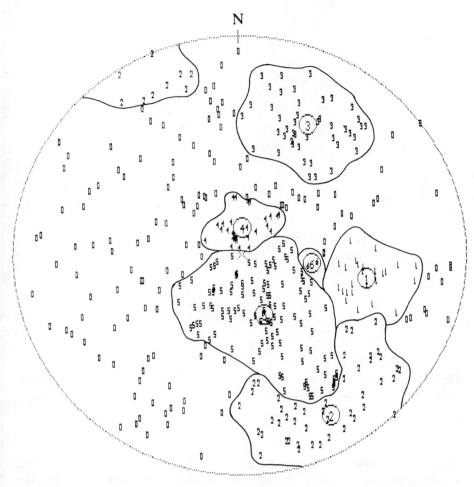

Figure 3.8 Lower hemisphere projection of discontinuity normals labelled by set, **unweighted** and clustered at a cone angle of 15°.

these two figures is simply a consequence of the overlaying process in the clustering algorithm. Discontinuities labelled 0 are not assigned to any set. Although there is broad agreement between the results in Figures 3.8 and 3.9, for example set number 5 in Figure 3.8 corresponds well with set number 3 in Figure 3.9, there are significant differences in detail. For example set 5 in Figure 3.9 does not appear in Figure 3.8; these differences are a result of the weighting process.

The angle ψ adopted for clustering has a significant influence on the number and size of the sets delineated during the clustering process. For example

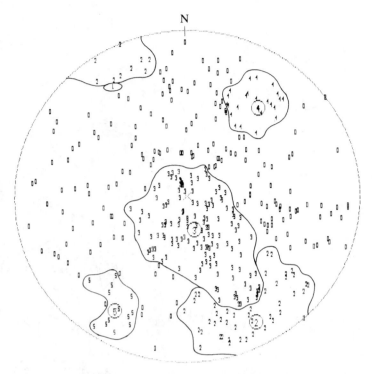

Figure 3.9 Lower hemisphere projection of discontinuity normals labelled by set, **weighted** and clustered at a cone angle of 15°.

clustering the unweighted data at angles of 5, 10, 15 and 20° gave 10, 9, 6 and 4 sets respectively; clearly the smaller the clustering angle the larger the number of separate sets that are identified. Clustering at an angle of 15° appears to give the most acceptable results for these data. It is interesting to note that this angle of 15° corresponds to a limiting probability close to the value of 0.05 recommended by Shanley and Mahtab (1976). Although clustering at larger cone angles does not significantly change the number of dense points it does increase the number of non-dense points that are assigned to sets initiated by dense points; this in turn increases the opportunity for chaining and amalgamation of sets. It is this chaining, and the associated overlaying process, that has caused set 3 in Figure 3.9 to 'invade the territory' of set 2, and for set 1 to be obliterated almost entirely by set 2. In the Author's opinion it is entirely appropriate that the choice of the clustering angle ψ remains with the user. In this way he or she can exercise an influence on the clustering process by drawing on personal knowledge of a particular site.

3.6 REPRESENTATIVE ORIENTATION FOR A SET

The orientation limits of each set can be delimited by contouring, by visual inspection of a projection of the discontinuity normals or by applying a clustering algorithm such as the one outlined in the previous section. The result of this process will be a list of orientations and associated weighting values for each set. Depending on how the set delineation was achieved, certain orientation values may appear in more than one set while others may not be assigned to any set. The unassigned data points can be regarded as a background, isotropic or random component in the discontinuity orientation fabric.

The ith of a total of N discontinuity normals in a given sample has a trend α_{ni} and a plunge β_{ni}. The Cartesian components n_{xi}, n_{yi} and n_{zi} of a vector $\mathbf{n}_i$ parallel to this normal are given by equation 3.7. If there is no requirement to correct for orientation sampling bias the magnitude of this vector, w_i can be assigned unit value. If there is a requirement to correct for orientation sampling bias, and the ith normal has been sampled by a scanline of trend α_s and plunge β_s, then the vector is assigned a magnitude, or weighting, $w_i = 1/\cos \delta_i$ where $\cos \delta_i$ is given by equation 3.5. The total weighted sample size, N_w, for the sample is given by

$$N_w = \sum_{i=1}^{N} w_i \qquad (3.12)$$

Each of the weighting factors w_i will be ≥ 1.0. Consequently N_w/N will usually lie between about 1.5 and 5; any statistical analysis based upon the artificially inflated sample size N_w will, therefore, give an erroneous impression of the precision of the data. Noting this fact, Priest (1985) recommended that each vector should instead be assigned a normalised weighting factor w_{ni} given by

$$w_{ni} = \frac{w_i N}{N_w} \qquad (3.13)$$

hence

$$\sum_{i=1}^{N} w_{ni} = N$$

Assigning each normal vector a magnitude w_{ni} ensures, therefore, that the total normalised weighted sample size is equal to the actual sample size, thereby permitting a valid statistical analysis of precision. For some applications it may be preferable to normalise the data on a set by set basis, rather than for the entire sample.

The representative, or mean, orientation for a set containing a total of M orientation values can be taken as the orientation of the resultant vector, $\mathbf{r}_n$ of the normal vectors $\mathbf{n}_i$, i = 1 to M (Watson, 1966). The Cartesian components r_{xn}, r_{yn} and r_{zn} of $\mathbf{r}_n$ are

$$r_{xn} = \sum_{i=1}^{M} n_{xi}$$

$$r_{yn} = \sum_{i=1}^{M} n_{yi} \qquad (3.14)$$

$$r_{zn} = \sum_{i=1}^{M} n_{zi}$$

In cases where a set covers a wide range of orientations, perhaps extending beyond the edge of a lower hemisphere projection, it is necessary to make a special adjustment when determining the mean orientation for the set. This adjustment is necessary because although a pair of normals of trend/plunge such as 125/20 and 305/10 plot on opposite sides of a lower hemisphere projection, they make an acute angle of only 30° with each other, and may well belong to the same set. The resultant of these two normals as listed is almost vertical, clearly an incorrect mean orientation for this 'set'. The solution to this problem is to take the reverse direction of the normal vector (obtained by changing the signs of the three components) for those discontinuities that make a lower hemisphere angle of more than 90° with the set mean, but that are judged to be part of the current set.

The magnitude $|r_n|$, trend α_{nr} and plunge β_{nr} of the resultant vector r_n are found by replacing u_x, u_y and u_z by r_{xn}, r_{yn} and r_{zn}, respectively in equations 1.3, 1.4 and 1.5. The dip direction and dip angle of the plane defined by the mean normal can be found from α_{nr} and β_{nr} by applying equations 1.1 and 1.2 in inverted form. The orientation of the resultant vector r_n, and hence the orientation of the mean plane, will be influenced more by those discontinuities that carry a higher weighting. In this way the orientation sampling bias is eliminated from the final interpretation of the orientation data. It is worth emphasising here that the vector calculations summarised in equations 3.14 should only be conducted on the discontinuity normals and **not** on their lines of maximum dip. A small but significant distortion in the results will occur if lines of maximum dip are used.

The magnitude, $|r_n|$, of the resultant vector provides a measure of the degree of clustering within the set. If $|r_n|/M$ approaches 1.0 the discontinuity normals are closely clustered whereas small values of this ratio indicate widely dispersed orientations.

Example 3.6 (Figure 3.10)

A cluster analysis indicated that the discontinuities listed in Table 3.4 belong to the same set. Determine the representative, or mean, orientation for the set and also the magnitude of the resultant vector (i) without correcting for orientation sampling bias, and (ii) by applying weighting and normalisation procedures to correct for orientation sampling bias.

Table 3.4 Discontinuity orientation data for Example 3.6 (hypothetical data)

Scanline 1, trend/plunge 348/15		Scanline 2, trend/plunge 170/78	
Discontinuity	Dip direction/ dip angle	Discontinuity	Dip direction/ dip angle
1	204/59	18	197/47
2	213/41	19	216/59
3	218/49	20	217/42
4	225/42	21	229/36
5	228/45	22	231/46
6	228/53	23	233/69
7	229/34	24	234/19
8	231/62	25	238/38
9	231/43	26	240/29
10	235/49	27	242/44
11	239/45	28	243/50
12	240/54	29	245/48
13	243/38	30	251/59
14	249/47	31	272/56
15	252/42		
16	255/54		
17	256/66		

Solution

(i) The trend and plunge of the normal to each discontinuity plane are found by applying equations 1.1 and 1.2. These normals are plotted on the lower hemisphere projection in Figure 3.10, as small dots for discontinuities sampled by scanline 1, and crosses for those from scanline 2. The Cartesian components n_{xi}, n_{yi} and n_{zi} of the unweighted vector $\mathbf{n_i}$ normal to the ith discontinuity are found from equations 3.7 by setting the weighting, w, to unity. Some of the resulting values are tabulated below:

Table 3.5 Cartesian components of normals in Example 3.6

Discontinuity i	Trend/plunge of normal	Cartesian components of normal		
		n_{xi}	n_{yi}	n_{zi}
1	024/31	0.7831	0.3486	0.5150
2	033/49	0.5502	0.3573	0.7547
3	038/41	0.5947	0.4646	0.6561
.	.	.	.	.
.	.	.	.	.
.	.	.	.	.

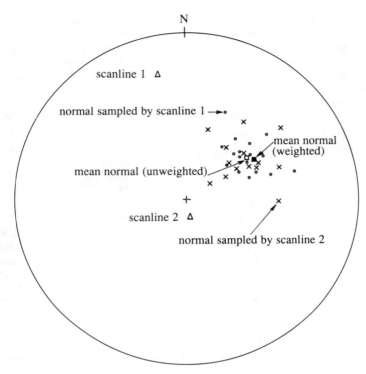

Figure 3.10   Lower hemisphere projection of discontinuity normals for Examples 3.6 and 3.7.

The Cartesian components r_{xn}, r_{yn}, and r_{zn} of the resultant vector, $\mathbf{r_n}$, are found from equation 3.14, noting that the sample size $N = 31$ in this case. This gives $r_{xn} = 12.466$, $r_{yn} = 17.544$ and $r_{zn} = 20.682$. Equations 1.3, 1.4 and 1.5 give the magnitude, trend and plunge of this resultant vector as 29.849, 054.6° and 43.9°, respectively. The orientation of this mean normal is plotted as a small open square on the projection in Figure 3.10. The dip direction and dip angle of the mean plane are, from equations 1.1 and 1.2, 234.6° and 46.1°, respectively.

(ii) The first 17 discontinuities were sampled along a scanline of trend/ plunge, $\alpha_s/\beta_s = 348/15$; the remainder were from a scanline of trend/plunge 170/78. In this example normalisation will be applied to the available data for the single set. The weighting factor, w_i for the ith discontinuity is found from equations 3.5 and 3.6. Equation 3.12 gives the total weighted sample size for this set, N_w, as 71.256. The normalised weighting factor, w_{ni}, for the ith discontinuity is, from equation 3.13 given by $w_{ni} = w_i N/N_w = 0.435 w_i$. The Cartesian components n_{xi}, n_{yi} and n_{zi} of the vector $\mathbf{n_i}$ are given by equations

3.7, by setting the weighting w = w_{ni}. Some of the resulting values are listed below:

Table 3.6 Weighted normal vectors in Example 3.6

Discontinuity i	Trend/plunge of normal	Weighting factors		Cartesian components of normal		
		w_i	w_{ni}	n_{xi}	n_{yi}	n_{zi}
1	024/31	1.2451	0.5417	0.4242	0.1889	0.2790
2	033/49	1.5542	0.6761	0.3720	0.2416	0.5103
3	038/41	1.5664	0.6815	0.4053	0.3167	0.4471
.	.	.	.	.	.	.
.	.	.	.	.	.	.
.	.	.	.	.	.	.

The Cartesian components of the resultant vector are, from equation 3.14, $r_{xn} = 11.677$, $r_{yn} = 19.208$ and $r_{zn} = 19.557$. Equations 1.3 to 1.5 give the magnitude, trend and plunge of this resultant vector as 29.795, 058.7° and 41.0° respectively. The orientation of this mean normal is plotted as a solid square on the projection in Figure 3.10. The dip direction and dip angle of the mean plane are, from equations 1.1 and 1.2, 238.7° and 49.0°.

In the above example the mean orientation for the unweighted values lies only about 4° from that for the weighted and normalised values. This close agreement is attributable partly to the fact that the data are associated with two nearly orthogonal scanlines and partly to the high degree of clustering within these hypothetical data. Priest (1985) has shown that mean orientations for weighted and unweighted data can differ by more than 25° if the set is widely dispersed.

3.7 THE FISHER DISTRIBUTION

Fisher (1953), in an important fundamental analysis of orientation statistics assumed that a population of orientation values was distributed about some 'true' value. This assumption is directly equivalent to the idea of discontinuity normals being distributed about some true value within a set. He assumed that the probability, $P(\theta)$, that an orientation value selected at random from the population makes an angle of between θ and $\theta + d\theta$ with the true orientation is given by

$$P(\theta) = \eta e^{K\cos\theta} d\theta \tag{3.15}$$

where K is a constant controlling the shape of the distribution and η is a variable that ensures the following:

(i) On a unit sphere, the area of an annulus of width $d\theta$ at an angle θ from the true orientation is proportional to $\sin \theta$. The value $P(\theta)$ must, therefore, also be proportional to $\sin \theta$.

(ii) The sum of all possible values of $P(\theta)$ must be unity i.e.

$$\int_0^\pi P(\theta)\,d\theta = 1$$

These requirements give the following value for η

$$\eta = \frac{K \sin \theta}{e^K - e^{-K}} \tag{3.16}$$

Combining equations 3.15 and 3.16, and dividing by $d\theta$ gives the following probability density distribution (see Appendix B)

$$f(\theta) = \frac{K \sin \theta\, e^{K \cos \theta}}{e^K - e^{-K}} \tag{3.17}$$

In view of its simplicity and flexibility, the Fisher distribution provides a valuable model for discontinuity orientation data. It is, however, a symmetric distribution and therefore provides only an approximation for asymmetric data. Einstein and Baecher (1983), Kelker and Langenberg (1976), Mardia (1972) and Watson (1966) describe a number of models, such as the Bingham distribution, that can provide better fits for asymmetric and girdle orientation data. Such models are inevitably more complex, both in their parameter estimation and in the formulation of probabilistic results, and will not be considered here. Interested readers are referred to the above papers for more information on these asymmetric models, and to Schaeben (1984) for a cluster algorithm that is capable of handling orientation data grouped in girdles. It is worth noting that much of the research effort in the area of orientation data analysis has been directed towards developing a range of clustering algorithms and relatively sophisticated models for orientation distributions, while ignoring the important problem of sampling bias.

The parameter K, often referred to as Fisher's constant, is a measure of the degree of clustering, or preferred orientation, within the population. Fisher (1953) shows that a sufficient estimate, k, of the population parameter K can be found from a sample of M unit vectors, for which the magnitude of the resultant vector is $|\mathbf{r_n}|$, by solving the following equation of maximum likelihood

$$\frac{e^k + e^{-k}}{e^k - e^{-k}} - \left(\frac{1}{k}\right) = \frac{|\mathbf{r_n}|}{M} \tag{3.18}$$

Most clusters will yield values of k in excess of about 5; in such cases equation 3.18 reduces to

$$k \approx \frac{M}{M - |\mathbf{r_n}|} \tag{3.19}$$

Fisher (1953) went on to show that, for large values of M, k is given by

$$k = \frac{M - 1}{M - |\mathbf{r_n}|} \tag{3.20}$$

Watson (1966) concluded that equation 3.20 is accurate when k exceeds 3. Mardia (1972) suggested that an unbiased estimate of K, when K is large, is given by

$$k = \frac{M - 2}{M - |\mathbf{r_n}|} \tag{3.21}$$

In practice the values of k estimated by equations 3.18 to 3.21 are usually very close, as demonstrated in the next example. Equation 3.20 has been adopted in the program CANDO. The probability $P(\theta_1 < \theta < \theta_2)$ that a random orientation value makes an angle of between θ_1 and θ_2 with the true orientation is given by

$$P(\theta_1 < \theta < \theta_2) = \int_{\theta_1}^{\theta_2} f(\theta) \, d(\theta)$$

Making the substitution $g = \cos \theta$, so that $\sin \theta \, d\theta = -dg$, gives

$$P(\theta_1 < \theta < \theta_2) = \frac{e^{K \cos \theta_1} - e^{K \cos \theta_2}}{e^K - e^{-K}} \tag{3.22}$$

When K is more than about 5 the term e^{-K} becomes very small and can be ignored for most practical purposes. The probability $P(\theta)$ that a random orientation value makes an angle of less than θ with the true orientation is found by letting $\theta_1 = 0$ and $\theta = \theta_2$ in equation 3.22, so that

$$P(<\theta) = \frac{e^K - e^{K \cos \theta}}{e^K - e^{-K}} \tag{3.23}$$

or, for large K, ignoring the term e^{-K}

$$P(<\theta) \approx 1 - e^{K(\cos \theta - 1)} \tag{3.24}$$

and in inverted form

$$\cos \theta \approx 1 + \frac{\ln(1 - P(<\theta))}{K} \tag{3.25}$$

Fisher (1953) also addressed the problem of placing confidence limits on the mean, or resultant vector, $\mathbf{r_n}$. He showed that the probability, $P_r(<\theta)$, that the resultant vector $\mathbf{r_n}$ makes an angle of less than θ with the true orientation is given by

$$P_r(<\theta) = 1 - \left(\frac{M - |\mathbf{r_n}|}{M - |\mathbf{r_n}| \cos \theta}\right)^{M-1} \tag{3.26}$$

and in inverted form

$$\cos \theta = \frac{M - ((1 - P_r(<\theta))^{\left(\frac{1}{1-M}\right)}(M - |\mathbf{r_n}|))}{|\mathbf{r_n}|} \tag{3.27}$$

The following approximations for $P_r(<\theta)$ are valid when M is large

$$P_r(<\theta) \approx 1 - e^{K|\mathbf{r_n}|(\cos \theta - 1)} \tag{3.28}$$

for which the inverse is

$$\cos \theta \approx 1 + \frac{\ln(1 - P_r(<\theta))}{K |\mathbf{r_n}|} \tag{3.29}$$

The equations presented in this section are strictly only applicable where each orientation value has unit magnitude. It is suggested here that these equations also provide valid approximations for data that have been weighted **and** normalised by the methods explained earlier. The final example in this chapter provides an illustration of the practical application of probabilistic results derived from the Fisher distribution.

Example 3.7 (Figure 3.10)

Apply the Fisher distribution to the orientation data in Example 3.6 and hence

(i)   estimate Fisher's constant for the set,
(ii) determine the expected number of discontinuity normals that should lie within (a) 10° and (b) 20° of the true orientation, and
(iii) calculate the angular radius of the zone of (a) 90% and (b) 99% confidence about the resultant vector.

Obtain answers first without correcting for orientation sampling bias and then by applying appropriate weighting and normalisation procedures.

Solution
(i) The magnitude, $|\mathbf{r_n}|$, of the resultant vector for the unweighted data has already been calculated in Example 3.6 to be 29.849. Noting that the sample size M = 31 and applying equations 3.18, 3.19, 3.20 and 3.21 gives the following estimates of Fisher's constant: 26.933, 26.933, 26.064 and 25.195 respectively. The resultant vector for the **weighted and normalised** data was found to have a magnitude of 29.795. Equations 3.18 to 3.21 give the following four estimates of Fisher's constant: 25.726, 25.726, 24.896 and 24.066.

(ii) Adopting the estimate of Fisher's constant of 26.064 for the unweighted data given by equation 3.20 and putting it, together with $\theta = 10°$, into equation 3.24 gives $P(<\theta) = 0.327$. Since there are 31 values, the expected number of normals lying within $10°$ of the true orientation is $31 \times 0.327 = 10.137$. Accepting the unweighted resultant vector as the best estimate of the true orientation, analysis of the data in Example 3.6 shows that 13 discontinuity normals actually lie within $10°$ of the mean. Inputting $\theta = 20°$ to equation 3.24 gives $P(<\theta) = 0.792$. The expected number of normals lying within $20°$ of the true orientation is, therefore, 24.552. In fact 25 normals in Example 3.6 lie within $20°$ of the mean. Since these are hypothetical data, the close agreement between the theoretical and observed frequencies should not be taken as a validation of the applicability of the Fisher distribution. In practice, graphs of the theoretical frequencies predicted by equations 3.23 and 3.24, together with the observed frequencies, for a range of angles θ would provide a good basis for assessing the applicability of the Fisher distribution to a given sample. One such graph is presented at the end of this chapter.

Adopting the estimate of Fisher's constant of 24.896 for the weighted and normalised data, and putting it, together with $\theta = 10°$, into equation 3.24 gives $P(<\theta) = 0.315$. The expected number of weighted normals lying within $10°$ of the true orientation is therefore 9.765. Accepting the weighted resultant vector as the best estimate of the true orientation, and analysing the data in Example 3.6, reveals that 10.006 weighted normals lie within $10°$ of the mean. The corresponding expected and observed frequencies for the weighted data when $\theta = 20°$ are 24.093 and 22.406. Clearly, reasonable agreement with the Fisher distribution can be achieved when the data are weighted and normalised.

(iii) For the unweighted data $|\mathbf{r_n}| = 29.849$, and K is taken to be 26.064. To determine the angular radius, or cone angle, for the zone of 90% confidence we need to calculate θ in equation 3.27 or equation 3.29 when $P_r(<\theta) = 0.90$. Equations 3.27 and 3.29 give angles θ of $4.495°$ and $4.409°$, respectively. The approximation given by equation 3.29 is, therefore, reasonably good. This result can be interpreted to mean that, accepting the Fisher distribution, we can be 90% certain that the true unweighted mean orientation for the set lies within about $4.5°$ of the unweighted resultant vector. For the unweighted data the angular radii given by equations 3.27 and 3.29 for 99% confidence are respectively $6.485°$ and $6.237°$.

For the weighted data $|\mathbf{r_n}| = 29.795$ and K is taken to be 24.896. The angular radii given by equations 3.27 and 3.29 are $4.604°$ and $4.516°$, respectively, for 90% confidence, and $6.641°$ and $6.388°$ respectively for 99% confidence.

At a given confidence level, the area of overlap between the cone angles for weighted and unweighted data provides a measure of the similarity between the predictions of the two approaches to data analysis. If there is only a small

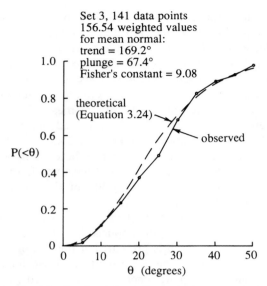

Figure 3.11 Proportion, P(<θ), of weighted discontinuity normals that make an angle of less than θ with the mean normal for set 3 in Figure 3.9.

amount of overlap, orientation sampling bias will significantly influence the conclusions of the analysis. In the above example, based on hypothetical orientation data, the mean normal for the unweighted and weighted data lie approximately 4.2° apart, so there is a moderate overlap between the cones constructed for unweighted and weighted data at both of the selected confidence levels. If the unweighted and weighted mean normals had been further apart, the associated lack of overlap would indicate that accepting the data in unweighted form would have imparted a significant distortion to the interpretation of the orientation data.

Figure 3.11 is a graph of the actual and theoretical (equation 3.24) values of P(<θ) for weighted discontinuity normals from set 3 in Figure 3.9. These data are real orientation values obtained from scanline surveys conducted by Priest (1975). The good agreement between the two curves indicates that the Fisher distribution can provide an adequate model for sets with isotropic distributions of orientation. Equation 3.29 shows that the 90 and 99% confidence cone angles about the mean weighted normal orientation of 169.2/67.4 for the set are 3.46° and 4.89°, respectively. It is interesting to note that for the unweighted data in Figure 3.8, the equivalent set (here set 5) has a mean normal orientation of 161.4/58.2, which, being 9.8° away from the mean weighted normal, is well outside the 90 and 99% confidence cones for the weighted set. In this case, therefore, failure to correct for orientation sampling bias would have had a significant influence on the interpretation of the orientation data.

EXERCISES FOR CHAPTER 3

3.1

It is proposed that discontinuity orientation data will be plotted on an equal angle lower hemisphere projection of radius 45 mm. Taking the +x coordinate axis as north (trend 0°) and the +y coordinate axis as east (trend 090°) calculate the x,y coordinates of points that represent the normals to discontinuities of dip direction/dip angle (i) 074/25 and (ii) 306/69.

3.2

A cluster analysis of 328 discontinuity normals is to be conducted by the methods explained in section 3.5. Calculate the critical frequency, t_{crit}, for cone angles ψ of (i) 5° and (ii) 10°.

3.3

A scanline of trend/plunge 136/55 intersected six discontinuities with the following dip directions/dip angles: 201/39, 213/50, 215/63, 230/52, 247/42 and 253/28. Assuming that these discontinuities belong to the same set, and applying a weighting to correct for orientation sampling bias, calculate: (i) the normalised weighting factors for the six discontinuities, (ii) Fisher's constant for the set normals and (iii) the dip direction/dip angle for the mean plane of the set.

3.4

The normalised and weighted sample size M for a particular discontinuity set is 68. The magnitude $|\mathbf{r_n}|$ of the resultant vector for the normalised and weighted discontinuity normals is 63.75. (i) Estimate Fisher's constant for the set, (ii) determine the expected number of discontinuity normals that should lie within 5° and 10° of the true normal, and (iii) calculate the angular radii of the zones of 80% and 95% confidence.

Answers to these exercises are given on page 461.

4

Discontinuity frequency

4.1 INTRODUCTION

Discontinuity frequency is one of the fundamental measures of the degree of fracturing in a rock mass. Frequency can be expressed in terms of the number of discontinuities that are observed or predicted to occur in a unit volume, a unit area or a unit length of a sample from a given rock mass. The aim of this chapter is to examine the property of discontinuity frequency from a theoretical and a practical point of view. Section 4.2 presents a brief analysis of volumetric and areal frequency. This section is followed by a discussion of linear frequency and how this property is influenced by the number and orientation of discontinuity sets and by the orientation of the sampling line. Section 4.4 contains a detailed investigation of the anisotropy, and the associated extreme values, of linear discontinuity frequency in a rock mass containing several discontinuity sets. The chapter concludes with a discussion of the probabilistic implications of random discontinuity occurrence.

4.2 VOLUMETRIC AND AREAL FREQUENCY

Volumetric frequency, which is the most fundamental of the three measures of discontinuity frequency, is based on the assumption that the occurrence of a discontinuity surface in a rock mass can be represented by the occurrence of a point located at the centroid, or some other unique position, on the discontinuity. The volumetric frequency, λ_v, is the average number of these points per unit volume of rock sample. This volumetric frequency can be applied to all discontinuities in a given mass or to some specified group of discontinuities such as a set defined by a group of similar orientations, as discussed in Chapter

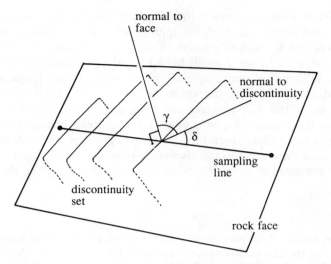

Figure 4.1   Discontinuity set intersected by a rock face and a sampling line.

3. Although volumetric frequency is an attractive measure of frequency in that it provides a fundamental measure of the number of discontinuities in a given rock mass, its direct estimation requires that a volumetric sample of the rock mass be taken and dissected in the manner explained by Fookes and Denness (1969). Moreover, in order to locate the centroids of the individual discontinuities it is necessary that the sample volume is sufficiently large to contain their boundaries. Dissection of large volumes of rock to estimate volumetric frequency in this way is expensive, time consuming and generally impractical. If a measure of volumetric frequency is needed, it is preferable in most cases to estimate it from measurements of areal or linear frequency taken at exposed planar rock faces, following methods such as those explained by Baecher *et al.* (1977). The difficulties associated with locating the centroids of discontinuities can be overcome by expressing discontinuity frequency in terms of the total area of discontinuities per unit volume of rock; this is an estimate of the product of mean discontinuity area and λ_v and is not, therefore, a single fundamental property of the rock structure.

Since many rock exposures are planar, or very nearly so, it is often feasible to express the frequency of discontinuities in terms of their areal frequency. Discontinuities intersecting a planar exposure will produce lines, which will be straight if the exposure and the discontinuities are planar. The occurrence of each discontinuity can be represented by the mid-point of its trace on the exposure. The areal frequency, λ_a, is the average number of these points per unit area of the exposure. As before, areal frequency can be applied to all discontinuities at a given face or to a specified set. The easiest way to sample and to estimate areal frequency is to photograph the rock face, as explained in Chapter 2, and then, after applying appropriate scale corrections, digitise the end points of the discontinuity traces. The resulting values of areal frequency will be sensitive to, in other words biased by, the orientation of the sampling plane. The influence of sampling plane orientation on areal frequency can be appreciated by considering the single set of parallel planar discontinuities illustrated in Figure 4.1. Ignoring the influence of discontinuity shape, the apparent areal frequency λ_{as} of a given set of parallel planar discontinuities exposed on a large planar rock face, or sampling plane, whose normal makes an angle γ with the normal to the discontinuity set can be obtained by applying the simple geometrical arguments adopted in section 3.4, giving the following result

$$\lambda_{as} = \lambda_a \sin \gamma \qquad (4.1)$$

where λ_a is the areal frequency on a sampling plane whose normal lies in the same plane as the discontinuity set . The sine function, rather than the cosine function of equation 3.4, is applicable here because the angle γ is measured between the normals to the sampling plane and the discontinuity set. Clearly when $\gamma = 90°$ then $\lambda_{as} = \lambda_a$, the expected result when the sampling plane is at right angles to the discontinuity set. As the angle γ is reduced the same number of discontinuity traces become spread over a wider area of sampling plane, as illustrated in Figure 4.1; finally $\lambda_{as} = 0$ when $\gamma = 0$. The variation of areal frequency with the orientation of the sampling plane is, in reality, rather more complex than the simple model in equation 4.1 since λ_{as} must also be a function of discontinuity shape.

If the discontinuities are large compared with the area of the exposure or sampling plane, many of them will extend beyond the limits of the exposure and thereby make it impossible to locate their mid-points. As before this problem can be avoided by determining instead the total discontinuity trace length per unit area of exposure; this gives an estimate of the product of mean discontinuity trace length and λ_{as}. The censoring and truncation effects imposed by exposures of limited extent are discussed in more detail in Chapter 6 which deals with discontinuity size and shape.

4.3 LINEAR FREQUENCY

The simplest, and most commonly used, measure of discontinuity frequency is the linear frequency λ defined as the average number of discontinuities intersected by a unit length of sampling line. The widespread use of linear frequency reflects the use of scanlines and boreholes for discontinuity sampling. As before, linear frequency can be applied to all discontinuities or to a specified set. It was shown in Chapter 3 that if the linear frequency along a line constructed normal to a set of parallel planar discontinuities is λ, then the observed frequency λ_s along a sampling line that makes an acute angle δ to the set normal is given by

$$\lambda_s = \lambda \cos \delta \qquad (4.2)$$

It is necessary to stipulate that the angle δ is acute since λ_s must always be positive. If there are D parallel planar discontinuity sets, the total frequency λ_s along the sampling line is given by the sum of the frequency components as follows

$$\lambda_s = \sum_{i=1}^{D} \lambda_i \cos \delta_i \qquad (-90° \leqslant \delta_i \leqslant 90°) \qquad (4.3)$$

where δ_i is the acute angle between the sampling line and the normal to the ith set, and λ_i is the frequency along the normal to the ith discontinuity set. If the sampling line has a trend α_s and a plunge β_s, and the mean normal to the ith discontinuity set has a trend α_{ni} and plunge β_{ni} then using equation 3.5 **without** taking the absolute value

$$\cos \delta_i = \cos (\alpha_s - \alpha_{ni}) \cos \beta_s \cos \beta_{ni} + \sin \beta_s \sin \beta_{ni} \qquad (4.4)$$

It is appropriate at this stage to adopt the vector notation introduced in section 1.2, since it offers an alternative and more economical presentation. If the orientation of the sampling line is represented by the unit vector **s** and the normal to the ith discontinuity set by a unit vector $\mathbf{n}_i$ in the right-handed Cartesian coordinate system of Figure 1.2, their direction cosines are, from equations 1.6, given by

$$s_x = \cos \alpha_s \cos \beta_s$$
$$s_y = \sin \alpha_s \cos \beta_s \qquad (4.5)$$
$$s_z = \sin \beta_s$$

and

$$n_{ix} = \cos \alpha_{ni} \cos \beta_{ni}$$
$$n_{iy} = \sin \alpha_{ni} \cos \beta_{ni} \qquad (4.6)$$
$$n_{iz} = \sin \beta_{ni}$$

The term $\cos \delta_i$ is given by the dot product

$$\cos \delta_i = \mathbf{s}.\mathbf{n}_i \qquad (4.7)$$

or, in full

$$\cos \delta_i = s_x n_{ix} + s_y n_{iy} + s_z n_{iz} \qquad (4.8)$$

If equation 4.4 or 4.8 is to be used to obtain $\cos \delta_i$ in equation 4.3 it is necessary first to ensure that δ_i is acute, i.e. that $\cos \delta_i$ is positive, for each set. This presents no difficulty since it is always possible to take, if necessary, the reverse direction for the normal to a given discontinuity set, to ensure that the frequency component is positive for that set. The reverse direction α'_{ni} β'_{ni} is obtained as follows

$$\text{if } \alpha_{ni} \leq 180° \text{ then } \alpha'_{ni} = \alpha_{ni} + 180°$$
$$\text{if } \alpha_{ni} > 180° \text{ then } \alpha'_{ni} = \alpha_{ni} - 180° \qquad (4.9)$$
$$\beta'_{ni} = -\beta_{ni}$$

The reverse unit vector $\mathbf{n}'_i$ is simply given by

$$\mathbf{n}'_i = -\mathbf{n}_i \qquad (4.10)$$

When input to equations 4.4 or 4.8 α'_{ni} and β'_{ni} , or $\mathbf{n}'_i$, give the angle δ'_i. It is helpful to remember that δ_i and δ'_i are supplementary angles, i.e. that $\delta_i + \delta'_i = 180°$. These ideas are best illustrated by a simple example.

Example 4.1 (Figures 4.2 and 4.4)

A rock mass is cut by four sets of parallel planar discontinuities with the following geometrical characteristics:

1st table for Example 4.1

Set i	Trend of normal α_{ni} Degrees	Plunge of normal β_{ni} Degrees	Normal frequency λ_i m^{-1}
1	144	14	6.81
2	331	57	2.27
3	034	61	4.78
4	222	39	1.84

Calculate the expected total discontinuity frequency along sampling lines with the following orientations

2nd table for Example 4.1

Sampling line	Trend α_s Degrees	Plunge β_s Degrees
A	not defined	90
B	345	20
C	240	25

Solution
(i) The values of δ_i for sampling line A, which is vertical, can be found directly from the plunge angles β_{ni} for each of the set normals, without

recourse to equation 4.4. In each case δ_i is given by $90° - \beta_{ni}$, hence $\delta_1 = 76°$, $\delta_2 = 33°$, $\delta_3 = 29°$ and $\delta_4 = 51°$. Clearly if the sampling line is vertical, all the δ_i will initially always be acute, as required for the summation. Summing the products of λ_i and $\cos \delta_i$ according to equation 4.3 gives $\lambda_s = 8.89\,\mathrm{m}^{-1}$.

(ii) The sampling line B has a trend 345° and a plunge 20°. Here it is convenient to use equation 4.4 to find the angles δ_i. This equation gives $\delta_1 = 140.22°$, $\delta_2 = 38.42°$, $\delta_3 = 53.27°$ and $\delta_4 = 100.52°$. Here δ_1 and δ_4 are both obtuse, so it is necessary to take the reverse directions of the associated normals by applying equations 4.9. The new values α'_{n1}, β'_{n1} and α'_{n4}, β'_{n4} are, respectively, $324, -14$ and $042, -39$ degrees. Applying equation 4.4 to these reversed orientations gives $\delta'_1 = 39.78°$ and $\delta'_4 = 79.48°$. Since δ'_1 and δ'_4 are, of course, respectively, the supplements of δ_1 and δ_4, they could have been found directly without explicitly reversing the the associated normals. Inputting δ'_1, δ_2, δ_3 and δ'_4 to equation 4.3 gives $\lambda_s = 10.21\,\mathrm{m}^{-1}$.

(iii) The sampling line C has a trend 240° and a plunge 25°. Applying equation 4.4 gives $\delta_1 = 89.41°$, $\delta_2 = 69.77°$, $\delta_3 = 91.45°$ and $\delta_4 = 20.64°$. Here δ_3 is obtuse so the associated normal must be reversed, giving α'_{n3}, β'_{n3} equal to 214° and $-61°$, respectively, and $\delta'_3 = 88.55°$. Inputting δ_1, δ_2, δ'_3 and δ_4 to equation 4.3 gives $\lambda_s = 2.70\,\mathrm{m}^{-1}$.

The angles δ_i and δ'_i add up to 180°, consequently $\cos \delta_i = -\cos \delta'_i$ or $|\cos \delta_i| = |\cos \delta'_i|$. This means that if $\cos \delta_i$ in equation 4.3 is replaced by $|\cos \delta_i|$ there is no need to carry out the reversals summarised in equations 4.9 and 4.10. Although this option of taking the absolute value is somewhat simpler than that adopted in the above example, it will be seen later that the process of reversing the direction of normals associated with obtuse δ_i is of fundamental significance in the evaluation of the global maximum for the total frequency λ_s.

Karzulovic and Goodman (1985) present an interesting method for estimating the normal frequencies for a known number, D, of discontinuity sets, of known orientations, by analysing the total frequencies obtained from a group of non-parallel sampling lines. If, as before, λ_i is the (unknown) frequency along the normal to the ith set and δ_{ij} is the (known) acute angle between the normal to the ith set and the jth sampling line, then the theoretical frequency λ_{sj} along the jth sampling line is, from equation 4.3, given by

$$\lambda_{sj} = \sum_{i=1}^{D} \lambda_i \cos \delta_{ij} \tag{4.11}$$

If the actual frequency measured along the jth sampling line is λ_{sj}^{a} and there are S non-parallel sampling lines, replacing λ_{sj} by λ_{sj}^{a} in equation 4.11 gives S equations in the D unknowns λ_i. If S is equal to D these equations can be solved simultaneously to give unique, but possibly imprecise, values for λ_i. If S is greater than D there is a degree of redundancy which leads to ambiguous results, depending upon which group of S sampling lines is employed to obtain the solution vector λ_i. Karzulovic and Goodman (1985), illustrating this difficulty by means of an example, recommend that all the sampling line data should be considered together to provide the optimum estimate for λ_i as follows. For a given estimate of λ_i the error associated with the jth sampling line is given by

$$\varepsilon_j = \lambda_{sj}^a - \lambda_{sj} \tag{4.12}$$

If there are S sampling lines, the total squared error is given by

$$\varepsilon_t = \sum_{j=1}^{S} (\varepsilon_j)^2$$

The aim is to find values of λ_i that minimise ε_t and thereby provide the optimum estimates of the normal frequencies for the discontinuity sets. This can be achieved by partially differentiating ε_t with respect to λ_i for i = 1 to D, equating the results to zero and then solving the resulting M equations simultaneously to obtain the λ_i. This approach gives the following result expressed in matrix form

$$[\mathbf{A}][\lambda_i] = [\mathbf{L}] \tag{4.13}$$

where [$\mathbf{A}$] is a symmetrical D by D square matrix. The term A_{kl} in row k and column l of [$\mathbf{A}$] is given by

$$A_{kl} = \sum_{j=1}^{S} \cos \delta_{kj} \cos \delta_{lj} \tag{4.14}$$

where δ_{kj} and δ_{lj} are the acute angles between the jth sampling line and the normals to sets k and l, respectively. The matrix [$\mathbf{L}$] has one column and D rows. The term L_k in row k of [$\mathbf{L}$] is given by

$$L_k = \sum_{j=1}^{S} \lambda_{sj}^a \cos \delta_{kj} \tag{4.15}$$

The solution vector [λ_i] is obtained from equation 4.13 by applying an appropriate numerical solver for simultaneous equations. Karzulovic and Goodman present a program, for a pocket calculator, that provides a solution for the particular case of 3 discontinuity sets. Using an example based upon hypothetical data from 5 non-parallel sampling lines they demonstrate that the approach can provide precise estimates of the normal frequencies.

The approach presented by Karzulovic and Goodman has one practical shortcoming: in order to apply the method it is necessary to know the orientation of each of the D discontinuity sets. If a discontinuity survey is conducted correctly, following the methods in Chapter 2, then frequency data would be collected at the same time as these orientation data. If these orientation and frequency data are available it is possible to compute the normal frequencies directly, following the methods explained in section 5.1, without recourse to equation 4.13. Despite this shortcoming, the approach of Karzulovic and Goodman offers a valuable insight into the topic of discontinuity frequency and provides the basis for a more general method that could perhaps provide the orientations, as well as the normal frequencies, for the sets.

4.4 DISCONTINUITY FREQUENCY EXTREMA

Earlier sections in this Chapter have demonstrated that linear discontinuity frequency in a fractured rock mass varies with the orientation of the line along which the frequency is measured or predicted. The logical questions to address now are whether there are, for a given rock structure, unique orientations that give maximum and minimum frequency, and, if such orientations exist, how they can be determined. These, and other questions relating to discontinuity frequency extrema, will be tackled in this section by drawing on the work of Hudson and Priest (1983). Most of the analysis in this section will be based on the assumption that the discontinuity network or rock structure can be represented by a number of sets comprising parallel planar discontinuities with specified orientations and normal frequencies. Later in this section it is shown that relaxation of this requirement, to allow for a component of randomly-orientated discontinuities, requires only a minor extension of the theory.

An alternative expression for total discontinuity frequency λ_s can be obtained by replacing $\cos \delta_i$ in equation 4.3 by the expression in equation 4.4, giving

$$\lambda_s = m_x \cos \alpha_s \cos \beta_s + m_y \sin \alpha_s \cos \beta_s + m_z \sin \beta_s \qquad (4.16)$$

or, employing the Cartesian components in equation 4.8

$$\lambda_s = m_x s_x + m_y s_y + m_z s_z = \mathbf{m.s} \qquad (4.17)$$

where

$$m_x = \sum_{i=1}^{D} \lambda_i \cos \alpha_{ni} \cos \beta_{ni} = \sum_{i=1}^{D} \lambda_i n_{ix}$$

$$m_y = \sum_{i=1}^{D} \lambda_i \sin \alpha_{ni} \cos \beta_{ni} = \sum_{i=1}^{D} \lambda_i n_{iy} \qquad (4.18)$$

$$m_z = \sum_{i=1}^{D} \lambda_i \sin \beta_{ni} = \sum_{i=1}^{D} \lambda_i n_{iz}$$

subject to the important requirement that all the angles δ_i, between the discontinuity set normals and the sampling line, are acute. Although the angles δ_i do not appear explicitly in equations 4.16 to 4.18, these equations are subject to the requirement that the appropriate ends of the discontinuity set

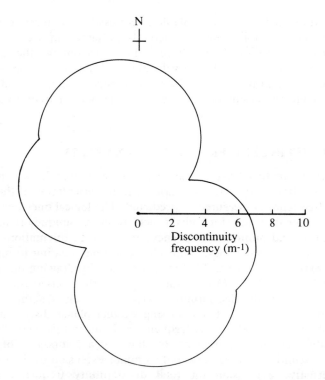

Figure 4.2   Variation of discontinuity frequency in a horizontal plane, Example 4.1.

normals have been selected so that the angles α_{ni} and β_{ni} are each associated with acute δ_i.

If a sampling line were rotated about an origin through a large number of arbitrary orientations in a given three-dimensional rock structure, it would be possible to use equations 4.17 and 4.18 to calculate total discontinuity frequency for each orientation. The frequency for a given sampling line orientation could then be represented by the length of a line, or vector, radiating from the origin and parallel to the sampling line. The end points of a large number of such frequency vectors would generate a three-dimensional surface representing the variation of discontinuity frequency for the given rock structure. A cross-section through one such surface, generated by taking a horizontal section through the locus generated by the four discontinuity sets in Example 4.1, is shown in Figure 4.2. Figure 4.3 (after Hudson and Priest, 1983) shows the theoretical and actual frequency loci for discontinuity traces exposed at a planar rock face. The loci in Figures 4.2 and 4.3 show that discontinuity frequency variation is a mathematically discontinuous function in three dimensions.

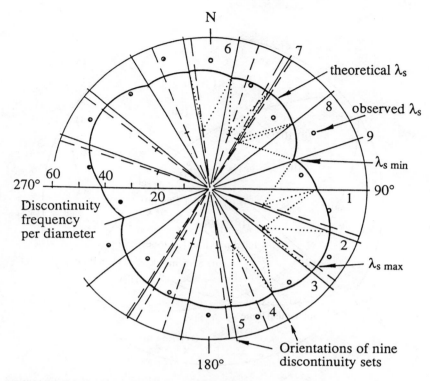

Figure 4.3 Theoretical and observed frequency loci (after Hudson and Priest, 1983).

This property is most noticeable when the rock structure contains sets of parallel planar discontinuities, as in Example 4.1. Abrupt changes in slope, or cusps, in the function occur where the sampling line lies parallel to one of the discontinuity sets involved. The cusps occur because transition of the sampling line from one side to the other of a discontinuity plane requires a reversal of the associated normal to maintain the angle δ_i acute. These cusps are rather like V-shaped valleys in the discontinuity frequency locus, tracing the orientations of the discontinuity sets involved. The direction defined by the intersection between any pair of discontinuity sets gives the point of intersection between the associated pair of cusps. Such a direction is always a local minimum $\lambda_{s\,min}$ for discontinuity frequency, which may or may not be the global minimum. Cusps are associated with local minima because any sampling line that is parallel to a discontinuity set will intersect no discontinuities from that set. A sampling line that is parallel to the line of intersection between two sets ignores the frequency components from both, and thereby generates a local minimum. The global minimum frequency can be found by inspecting

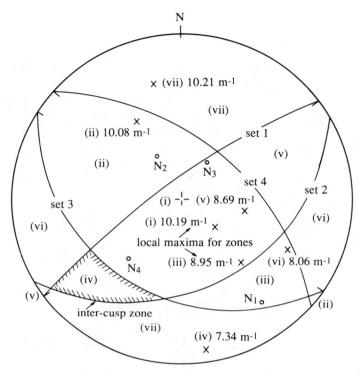

Figure 4.4   Lower hemisphere projection of four discontinuity sets from Example 4.1.

the frequency along each line of intersection. If there are D discontinuity sets ($D \geqslant 2$) the number, K_t, of separate intersection directions is given by

$$K_t = \tfrac{1}{2}(D^2 - D) \qquad (4.19)$$

The orientations of these intersection directions can be found as follows. If the normals to discontinuity sets 1 and 2 are unit vectors $\mathbf{n_1}$ and $\mathbf{n_2}$ with direction cosines $n_{1x}\ n_{1y}\ n_{1z}$ and $n_{2x}\ n_{2y}\ n_{2z}$, respectively, found from equations 1.6, then the vector $\mathbf{i}$ representing the line of intersection between the two planes is given by the cross-product $\mathbf{i} = \mathbf{n_1} \times \mathbf{n_2}$ which has Cartesian components

$$\begin{aligned}
i_x &= n_{1y}n_{2z} - n_{1z}n_{2y} \\
i_y &= n_{1z}n_{2x} - n_{1x}n_{2z} \\
i_z &= n_{1x}n_{2y} - n_{1y}n_{2x}
\end{aligned} \qquad (4.20)$$

The positive direction of $\mathbf{i}$ is given by the drive direction of a right-handed screw rotated through the angle ($< \pi$) from $\mathbf{n_1}$ to $\mathbf{n_2}$. The trend and plunge of $\mathbf{i}$ can be found from equations 1.4 and 1.5. It is often, but not always, the case

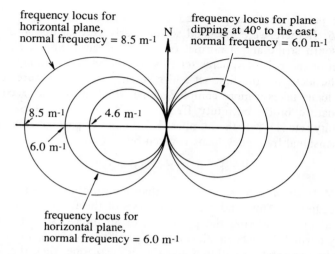

frequency locus for
horizontal plane,
normal frequency = 8.5 m-1

N

frequency locus for plane
dipping at 40° to the east,
normal frequency = 6.0 m-1

8.5 m-1   4.6 m-1

6.0 m-1

frequency locus for
horizontal plane,
normal frequency = 6.0 m-1

Figure 4.5 Frequency loci for a vertical set of parallel planar discontinuities with a north–south strike.

that the global minimum frequency lies along the line of intersection between the two sets that have the largest normal frequencies.

Hudson and Priest (1983) have shown that the variation of total discontinuity frequency in any inter-cusp zone can be graphed in three dimensions by a portion of the surface of a sphere. The notional complete spheres occur in diametrically opposing pairs, which pass through the origin of the three-dimensional frequency vector diagram. An inter-cusp zone is simply a range of orientations bounded by planes passing through the origin and lying parallel to a number of the sets forming the discontinuity network. This principle is illustrated on the lower hemisphere projection in Figure 4.4 which shows the 4 discontinuity sets from Example 4.1; the orientation range for one of the inter cusp zones bounded by sets 1, 2 and 3 has been shaded (the other zone lies on the upper hemisphere of the projection). In general, inter-cusp zones take the shape of spherical polygons, usually either spherical triangles or spherical quadrilaterals.

The frequency locus for a single set of parallel planar discontinuities is a pair of touching spheres; cross-sections through this locus, and through the origin, give pairs of touching circles. This geometry is illustrated in Figure 4.5 which shows cross-sections in a horizontal plane, and also in a plane dipping at 40° to the east, through the frequency locus for a vertical set of parallel planar discontinuities with a north–south strike and a normal frequency of $6.0 \, m^{-1}$. It must be emphasised that although discontinuity frequency is additive, the graphs of discontinuity frequency for multiple sets cannot be obtained simply by superimposing the pairs of spheres associated with each individual set. This important point can be appreciated by considering the frequency locus in Figure 4.5. If there were a second set of nearly vertical discontinuities with a north–south strike and a normal frequency of say $8.5\,\mathrm{m}^{-1}$, simple super-imposition of the pair of spheres for this second set would almost completely obscure the locus for the first set and give an erroneous picture. Clearly the complete locus takes a more complex shape which must take account of the additive nature of discontinuity frequency. If there are D parallel planar discontinuity sets ($\mathrm{D} \geqslant 1$) the number, K_c of **pairs** of part spheres forming the three-dimensional frequency locus is given by

$$K_c = \tfrac{1}{2}(D^2 - D + 2) \qquad (4.21)$$

Equation 4.21 shows that K_c is greater than the number of sets D, for values of D exceeding 2. This, and other properties of the frequency locus, can be appreciated by considering the properties of an inter-cusp zone. If the dis-continuity normals have been adjusted so that all the angles δ_i are acute for one sampling line orientation within a given inter-cusp zone, then the δ_i are acute for all other sampling line orientations within, or on the boundaries of, the inter-cusp zone. Only when a sampling line passes from one zone to another, by passing through the plane of one of the sets, does it become necessary to reverse the normals for the plane that has been crossed. Once the $\delta_i \leqslant 90°$ criterion has been satisfied for a given inter-cusp zone, equations 4.16 to 4.18 give the continuous discontinuity frequency function for that zone. Hudson and Priest (1983) showed that the trend α_m and plunge β_m of a direction associated with a local maximum for discontinuity frequency in the zone can be found by partially differentiating equation 4.16 with respect to α_s and β_s, equating the results to zero and then solving simultaneously to obtain α_m and β_m. This gives

$$\alpha_m = \arctan\left(\frac{m_y}{m_x}\right) + Q \qquad (4.22)$$

$$\beta_m = \arctan\left(\frac{m_z}{\sqrt{m_x^2 + m_y^2}}\right) \qquad (4.23)$$

where m_x, m_y and m_z are given by equation 4.18 and the parameter Q, given in Table 1.1, depends upon the signs of m_x and m_y to ensure that α_m lies in the correct quadrant. The angles α_m and β_m in fact simply give the orientation of a line radiating from the origin of the frequency locus and passing through the centre of the sphere describing the variation of frequency for the inter-cusp zone. If α_m and β_m specify an orientation **within** the given inter-cusp zone, substitution of their values for α_s and β_s in equation 4.16 gives the local maximum discontinuity frequency $\lambda_{s\,max}$ as follows

$$\lambda_{s\,max} = \sqrt{m_x^2 + m_y^2 + m_z^2} \qquad (4.24)$$

Equations 4.22 to 4.24 show that m_x, m_y and m_z are respectively the x, y and z components of the $\lambda_{s\,max}$ vector.

It is quite possible that α_m and β_m could specify an orientation **outside** the given inter-cusp zone. If this occurs there is no stationary point in the discontinuity frequency function for that particular zone. In this case, substitution of α_m and β_m for α_s and β_s in equation 4.16 (together with any necessary reversal of normals to ensure acute δ_i) gives a value of λ_s that is **greater than** $\lambda_{s\,max}$ given by equation 4.24. In fact this $\lambda_{s\,max}$ does not lie on the true discontinuity frequency locus, but on the surface of a sphere extending the selected inter-cusp zone **inside** this locus. These false local maxima can, therefore, be identified simply by comparing $\lambda_{s\,max}$ given by equation 4.24 with λ_s given by equation 4.16 with α_s and β_s replaced by α_m and β_m.

In order to determine the global maximum discontinuity frequency it is necessary to 'visit' each of the inter-cusp zones, determine α_m, β_m and $\lambda_{s\,max}$, and establish whether $\lambda_{s\,max}$ is a true local maximum. An inter-cusp zone is 'visited' simply by reversing discontinuity normals to ensure that all δ_i are acute for any arbitrary sampling line orientated within the zone. If there are D discontinuity sets there will be, by equation 4.21, K_c separate zones that require examination. The key to determining the global maximum discontinuity frequency is to ensure that each of the zones is visited and examined systematically.

For a single set of parallel planar discontinuities the directions of global minimum and maximum discontinuity frequency are orthogonal. Although this is not true in the general case of D separate discontinuity sets, most rock structures yield a global minimum and maximum that are within about 20–30° of orthogonal. The process of determining discontinuity frequency extrema for multiple discontinuity sets can be illustrated by considering the data in Example 4.1.

Example 4.2 (Figures 4.4 and 4.6)

Taking the discontinuity data in Example 4.1 determine the orientation and magnitude of (i) minimum and (ii) maximum total discontinuity frequency.

Solution
(i) The minimum frequency must occur along the line of intersection between a pair of discontinuity sets. For 4 discontinuity sets there will be, by equation 4.19, six separate intersections. The orientations of these lines of intersection can be found either from equations 4.20 or by applying hemispherical projection methods. The intersection orientations on the lower hemisphere, and the associated values of total discontinuity frequency found from equation 4.16, are tabulated below

1st table for Example 4.2

Intersecting sets	Orientation of intersection		Total frequency m^{-1}
	Trend Degrees	Plunge Degrees	
1,2	234.97	3.90	3.34
1,3	241.07	26.27	2.57
1,4	036.16	50.85	6.51
2,3	189.85	26.83	6.45
2,4	109.00	25.76	7.95
3,4	129.52	3.05	7.52

The above table shows that the global minimum frequency of $2.57\,\mathrm{m}^{-1}$ occurs along the line of intersection between sets 1 and 3, which has a trend 241.07° and a plunge 26.27°. It is worth noting that, in this case, sets 1 and 3 both have higher normal frequencies than the other two sets.

(ii) When determining the global maximum frequency it is helpful to employ hemispherical projection methods for plotting the input data and the results. Figure 4.4 shows an equal angle lower hemisphere projection of the great circles and the normals to the four discontinuity sets in this example. There is no simple way of representing the magnitudes of the normal frequencies on this projection. In this example there are 4 discontinuity sets, so setting D = 4 in equation 4.21 gives $K_c = 7$, indicating that there are 7 pairs of inter-cusp zones that must be examined to determine the global maximum frequency. The great circles divide the projection circle into seven distinct regions, labelled (i), (ii), (iii)...(vii) which de-limit the orientation ranges of the 7 inter-cusp zones that require examination. On the lower hemisphere plot in Figure 4.4, all zones except (i), (iii) and (iv) extend beyond the edge of the projection, re-entering at a diametrically opposite point.

It was noted earlier that when a sampling line passes from one side to the other, of a plane representing a given discontinuity set i, it is necessary to reverse the direction of the normal to that set to ensure that the associated angle δ_i remains acute. This process can be visualised on the projection in Figure 4.4. Consider first zone (i); since this zone contains the vertical direction, which plots at the centre of the projection, for a given set i, δ_i will always be acute if $\beta_{ni} \geq 0$. Orientations are, in this book, quoted in terms of positive angles of plunge, so it is not necessary to reverse any of the normals to determine the local maximum frequency for zone (i) in this example. 'Moving' north-west from zone (i) into zone (ii) involves crossing plane 1 (strictly speaking this is a change in orientation, not a physical movement). Consequently, to determine the local maximum frequency for zone (ii) it is necessary to reverse the direction of the normal to set 1. Zone (ii) can also be reached by 'moving' south-east from zone (i) crossing, and thereby requiring a reversal of the normals to, sets 2, 3 and 4; this achieves the same effect as only reversing set 1.

Here it is desirable to introduce a shorthand notation to represent the reversal of a normal from lower to upper hemisphere. Set normals with positive plunges, which plot on the lower hemisphere, will be represented by a positive digit. Set normals that have been reversed to give a negative plunge, and which would therefore plot on the upper hemisphere, will be represented by a negatively signed digit. Consequently zone (i) requires either 1, 2, 3, 4 or alternatively −1, −2, −3, −4 to determine the local maximum. Zone (ii) requires either −1, 2, 3, 4 or 1, −2, −3, −4. These pairs of digit strings designate a pair of part spherical loci of discontinuity frequency variation which lie on diametrically opposite sides of the origin. The strings of digits for each of the seven pairs of inter-cusp zones, determined by examining the lower hemisphere projection in Figure 4.4, are tabulated below

2nd table for Example 4.2

Inter-cusp zone	Digit strings
(i)	1,2,3,4 and −1,−2,−3,−4
(ii)	−1,2,3,4 and 1,−2,−3,−4
(iii)	1,−2,3,4 and −1,2,−3,−4
(iv)	1,2,−3,4 and −1,−2,3,−4
(v)	1,2,3,−4 and −1,−2,−3,4
(vi)	−1,2,−3,4 and 1,−2,3,−4
(vii)	1,−2,−3,4 and −1,2,3,−4

It is interesting to note that each pair of digit strings in the above table contains a total of four reversals. It also worth noting that zones such as −1, −2, 3, 4 and 1, 2, −3, −4 do not exist in this particular rock structure. Equations 4.22 to 4.24 can now be used to determine the orientations and magnitudes of the local maxima associated with the seven inter-cusp zones. The results are tabulated below and also plotted in Figure 4.4.

These results show that the global maximum discontinuity frequency is $10.21 \, \text{m}^{-1}$ and occurs along a line of trend 346.67° and plunge 18.73° in zone (vii). Figure 4.4 shows that the local maxima for zones (iii), (iv), (v) and (vi) plot beyond the orientation boundaries of their zones and do not, therefore, constitute feasible local maxima. This fact can be verified by using equation 4.16, with appropriate reversals of normals, to compute total discontinuity frequency along each direction $\alpha_m \beta_m$. The results, listed on the right hand side of the above table, show that the $\lambda_{s\,max}$ values computed for zones (iii), (iv), (v) and (vi) do not lie on the discontinuity frequency locus.

3rd table for Example 4.2

Inter-cusp zone	a_m Degrees	β_m Degrees	$\lambda_{s\ max}$ m^{-1}	Total frequency along $a_m\ \beta_m\ m^{-1}$
(i)	133.23	60.78	10.19	10.19
(ii)	330.37	33.72	10.08	10.08
(iii)	139.11	34.60	8.95	9.12
(iv)	171.90	4.13	7.34	9.37
(v)	103.02	49.16	8.69	9.54
(vi)	117.08	20.09	8.06	8.16
(vii)	346.67	18.73	10.21	10.21

Examples 4.1 and 4.2 illustrate the high degree of discontinuity frequency anisotropy that can be encountered, even when there are several discontinuity sets. In these examples the total frequency ranges from $2.57\ m^{-1}$ along a line of trend 241.07° and plunge 26.27° to $10.21\ m^{-1}$ along a line of trend 346.67° and plunge 18.73°. These frequency extrema, which lie approximately 85° apart, define a unique plane, termed by Hudson and Priest (1983) 'the plane of extreme frequencies'. In the above examples, this plane has a dip direction of 285.85° and a dip angle of 34.81°. Since it is difficult to represent adequately the complete three-dimensional locus of discontinuity frequency, it can be instructive to plot the two-dimensional locus of discontinuity frequency in a planar cross-section passing through the origin of the locus. This cross-section can take an orientation that is related to the engineering structure under analysis, or, to reveal the complete range of values, can be constructed in the plane of extreme frequencies. A two-dimensional locus in the plane of extreme frequencies for Examples 4.1 and 4.2 is presented in Figure 4.6. An appreciation of these extreme values, and the associated anisotropy in discontinuity frequency is crucial not only for designing efficient sampling strategies but also for rock mass classification and understanding the mechanical and hydrological properties of fractured rock masses.

So far, the analysis in this section has been based upon the assumption that the rock structure is made up of discontinuities in parallel planar sets. It was noted in Chapter 3 that discontinuities rarely occur in perfectly parallel sets, but tend to be distributed about a mean or central orientation. There are several ways in which the above theory can be extended to accommodate variable orientation within sets.

The first approach is to assume that in a given sample of N discontinuities, each discontinuity belongs to a separate set with unit normal frequency. This approach carries with it the implicit assumption that each discontinuity is persistent across the zone of interest. If a discontinuity extends across only a proportion p of the rock mass under consideration, it could be assigned a

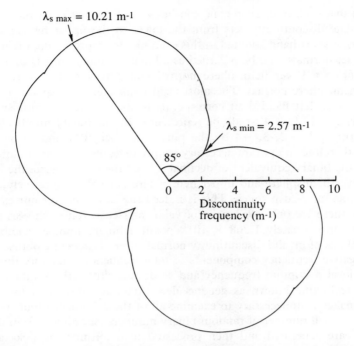

Figure 4.6 Two-dimensional locus of total discontinuity frequency for the plane of extreme frequencies in Example 4.2.

normal frequency of p to represent its impersistent geometry. The methods explained in this section are directly applicable here, simply by letting the number of sets D be equal to the number of discontinuities N, letting the orientation of the ith set be equal to the orientation of the ith discontinuity, and letting the normal frequency for each set be equal to unity, or to p if impersistent. Equations 4.16 to 4.18 can be applied directly to determine total discontinuity frequency in any specified direction. The only difficulty is the lengthy nature of the computations required to examine each of the discontinuity intersections to determine global minimum frequency and to examine each of the inter-cusp zones to determine maximum frequency. For example, if there are 100 discontinuities in the sample, i.e. there are 100 sets in the analysis, equation 4.19 shows that there are 4950 separate intersection directions and equation 4.21 shows that there are 4951 pairs of inter-cusp zones which must be examined. The various possible discontinuity intersections can be identified by adopting a pair of nested loops, the outer one counting from $i = 2$ to D, the inner one counting from $j = 1$ to $(i - 1)$. These loops generate the pointers i and j to the sets involved in all possible intersections.

Identifying the various inter-cusp zones is not nearly so simple. Example 4.2

showed that each inter-cusp zone can be 'visited' by reversing the normals to appropriate discontinuity sets from the lower to the upper hemisphere. The digit string short hand adopted in this example, for representing the reversal of certain set normals, can be regarded as a binary number with D digits, with 0 representing a lower hemisphere normal and 1 representing a reversed, or upper hemisphere normal. The most right hand digit corresponds to the first set; the most left hand digit corresponds to the Dth set. By this system the digit string $-1, 2, 3, 4$ would be represented by the binary number 0001, the digit string $-1, -2, 3, -4$ by the binary number 1011 and so on. At first glance, therefore, it appears necessary simply to generate binary numbers from zero to the binary equivalent of decimal 2^{D} and then to associate the 0s and 1s with lower hemisphere and upper hemisphere normals, respectively, to cover all possible inter-cusp zones. This is indeed the case, but, for our example of 100 sets there are only 4951 pairs of valid inter-cusp zones whereas there are 2^{100}, or approximately 1.268×10^{30}, possible binary number combinations. The millions of invalid discontinuity normal reversals generate obtuse δ_i which give negative frequency components to total frequency; therefore they cannot yield a local maximum frequency and so do not clutter the solution. A most elegant technique known as genetic algorithms, and described by Goldberg (1987) makes it unnecessary to examine all of the 2^{D} binary numbers. In this method a small number of random binary numbers (say about 50) in the range 0 to 2^{D} are generated and then processed to determine the associated discontinuity frequency maxima. The binary numbers that yield, say, the 10 best solutions (in this context the ten largest $\lambda_{s\,max}$) become 'parents' that are allowed to reproduce a total of 50 copies, which then enter into the mating pool. (In contrast to the real world, mating follows, rather than precedes, reproduction.) Two important features of this reproduction are (i) natural selection: the number of offspring from a given parent is proportional to its value of $\lambda_{s\,max}$ and (ii) mutation: a small number of randomly selected binary digits (typically between 1 and 50 per thousand digits) are changed from 0 to 1 or from 1 to 0. The 'offspring' that are produced in this way enter the mating pool and are grouped randomly in pairs for the swapping of strings of binary code; a process referred to as 'crossover'. The offspring, which have been modified by crossover, are then processed to identify the ten best solutions that will become the parents for the next generation. The process proceeds from generation to generation until a stable optimal solution, corresponding to the normal reversals associated with the global maximum discontinuity frequency, has been obtained. Goldberg comments that this method, which of course mirrors biological natural selection, is an extremely efficient but relatively simple way of arriving at an optimal solution. The method is equally applicable to cases where there is simply a large number of discontinuity sets in a given rock structure. For example, 8 sets would yield 29 pairs of inter-cusp zones and 256 possible combinations of binary digits.

A somewhat less elegant, but perhaps more direct, method for determining

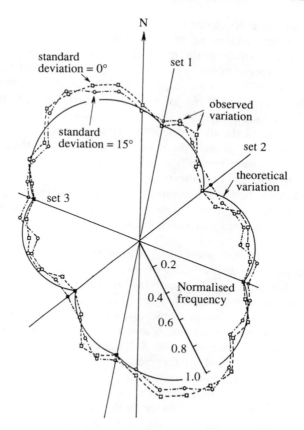

Figure 4.7   Observed and theoretical variation in normalised discontinuity frequency for three discontinuity sets (after Priest and Samaniego, 1983).

maximum discontinuity frequency is simply to compute total frequency for the complete range of possible sampling directions, taking α_s from 0 to 359° in an outer loop and β_s from 0 to 90° in an inner loop, taking care to adjust the set normals so that δ_i are acute for each sampling line. The maximum frequency identified in this way will be very close to the global maximum.

Another way of incorporating not only variable orientations within sets, but also impersistent discontinuities, in the study of discontinuity frequency has been proposed by Priest and Samaniego (1983). They used statistical data for the various sets to generate two-dimensional random realisations of discontinuity frequency, as explained in section 6.7. They then produced a two-dimensional frequency locus by rotating a sampling line through 360° in the plane of the realisation and noting the number of intersections for each sampling line orientation. Figure 4.7 shows the theoretical discontinuity frequency locus, from equations 4.16 to 4.18 based upon the assumption that there are three sets containing parallel planar discontinuities orientated as shown, with their normals in the plane of the locus. The normal frequencies for sets 1, 2 and 3 were taken to be 0.8, 2.8 and $1.6\,m^{-1}$ and the mean trace lengths were 2.0, 6.0 and 4.0 m, respectively. The frequency values have been normalised by expressing them as a dimensionless ratio of the maximum frequency for the locus. The two observed normalised frequency loci are for random realisations of the three discontinuity sets, generated on the assumption that the trace lengths obey the negative exponential distribution and that the trace orientations are normally distributed about the mean, with standard deviations of 0° and 15° as indicated. Priest and Samaniego concluded that the good agreement between theoretical and observed frequency in loci such as this suggests that the theory presented in equations 4.16 to 4.18 is applicable to real rock masses containing impersistent discontinuities of variable orientation.

In general, distributed orientations within the sets tend to decrease the difference between the discontinuity frequency extrema. An alternative way of representing this effect is by specifying an additional group of randomly orientated discontinuities whose frequency is effectively invariant with sampling line orientation. This isotropic discontinuity frequency is subtracted from the input normal frequencies λ_i and then added to any computed total frequency λ_s. In Examples 4.1 and 4.2, taking an isotropic frequency of $1.15\,m^{-1}$ gives new normal frequencies of 5.66, 1.12, 3.63 and $0.69\,m^{-1}$ for sets 1, 2, 3 and 4, respectively. These normal frequencies give global minimum and maximum frequencies of 2.213 and $8.687\,m^{-1}$, respectively when the isotropic component is added to the computed extrema of 1.06 and $7.54\,m^{-1}$. The trends/plunges of the minimum and maximum frequency directions are 241.0/26.3 and 342.3/17.9, respectively, which are very close to the earlier solutions. The specification of an isotropic frequency component has, in this case, reduced the difference between the extreme values of discontinuity frequency from 7.64 to $6.48\,m^{-1}$. Hudson and Priest (1983) have shown that if there is a large number of discontinuity sets with different orientations, but similar normal frequencies, the total discontinuity frequency locus itself tends to become effectively isotropic.

4.5 DISCONTINUITY OCCURRENCE

In section 1.3 it was noted that there can be several phases during which discontinuities are formed within a rock mass. This process usually leads to a highly complex structure of mutually intersecting discontinuities. Snow (1970) was the first of many researchers, including Priest and Hudson (1976) and Baecher et al. (1977), to conclude that this formation process would lead to an effectively random occurrence of discontinuities along an arbitrary line through the rock mass. Field measurements by Priest and Hudson (1976) and by Wallis and King (1980) have demonstrated that this conclusion is valid when all discontinuities are grouped together; it has yet to be shown that the conclusion is valid for individual sets. Recent studies by Chelidze and Gueguen (1990) have investigated the fractal properties of discontinuities. Hudson and Priest (1976) have shown that the superimposition of non-random individual sets gives rise to a random occurrence process when the sets are aggregated. The random occurrence of discontinuities along a line is an example of a one-dimensional Poisson process (Larson, 1974). A Poisson process is defined by stipulating that any small increment along the line has the same, but very small, chance of containing a discontinuity occurrence — here referred to as an *event*. If the total event frequency (discontinuity frequency) is λ, it can be shown (Larson, 1974) that the probability $P(k, x)$ of exactly k events (discontinuity intersections) occurring in an interval of length x, selected at random along the line, is given by

$$P(k, x) = \frac{e^{-\lambda x}(\lambda x)^k}{k!} \qquad (4.25)$$

This equation is identical to equation 3.8.

If it can be shown that discontinuities obey a Poisson process, equation 4.25 can be used to formulate some valuable probabilistic statements about the rock mass as follows:

The probability of zero events in an interval is found by setting k = 0, giving

$$P(0, x) = e^{-\lambda x} \qquad (4.26)$$

The probability of less than k events in an interval x is given by

$$P(<k, x) = P(0, x) + P(1, x) + P(2, x) + \ldots + P(k - 1, x) \qquad (4.27)$$

The probability of k or more events in an interval x is given by

$$P(\geqslant k, x) = 1 - P(<k, x) \qquad (4.28)$$

Equation 4.26 could be used, for example, to determine the probability that a given length of borehole will contain no discontinuity intersections. The fact that discontinuities occur randomly along arbitrary lines through rock masses has a number of important implications concerning the distribution of spacings between the discontinuity intersection points. These implications are discussed in Chapter 5.

The application of equations 4.25 to 4.28 can best be illustrated by an example.

Example 4.3

Packer permeability tests were carried out at approximately regular intervals in six vertical boreholes, each of which was drilled to a depth of 40 m in a fractured slate rock mass. A constant packer spacing was adopted throughout, giving an effective test length of 0.8 m. Of the 116 tests carried out, 17 gave a zero discharge, indicating that the test length contained no discontinuities. Use these data to estimate (i) discontinuity frequency in the vertical direction, (ii) the number of test lengths that contained (a) exactly 3, (b) less than 3, (c) 3 or more discontinuities, and (iii) the test length required to ensure that 70% of subsequent tests in these boreholes will contain 3 or more discontinuities.

Solution

(i) Here equation 4.26 is relevant. The estimated value of $P(0, x)$ is given by the proportion of the tests that gave zero discharge, in this case 17 out of 116 or 0.1466. Inverting equation 4.26 gives

$$\lambda = \frac{-\ln P(0, x)}{x}$$

The interval x is given by the test length of 0.8 m, so $\lambda = 2.40\,\mathrm{m}^{-1}$.
   (ii)
(a) Inserting $\lambda = 2.4\,\mathrm{m}^{-1}$, $x = 0.8\,\mathrm{m}$ and $k = 3$ into equation 4.25 gives
   $P(3, 0.8) = 0.173$, or in this case approximately 20 out of 116 tests.
(b) Inserting $k = 3$ into equation 4.27 gives

$$P(<3, x) = P(0, x) + P(1, x) + P(2, x)$$

Evaluating the three right hand terms for $\lambda = 2.4\,\mathrm{m}^{-1}$ and $x = 0.8\,\mathrm{m}$ in equation 4.25 gives $P(0, 0.8) = 0.147$, $P(1, 0.8) = 0.281$, $P(2, 0.8) = 0.270$, and so $P(<3, x) = 0.698$, or approximately 81 out of 116 tests.
(c) Inserting the result found in (b) above for $k = 3$ into equation 4.28 gives
   $P(\geqslant3, x) = 0.302$, or approximately 35 out of 116 tests.
   (iii) Inserting $k = 3$ and combining equations 4.27 and 4.28 gives

$$P(\geqslant3, x) = 1 - (P(0, x) + P(1, x) + P(2, x))$$

Hence, utilising equation 4.25

$$P(\geqslant3, x) = 1 - \left(e^{-\lambda x} + \lambda x e^{-\lambda x} + \frac{(\lambda x)^2 e^{-\lambda x}}{2}\right)$$

It is stipulated that $P(\geqslant3, x) = 0.70$. Iterative solution of the above expression shows that, for $\lambda = 2.4\,\mathrm{m}^{-1}$ this occurs when $x = 1.507\,\mathrm{m}$.

Although the above example serves to demonstrate a practical application of equations 4.25 to 4.28, some further comments are justified. A zero discharge from a test length implies that no hydraulically conductive discontinuities have been intersected. It is quite possible that closed discontinuities, which are mechanically significant but effectively non-conducting, could remain undetected. The above example also relies on the fact that the slate rock material is effectively impermeable. Interpretation of these data would be slightly more complex if the rock material surrounding the borehole were relatively permeable. These points, and others relating to the flow of water through fracture networks, are discussed further in Chapter 11.

In the above example, the precision of the discontinuity frequency estimate is dependent upon the number of zero discharge tests. The chance occurrence of a few more, or a few less, zero discharge tests would have had a significant influence on the computed discontinuity frequency. This effect can be demonstrated by accepting the estimated vertical discontinuity frequency as $2.4 \, \text{m}^{-1}$ and using equation 4.26 to compute the probability that no discontinuities will occur in a test length of 0.8 m. This approach gives $P(0, 0.8) = 0.147$. If each of a total of n tests is regarded as a Bernoulli trial, it is possible to use the binomial theorem to compute the probability, $P(r)$, of obtaining exactly r zero discharge tests, given that there is a probability $P(0, 0.8)$ of obtaining zero discharge in any given test.

$$P(r) = \frac{n!}{r! \, (n - r)!} (P(0, 0.8))^r (1 - P(0, 0.8))^{n-r} \qquad (4.29)$$

Here n = 116 and $P(0, 0.8) = 0.147$, so the probability of obtaining exactly 17 zero discharge tests (as was actually achieved) when $\lambda = 2.4 \, \text{m}^{-1}$ is

$$P(17) = \frac{116!}{17! \, (99)!} (0.147)^{17} (0.853)^{99} = 0.104$$

This result shows that there is a probability of $(1 - 0.104) = 0.896$ of not obtaining exactly 17 zero discharges, so there is an 89.6% chance of not estimating λ to be $2.4 \, \text{m}^{-1}$ by this method in this rock mass. The problem can be viewed in another way by considering the probability that exactly 17 zero discharges will be obtained for any other value of λ. For example, if the true value of discontinuity frequency were $2.1 \, \text{m}^{-1}$, then $P(0, 0.8) = 0.186$ and $P(17) = 0.055$, indicating that there is a possibility that the true frequency could be significantly different from the estimate. The topic of precision in the estimate of discontinuity frequency from a fracture survey is discussed further in Chapter 5 in the context of discontinuity spacing.

Before leaving the subject of discontinuity frequency it is worth noting that if discontinuity intersections along a line obey a one-dimensional Poisson process, then it is reasonable to assume that the occurrence of discontinuity trace mid-points in a plane will obey a two-dimensional Poisson process, and that the occurrence of discontinuity centres in a volume will obey a three-dimensional Poisson process. The two-dimensional Poisson process is defined by replacing the interval of length x, in equation 4.25, by an interval of area, and by replacing the linear frequency λ by the areal frequency λ_a. Similarly the three-dimensional Poisson process is defined by substituting an interval of volume and the volumetric frequency λ_v in equation 4.25. For many applications it is desirable to be able to generate one- two- or three-dimensional Poisson processes numerically. Here it is convenient to generalise the approach for an n-dimensional Poisson process with a spatial event frequency λ_n. If the total size (length, area or volume) of the n-dimensional generation space is s_n and this space is divided up into a large number, m, of equally sized elements, then the probability, P_n, of occurrence of a discontinuity centre in any given element is given by

$$P_n = \frac{\lambda_n s_n}{m} \tag{4.30}$$

The generation process can be achieved by assigning discontinuity occurrences to a total of $m_s = \lambda_n s_n$ elements selected at random from the generation space. This random selection can be based upon a total of m_s randomly generated groups of n Cartesian coordinates, which serve to identify the mid-point of each selected element in the n-dimensional generation space. This approach has the advantage of avoiding the need to examine each of the m elements of space, or indeed of having to decide upon a value for m. Once the occurrence location for a discontinuity has been established in this way, random values for its orientation, trace length and aperture can be generated from the appropriate parent distributions. The generation of random realisations in this way is utilised, and discussed further, in sections 6.8 and 11.5.

EXERCISES FOR CHAPTER 4

4.1

A preliminary discontinuity survey at a planar surface exposure of a jointed limestone rock mass was carried out by measuring discontinuity characteristics along a 15 m scanline of trend/plunge 340/10. The following data were obtained:

Discontinuity set	Mean orientation of set, dip direction/dip angle	Number of discontinuities intersected from this set
1	015/45	27
2	156/55	76
3	239/70	53

In addition to the above discontinuity sets there were 21 randomly-orientated discontinuities intersected along the scanline. Calculate the total number of discontinuities that you would expect to intersect along a 10 m length of borehole of trend/plunge 190/70 through the same rock mass and discontinuity network.

4.2

A rock mass is cut by four sets of parallel planar discontinuities with the following geometrical characteristics:

Discontinuity set	Trend of normal degrees	Plunge of normal degrees	Normal frequency m^{-1}
1	062	31	3.86
2	134	64	1.24
3	237	47	1.75
4	306	58	2.65

The rock is also cut by a randomly orientated group of discontinuities with an effectively isotropic frequency of $0.45\,m^{-1}$. Calculate (i) the expected total discontinuity frequency along a vertical sampling line, (ii) the orientation and magnitude of the theoretical global minimum discontinuity frequency, and (iii) the orientation and magnitude of the theoretical global maximum discontinuity frequency.

4.3

List the digit strings that identify the seven pairs of discontinuity frequency inter-cusp zones in Exercise 4.2 by reference to the reversal of discontinuity normals as outlined in Example 4.2.

4.4

Down hole pumping tests in an igneous rock mass were conducted by isolating test zones of a 60 m length of borehole with inflatable packers. Water under constant pressure was pumped into each isolated section and the acceptance rate was monitored. It is assumed that a negligible acceptance rate occurs when an isolated section of borehole is not intersected by a discontinuity. The following results were obtained:

Test length m	Total number of tests	Number of tests with negligible acceptance rate
0.50	120	15
0.75	80	4
1.00	60	1
1.25	48	0

Assuming that discontinuity occurrence is random, estimate the discontinuity frequency along the borehole axis.

Answers to these exercises are given on page 461.

5

Discontinuity spacing

5.1 INTRODUCTION

In its most general sense, discontinuity spacing is the distance between one discontinuity and another. Discontinuity spacing, which is linked to the reciprocal of discontinuity frequency, is widely used as a measure of the 'quality' of a rock mass for classification schemes such as those outlined in Appendix C. It is necessary to start this chapter by specifying a number of definitions of discontinuity spacing. The statistical distributions of discontinuity spacings measured along a scanline are discussed in section 5.2, followed by an examination of Rock Quality Designation and its relation with discontinuity spacing and frequency in section 5.3. The final section contains a discussion of the accuracy and precision of discontinuity spacing estimates, in particular the inaccuracy caused by short scanlines and the imprecision caused by small sample sizes.

A random sample of discontinuity spacing values can be obtained from a linear scanline survey, as described in Chapter 2. Such a survey provides a list of the distances along the scanline to the points where it is intersected by the various discontinuities that have been sampled. Subtraction of consecutive intersection distances provides a list of discontinuity spacings. The problem of partial spacing values at the start and at the end of the scanline can be overcome simply by ensuring that the scanline starts and ends at discontinuity intersection points.

Discontinuity spacing is here defined as the distance between a pair of discontinuities measured along a line of specified location and orientation. It is useful to distinguish three different types of discontinuity spacings:

(i) The spacing between a pair of immediately adjacent discontinuities, measured along a line of general, but specified, location and orientation is here referred to as **total spacing**.

(ii) The spacing between a pair of immediately adjacent discontinuities from a particular discontinuity set, measured along a line of any specified location and orientation is here referred to as the **set spacing**.

(iii) The set spacing when measured along a line that is parallel to the mean normal to the set (see Chapter 3) is the **normal set spacing**.

Discontinuity set spacings can be estimated by selecting only those discontinuities in a scanline sample that have an orientation within some specified range. If X_d is a random value of set spacing for a set whose normal makes an acute angle δ with the sampling line, then the normal set spacing X_n is, following the simple geometrical approach in section 3.3, given by

$$X_n = X_d \cos \delta \qquad (5.1)$$

The discontinuity spacing data obtained from a scanline sample are amenable to statistical processing in the same way as any other continuous variable. The reader is advised to study the brief introduction to statistics and probability density, given in Appendix B, before proceeding further with this chapter.

Let X_{ti} be the ith random value of total spacing, X_{di} be the ith random value of set spacing and X_{ni} be the ith random value of normal set spacing. The best estimates of mean spacing, variance and the kth moment of spacing can be found, for a sample of size n, by inserting X_{ti}, X_{di} or X_{ni} into equations B.1, B.2 and B.3 as appropriate. Utilising equation B.1, the best estimates of mean total spacing, mean set spacing and mean normal set spacing are, respectively $\bar{X}_t$, $\bar{X}_d$ and $\bar{X}_n$. The best estimate of discontinuity frequency λ_t along a given line for all sets aggregated is given by $1/\bar{X}_t$. The best estimate of discontinuity frequency λ_d along a given line for a particular set is given by $1/\bar{X}_d$. The best estimate of discontinuity frequency λ_n along the normal to a particular set is given by $1/\bar{X}_n$. These estimates of discontinuity frequency can be used as input values in the analysis of discontinuity frequency, presented in Chapter 4. The subscripts t, d and n for discontinuity frequency λ will henceforth only be used where it is particularly important to emphasise the nature of the value.

The simple reciprocal relation between mean spacing and discontinuity frequency, discussed in the previous paragraph, does not present the complete picture. Although it is easy to visualise the concept of a single i^{th} spacing value, X_{ti}, X_{di} or X_{ni}, it is not so easy to visualise the physical significance of the associated single i^{th} 'frequency' values given by the reciprocals $\Lambda_{ti} = 1/X_{ti}$, $\Lambda_{di} = 1/X_{di}$ and $\Lambda_{ni} = 1/X_{ni}$. This difficulty arises because the word 'frequency' implies several values. The term will be reserved, therefore, for the reciprocal of the best estimate of **mean spacing** as explained above. The quantities Λ_{ti}, Λ_{di} and Λ_{ni} which are derived from single spacing values will

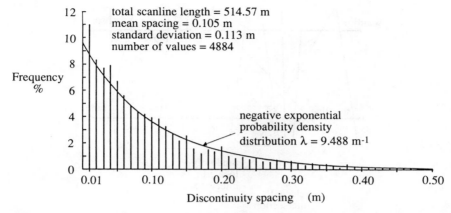

Figure 5.1 Discontinuity spacing histogram for all scanlines in the first 85 m of tunnel, Chinnor UK (after Priest and Hudson, 1976).

henceforth be referred to as 'repetition values'; for example if a pair of discontinuities has a spacing of 0.36 m they have a repetition of 2.78 m^{-1}. Although the analysis presented in this Chapter will be based upon spacing values, it could equally well be presented in terms of repetition values. Analysis of repetition values is, however, probably more of academic interest rather than of practical value.

5.2 DISCONTINUITY SPACING DISTRIBUTIONS

Although mean discontinuity spacing provides a direct measure of rock quality, a number of researchers have found it instructive to investigate the distribution of discontinuity spacings by plotting histograms of the sampled values of total spacing, X_t. The histogram in Figure 5.1, from Priest and Hudson (1976), is typical of those that have been obtained. On the basis of their field measurements Priest and Hudson concluded that the distribution of total discontinuity spacings for a variety of sedimentary rock types could be modelled by the negative exponential probability density distribution, listed in Table B.1. This conclusion has been supported by others, notably Wallis and King (1980) working on a Precambrian porphyritic granite, and by Baecher (1983) working on a variety of igneous, sedimentary and metamorphic rocks. Although there are strong empirical arguments for accepting the negative exponential distribution as a model for the distribution of total discontinuity spacings, there is also a powerful logical argument, summarised below, for accepting this distribution.

It was noted in Chapter 1 that several phases of discontinuity formation often occur in a given rock mass, which usually lead to a complex structure of

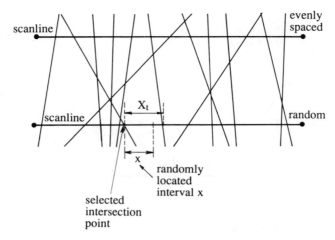

Figure 5.2 Random intersections along a line produced by variable discontinuity orientations.

mutually intersecting discontinuities with highly variable orientations. It is reasonable to assume that intersections between these discontinuities and a random straight sampling line will tend to be random. This is because it is not only the location but also the orientation of each discontinuity that controls the exact intersection point with the sampling line. Consequently, even when the intersections are apparently non-random along one particular sampling line, if the discontinuities are not all parallel their different orientations will tend to produce random intersections along a line just a few centimetres away. This effect is illustrated diagrammatically in Figure 5.2, where evenly spaced intersections along one scanline give rise to random intersections along a neighbouring scanline. If it were accepted that discontinuity spacings obey some other distribution, such as the normal distribution, then it would also be necessary to accept that there is a mechanism for neighbouring discontinuities to 'communicate' in some way, to preserve the ordered pattern. Although it is possible to hypothesise such mechanisms, based perhaps upon cyclic mineralogy or the decay of stress concentrations adjacent to fractures, in the Author's opinion, and in the absence of firm evidence, it is preferable to adopt the simpler hypothesis of random occurrences.

If discontinuity occurrence along a line is random then the location of one discontinuity intersection has no influence upon the location of any other; in this case the intersections obey a one-dimensional Poisson process. It was noted in Chapter 4 that if the total event frequency (in this case discontinuity frequency) for a one-dimensional Poisson process is λ, then the probability $P(k, x)$ of obtaining exactly k events (in this case discontinuity intersections) in an interval x placed randomly along the line is given by equation 4.25 as

$$P(k, x) = \frac{e^{-\lambda x}(\lambda x)^k}{k!}$$

Since the discontinuity intersection points are random, a simple way of locating a random interval x is to place the left hand end of the interval at an intersection point, as shown in Figure 5.2. Let X_t be the random value of total discontinuity spacing occurring to the right hand side of the selected intersection point. The probability, $P(X_t > x)$, that X_t will be greater than x is the same as the probability that there are no discontinuity intersections within the interval x. Setting $k = 0$ in equation 4.25, reproduced above, gives

$$P(X_t > x) = P(0, x) = e^{-\lambda x} \tag{5.2}$$

For brevity, λ is taken to be the total discontinuity frequency λ_t, hence

$$P(X_t \leq x) = 1 - e^{-\lambda x}$$

But $P(X_t \leq x)$ is the cumulative probability distribution $F(x)$, so

$$F(x) = 1 - e^{-\lambda x} \tag{5.3}$$

The probability density distribution is given by the first derivative of $F(x)$ with respect to x, as explained in Appendix B, hence

$$f(x) = \frac{dF(x)}{dx} = \lambda e^{-\lambda x}$$

This result shows that, if the discontinuity occurrences are random, the probability density distribution of total discontinuity spacings is negative exponential with a mean spacing given by $1/\lambda$. The proof set out above does not, in fact, rely upon locating the left hand end of the random interval x conveniently at a discontinuity intersection point; the left hand end of the interval can be at any random location. If this is allowed, exactly the same result is obtained but via a rather more complicated proof. A version of this more comprehensive proof is presented in Example 6.4, which deals with the analysis of discontinuity trace length.

The fact that observed distributions of total discontinuity spacings tend to be of negative exponential form suggests, but does not confirm, that the discontinuity occurrences are random. It has not yet been shown whether the distributions of set spacings, or of normal set spacings, are negative exponential or not. Hudson and Priest (1979) have, however, demonstrated that a negative exponential distribution of total spacings can be produced by the combination of non-negative exponential distributions of set spacings. The combination process, summarised diagrammatically in Figure 5.3, shows that a process of random mutual interference leads to a breakdown of the ordered pattern of spacings found in the uniform and normal distributions. Hudson and Priest carried out numerical simulations of this combination/interference process for uniform, normal and negative exponential distributions of set

Component distributions

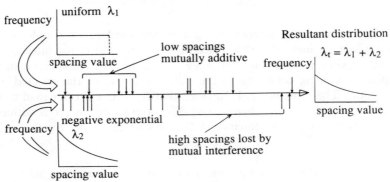

Figure 5.3 Combination of two discontinuity spacing distributions (after Hudson and Priest, 1979).

spacings with component frequencies ranging from 0.2 to 0.8 and a total frequency of 1.0. Their results, reproduced in histogram form in Figure 5.4, show a clear tendency for the distributions of total spacings to converge towards a negative exponential form. It is interesting to note that a normal distribution of set spacings is almost completely obliterated when its component frequency is about 0.5 or less.

Example 5.1

During the logging of 93 m of fractured borehole core it was found that 259 separate pieces had a length of more than 0.1 m. Assuming that the discontinuities occur at random locations along the core, estimate (i) the mean total discontinuity spacing, (ii) the number of separate pieces of core that are longer than 0.2 m and therefore suitable for laboratory testing, and (iii) the number of separate pieces of core between 0.1 and 0.2 m long and therefore suitable for point load testing.

Solution

(i) Let $\bar{X}_t$ be the mean total discontinuity spacing for the borehole core. The total discontinuity frequency λ_t is given by

$$\lambda_t = 1/\bar{X}_t$$

It is assumed that the length of each separate intact piece of core is a discontinuity spacing value. If L is the total length of the borehole core then the total number, n_{int}, of separate intact pieces is given by the total number of discontinuities

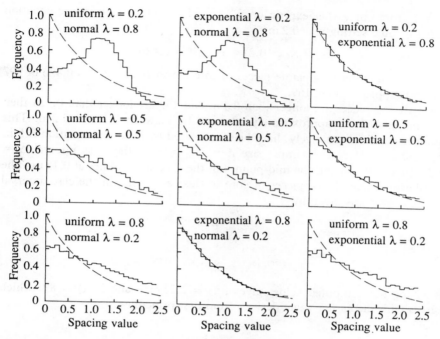

Figure 5.4 The effect of combining pairs of discontinuity spacing distributions; negative exponential frequency distribution plotted on each diagram for $\lambda = 1.0$ (after Hudson and Priest, 1979).

$$n_{int} = \lambda_t L = \frac{93}{\bar{X}_t}$$

It was shown earlier in equation 5.2 that the probability, $P(X_t > x)$, that a random value of total discontinuity spacing X_t is greater than x is, for negative exponential spacings, given by $P(X_t > x) = e^{-\lambda_t x}$. Noting that in this case $x = 0.1\,m$ and equating the numerical proportion $259/n_{int}$ with $P(X_t > x)$ gives

$$\frac{259\,\bar{X}_t}{93} = e^{-0.1/\bar{X}_t}$$

or

$$\bar{X}_t = 0.359\,e^{-0.1/\bar{X}_t}$$

Solving this equation gives $\bar{X}_t = 0.234\,m$.

(ii) The total discontinuity frequency λ_t is given by

$$\lambda_t = \frac{1}{\bar{X}_t} = 4.267\,m^{-1}$$

Hence from our earlier expression $n_{int} = \lambda_t L \approx 397$. Again, using equation 5.2, this time setting $x = 0.2\,m$

$$P(X_t > 0.2) = e^{-0.2\lambda_t} = 0.426$$

Hence the number of separate pieces of core longer than 0.2 m is 0.426 of 397 which is approximately 169.

(iii) If 259 pieces are longer than 0.1 m and 169 are longer than 0.2 m then 259 minus 169, or approximately 90 must lie between 0.1 and 0.2 m. This number could, alternatively, have been estimated by means of equation B.8 in Appendix B. Here the sample size $n = n_{int} = 397$, the class interval $\Delta = 0.2 - 0.1 = 0.1\,m$ and the mid-point x of the class interval lies at 0.15 m. The number of values $N(x)$ (pieces of core in this case) lying in the class interval centred upon x is given by

$$N(x) = n\,\Delta f(x)$$

where

$$f(x) = \lambda_t e^{-\lambda_t x}$$

Inserting the computed values gives $f(x) = 2.25\,m^{-1}$ and $N(x) \approx 89$, which agrees with the earlier value derived from first principles.

5.3 ROCK QUALITY DESIGNATION

The fact that discontinuity spacings tend to obey a negative exponential distribution has a number of important implications in the analysis of rock structure. The first of these implications is concerned with the calculation and use of the quantity called the Rock Quality Designation (RQD). RQD, which was proposed by Deere (1964) as a measure of the quality of borehole core, is defined as the percentage length of a given length of core (or length of borehole) that consists of sound, intact pieces that are 0.1 m (4 in) or longer. The value 0.1 m is here referred to as the threshold value. Since RQD is relatively easy to calculate, and provides an unambiguous numerical value, it has become widely accepted as a measure of discontinuity spacing. Indeed RQD forms an important input parameter to the rock mass classification schemes developed by Bieniawski (1973) and by Barton et al. (1974) outlined in Appendix C. This wide acceptance of RQD makes it desirable to understand how it is related to the more fundamental properties of the rock structure, such as discontinuity frequency. For the purposes of the analysis described below, a borehole is regarded as a line, intersecting discontinuities whose total spacings represent intact pieces of core. The ends of each run of core are assumed to occur at discontinuities and it is also assumed that there is 100% core recovery. RQD can now be defined more formally as follows

$$RQD = 100 \sum_{i=1}^{n} \frac{\bar{X}_{ti}}{L} \tag{5.4}$$

where X_{ti} is the length of the ith total spacing (i.e. the ith piece of core) that exceeds the threshold level t, out of a sample of n spacing values. The parameter L is the length of the sampling line along which RQD is required. This summation can be formulated as an integration of the probability density distribution $f(x)$ of discontinuity spacings. The probability that a randomly selected spacing takes a value between x and $x + dx$ is, from equation B.10, given by $f(x)dx$. If the discontinuity frequency is λ along a sampling line of length L, there will be a total of λL discontinuities and, ignoring end effects, λL spacing values. Hence the number of spacings between x and $x + dx$ is given by $\lambda L\, f(x)dx$ and the total length of these is $x\, \lambda L\, f(x)dx$. The theoretical RQD for a general threshold value t, which is here denoted $TRQD_t$, can be found by summing these total lengths for all values of x between the threshold t and the maximum possible value, which is taken to be L, and then expressing the result as a percentage of L, as follows

$$TRQD_t = 100 \int_t^L \frac{x\, \lambda L\, f(x)}{L}\, dx$$

which gives

$$TRQD_t = 100\, \lambda \int_t^L x\, f(x)\, dx \tag{5.5}$$

The result in equation 5.5 is totally general and does not depend upon the form of the density distribution $f(x)$. If the spacings obey the negative exponential distribution, then $f(x) = \lambda e^{-\lambda x}$ and

$$TRQD_t = 100\, \lambda^2 \int_t^L x\, e^{-\lambda x}\, dx$$

Here we can use the expression for m_{X1} given in equation B.19 of Example B.2. Inserting the limits t and L instead of 0 and ∞ gives

$$TRQD_t = 100[e^{-\lambda t}(1 + \lambda t) - e^{-\lambda L}(1 + \lambda L)] \tag{5.6}$$

If L is large, and it usually is, then the term $e^{-\lambda L}$ will be very small, hence

$$TRQD_t = 100\, e^{-\lambda t}(1 + \lambda t) \tag{5.7}$$

Equation 5.7, which was first derived by Priest and Hudson (1976), gives the link between RQD and discontinuity frequency, and, since mean spacing is given by $1/\lambda$, this equation also gives the link between RQD and mean discontinuity spacing. Figure 5.5, taken from Priest and Hudson (1976) shows a plot of $TRQD_t$ against mean discontinuity spacing for threshold levels ranging between 0.1 and 1.0 m. It is interesting to note that adopting the

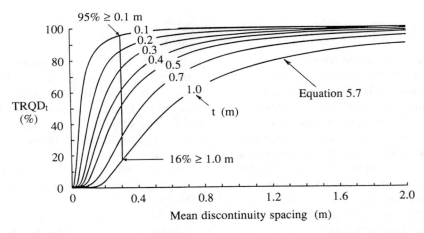

Figure 5.5 Variation of $TRQD_t$ with mean discontinuity spacing for a range of $TRQD_t$ threshold values t (after Priest and Hudson, 1976).

conventional RQD threshold level of 0.1 m gives an RQD that is sensitive to mean spacings up to only approximately 0.3 m; RQD increases by only 5% in response to increases in mean spacing beyond this value. An improved sensitivity in RQD to higher values of mean spacing can be achieved by increasing the threshold level. Such an approach would be appropriate when designing a large excavation in rock that, despite having a high mean discontinuity spacing, could present significant stability or water inflow problems.

Figure 5.6, from Priest and Hudson (1976) shows a graph of $TRQD_t$, given by equation 5.7 for a threshold value of t = 0.1 m, plotted against discontinuity frequency λ. The experimental data points for a variety of sedimentary rock types show that equation 5.7 provides a good approximation for RQD over discontinuity frequencies ranging from 2 to 38 m^{-1}. Priest and Hudson have shown that a linear approximation to equation 5.7 for t = 0.1 m is given by the tangent to the curve at the inflection point where $\lambda = 1/t = 10\,m^{-1}$. The equation for this tangent is given by

$$TRQD_{0.1} \approx 110.4 - 3.68\lambda \qquad (5.8)$$

The above equation provides a reasonable approximation for the range $6 < \lambda < 16\,m^{-1}$. It is worth noting that the ISRM (1978) has proposed the following approximate relation between RQD and the volumetric joint count J_v

$$
\begin{aligned}
RQD &= 115 - 3.3J_v \qquad \text{for } J_v \geqslant 4.5\,m^{-1} \\
RQD &= 100 \qquad\qquad\quad\; \text{for } J_v < 4.5\,m^{-1}
\end{aligned}
\qquad (5.9)
$$

where J_v is defined as the sum of the number of joints per metre for each joint set present. The similarity between equation 5.8, which is based on funda-

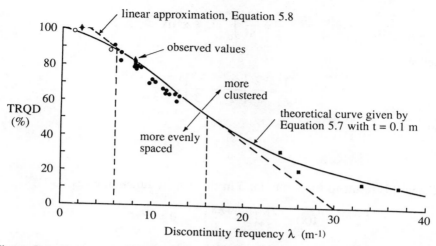

Figure 5.6 Relation between TRQD and mean discontinuity frequency (after Priest and Hudson, 1976).

mental analysis, and equation 5.9, which is empirical, reinforces the validity of the theoretical approach based upon a negative exponential distribution of discontinuity spacings.

Example 5.2

The probability density distribution $f(x)$ of discontinuity spacing values x measured on a long sampling line set up on the planar surface of a jointed rock mass is given by the following triangular distribution

$$f(x) = \frac{2(a - x)}{a^2} \qquad 0 \leqslant x \leqslant a$$

Obtain from $f(x)$ an expression for the theoretical Rock Quality Designation $TRQD_t$ for the rock mass, in terms of the discontinuity frequency λ and the $TRQD_t$ threshold value t.

Solution

The theoretical mean discontinuity spacing $\mu_x = 1/\lambda$ is given by equation B.14 as follows

$$\mu_x = \frac{1}{\lambda} = \int_0^\infty x\, f(x)\, dx$$

Inserting the appropriate limits of integration for the triangular distribution gives

$$\frac{1}{\lambda} = \frac{2}{a^2} \int_0^a ax - x^2 \, dx$$

hence

$$\frac{1}{\lambda} = \frac{2}{a^2} \left[\frac{ax^2}{2} - \frac{x^3}{3} \right]_0^a = \frac{a}{3}$$

so

$$a = \frac{3}{\lambda}$$

Using this result to substitute for a in the density function gives

$$f(x) = \frac{2\lambda}{3} \left(1 - \frac{\lambda x}{3}\right) \qquad 0 \leqslant x \leqslant \frac{3}{\lambda}$$

Equation 5.5 gives the theoretical RQD as

$$TRQD_t = 100\lambda \int_t^L x \, f(x) \, dx$$

where L is the length of the sampling line. Since the sampling line is long it is assumed that $3/\lambda < L$, so it is necessary to insert $3/\lambda$ as the upper limit of the integration. Adopting the triangular distribution for f(x) in equation 5.5 and inserting the limits of integration gives

$$TRQD_t = 100 \left(\frac{2\lambda^2}{3}\right) \int_t^{(\frac{3}{\lambda})} x - \frac{\lambda x^2}{3} \, dx$$

or

$$TRQD_t = 100 \left(\frac{2\lambda^2}{3}\right) \left[\frac{x^2}{2} - \frac{\lambda x^3}{9}\right]_t^{\frac{3}{\lambda}}$$

so

$$TRQD_t = 100 \left(\frac{2\lambda^2}{3}\right) \left(\frac{9}{2\lambda^2} - \frac{t^2}{2} - \frac{3}{\lambda^2} + \frac{\lambda t^3}{9}\right)$$

giving the result

$$TRQD_t = 100 \left(1 - \frac{\lambda^2 t^2}{3} + \frac{2\lambda^3 t^3}{27}\right)$$

It is interesting to compare the theoretical values of RQD predicted by the above result, based upon a triangular spacing distribution, with those predicted by equation 5.7, based upon a negative exponential distribution, which, of course, is approximately triangular in shape. For example, selecting a threshold value of $t = 0.1\,m$, for a discontinuity frequency $\lambda = 5\,m^{-1}$ the above equation gives $TRQD_{0.1} = 92.6\%$ while equation 5.7 gives 91.0%. At the same threshold value, but a frequency $\lambda = 15\,m^{-1}$, the above equation gives $TRQD_{0.1} = 50.0\%$ while equation 5.7 gives 55.8%. Clearly, for the purposes of estimating RQD, the triangular distribution provides a reasonable approximation to the negative exponential distribution.

Example 5.3

The overall RQD for 134 m of borehole core, sampled from a fractured rock mass was found to be 58%. Assuming that the discontinuity spacings obey the negative exponential distribution, estimate the length of this core that could be expected to consist of intact pieces between 0.1 and 0.2 m long.

Solution
Here it is first necessary to estimate the discontinuity frequency λ for the borehole core. Unfortunately, since equation 5.7 cannot be inverted to give λ explicitly in terms of $TRQD_t$, it is necessary to adopt an iterative method for determining λ. A good starting point for this iteration can be found by inverting the linear approximation in equation 5.8, hence

$$\lambda \approx \frac{110.4 - TRQD_{0.1}}{3.68}$$

In this case $TRQD_{0.1} = 58\%$ so $\lambda \approx 14.2\,m^{-1}$. From this starting value, repeated iterations of equation 5.7 give $\lambda = 14.34\,m^{-1}$.

The percentage length of the borehole core consisting of intact pieces longer than 0.1 m is already known, from the value of RQD, to be 58%. For a total core length of 134 m this represents 78.3 m of core. The percentage length of core consisting of intact pieces longer than 0.2 m is found by inserting $t = 0.2\,m$ into equation 5.7 together with the computed value of λ; hence $TRQD_{0.2} = 22\%$ which represents 29.5 m of core. The expected length of core consisting of intact pieces between 0.1 and 0.2 m is therefore $78.3 - 29.5 = 48.8\,m$.

It is important to appreciate the distinction between the above result, which gives the **length** of core consisting of intact pieces in the range 0.1 to 0.2 m, and the result obtained in Example 5.1 which gave the **number** of intact pieces in this range for a different core sample. Application of the principles adopted in Example 5.1 to the above example gives the number of intact pieces in the range 0.1 to 0.2 m as approximately 349. Since these have an estimated total length of 48.8 m they have a mean length of $48.8/349 \approx 0.14\,m$.

5.4 ACCURACY AND PRECISION OF DISCONTINUITY SPACING ESTIMATES

The estimation of mean discontinuity spacing from scanline surveys can form a crucial part of a site investigation. Although the mean value of total spacing, set spacing or normal set spacing can be estimated for a given sample by applying equation B.1, the result gives no indication of how reliable the estimate is. There are two separate criteria by which this reliability can be judged. The first criterion concerns the tendency for the estimated mean value to be biased by some persistent factor that causes the result to be consistently in error; this is usually termed **inaccuracy**. The second criterion concerns the tendency for small samples taken from variable populations to yield mean values that exhibit inconsistent random deviations from the true population mean; this effect is usually termed **imprecision**.

5.4.1 Inaccuracy caused by short sampling lines

Sen and Kazi (1984) present an analysis of the inaccuracies in mean spacing and RQD estimates caused by the relatively short sampling lines that are required where a rock face is of limited extent or where borehole core is logged in short runs. They noted that a sampling line of length L cannot observe discontinuity spacings that are larger than L. This process, discussed in Chapter 6 in the context of discontinuity size, is referred to as curtailment, with either truncation or censoring, depending on whether a record is kept of the number of spacing values that cannot be measured. If the probability density distribution of spacings in the population is $f(x)$, and if no record is kept of the number of spacings that cannot be measured, in other words they are simply ignored, the observed truncated distribution of spacings $f_L(x)$ will be directly proportional to $f(x)$ subject to the truncation $0 \leq x \leq L$; or more formally

$$f_L(x) = c\, f(x) \qquad 0 \leq x \leq L \tag{5.10}$$

where c is a constant. Now if $f_L(x)$ is a probability density distribution then, applying equation B.11 and inserting L as the upper limit of integration, gives

$$\int_0^L f_L(x)\, dx = 1$$

hence

$$c \int_0^L f(x)\, dx = 1$$

or

$$c = \frac{1}{\displaystyle\int_0^L f(x)\, dx} = \frac{1}{F(L)}$$

where $F(L)$ is the cumulative probability density distribution, hence

$$f_L(x) = \frac{f(x)}{F(L)} \qquad 0 \leqslant x \leqslant L \tag{5.11}$$

If $f(x)$ is negative exponential then

$$f_L(x) = \frac{\lambda e^{-\lambda x}}{1 - e^{-\lambda L}} \qquad 0 \leqslant x \leqslant L \tag{5.12}$$

The expected value, or mean, μ_{XL} of $f_L(x)$ is, applying equation B.14, given by

$$\mu_{XL} = \frac{\lambda}{1 - e^{-\lambda L}} \int_0^L x e^{-\lambda x} dx \qquad 0 \leqslant x \leqslant L$$

Here we can use the expression for m_{X1} given in equation B.19 of Example B.2. Inserting the limits 0 and L instead of 0 and ∞ gives

$$\mu_{XL} = \frac{1 - e^{-\lambda L} - \lambda L e^{-\lambda L}}{\lambda(1 - e^{-\lambda L})} \tag{5.13}$$

When L is large, $e^{-\lambda L}$ approaches zero and μ_{XL} approaches $1/\lambda$, which is the theoretical mean value for the untruncated distribution. Equation 5.13 corrects a minor typographical error in equation 5 presented by Sen and Kazi (1984).

The theoretical variance σ^2_{XL} of $f_L(x)$ can be found by inserting the limits 0 and L into equation B.20 and then applying equation B.16, hence

$$\sigma^2_{XL} = \frac{2 - e^{-\lambda L}(2 + 2\lambda L + \lambda^2 L^2)}{\lambda^2(1 - e^{-\lambda L})} - (\mu_{XL})^2 \tag{5.14}$$

where μ_{XL} is given by equation 5.13. As before, when L is large σ^2_{XL} approaches $1/\lambda^2$, which is the variance of the untruncated distribution. Again equation 5.14 corrects a minor typographical error in the work of Sen and Kazi.

The theoretical RQD, $TRQD_t$, for a threshold value t and a sampling line of length L is found by substituting $f_L(x)$, given by equation 5.11, for $f(x)$ in equation 5.5. The discontinuity frequency term λ in equation 5.5 must also be replaced by $1/\mu_{XL}$, where μ_{XL} is the mean of $f_L(x)$. If $f(x)$ is negative exponential then $f_L(x)$ is given by equation 5.12 and μ_{XL} is given by equation 5.13, hence $TRQD_t$ is given by

$$TRQD_t = \frac{100 \lambda^2}{1 - e^{-\lambda L} - \lambda L e^{-\lambda L}} \int_t^L x e^{-\lambda x} dx$$

Again, inserting the limits t and L into the expression for m_{X1} in equation B.19 of Example B.2 gives

$$TRQD_t = \frac{100}{1 - e^{-\lambda L} - \lambda L e^{-\lambda L}} [e^{-\lambda t}(1 + \lambda t) - e^{-\lambda L}(1 + \lambda L)] \tag{5.15}$$

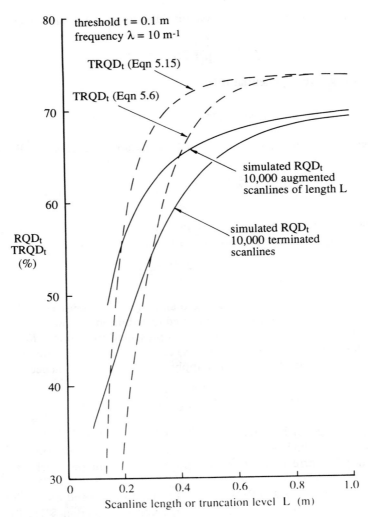

Figure 5.7 Theoretical and simulated RQD for short scanlines.

The above equation corrects a typographical error in equation 28 of Sen and Kazi (1984). It is interesting to compare the result in equation 5.15 with that presented in equation 5.6 which also gives $TRQD_t$ for a sample of spacings truncated at L. Figure 5.7 shows graphs of these two equations for discontinuity frequency $\lambda = 10 \, \mathrm{m}^{-1}$, a threshold $t = 0.1 \, \mathrm{m}$ and truncation levels L in the range 1.0 down to about 0.1 m. These graphs indicate that equations 5.6 and 5.15 only give significantly different values when L is less than about 0.5 m, or in more general terms, when the product λL, which gives the

(a)

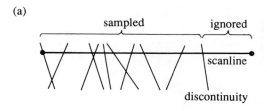

(b)

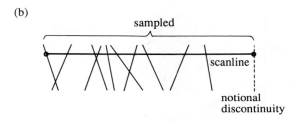

Figure 5.8   Scanline sampling of discontinuity spacings: (a) terminated, (b) augmented.

expected number of discontinuities in the length L, falls below about 5. Both equations predict a rapid reduction in theoretical RQD when λL falls below about 5. This is because, as the truncation level L gets smaller, an increasing proportion of spacing values will exceed L and will therefore be discarded. Loss of these higher spacing values, and retention of the smaller ones, causes a rapid fall in $TRQD_t$.

The above analysis does not, however present the complete picture. Consider the physical situation of measuring RQD along a short sampling line, say 1 m long, that commences at a discontinuity. It is a straightforward matter to log the discontinuity spacing values, keeping a record of those that exceed the selected threshold level. At the end of the sampling line, however, there will be a final incomplete spacing value. There are two ways of handling this final spacing value. The first approach, illustrated in Figure 5.8a, is simply to ignore this final partial spacing and to terminate the sampling line at the final observed discontinuity intersection point; this approach will be referred to as 'termination'. The second approach, illustrated in Figure 5.8b, is to regard the end of the sampling line as a discontinuity and therefore to process the final partial spacing in the same way as all the other spacings; this approach will be referred to as 'augmentation'. The effects of termination and augmentation on short sampling lines are not represented in equations 5.6 and 5.15. These effects can, however, be demonstrated by simulation. Figure 5.7 shows the mean values of simulated RQD determined for a threshold t = 0.1 m from 10 000 scanlines of lengths ranging from 1.0 m down to 0.1 m in a rock mass

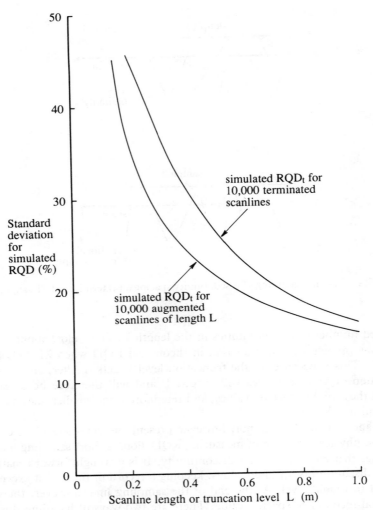

Figure 5.9 Standard deviation of simulated RQD for terminated and augmented short scanlines.

with a discontinuity frequency $\lambda = 10.0\,\mathrm{m}^{-1}$. The end effects associated with these short scanlines give simulated RQD values for the terminated and the augmented scanlines that, for λL greater than about 5, are between 4 and 8 percentage points lower than the values predicted by equations 5.6 and 5.15. As with the theoretical predictions, there is a rapid drop in RQD as λL falls below 5. The conclusion is that short sampling lines have only a small influence on the expected value of RQD as long as $\lambda L \geqslant 5$, in other words as long as at least 5 discontinuities occur within the sampled length.

A single short sampling line produces a small sample size and, therefore, introduces problems of imprecision. This effect is illustrated in Figure 5.9 which shows the standard deviation in simulated RQD for the 10 000 terminated and augmented scanlines of lengths ranging from 1.0 down to 0.1 m. Even at a scanline length of 1.0 m the standard deviation is at least 15%, which, for an observed RQD of say 65% would give only 50% confidence that the correct value of RQD lies between 55 and 75%. These and other aspects of imprecision caused by small sample sizes are discussed further in the next subsection. Meanwhile the reader may find it valuable to study the following examples, which serve to illustrate the practical implications of the theory presented above.

Example 5.4

It is known that the mean total discontinuity spacing in a vertical direction in a given rock mass is 0.26 m. Assuming a negative exponential distribution of spacings, estimate the mean discontinuity spacing that could be expected when determined from vertical scanlines of lengths 1.0, 2.0 and 3.0 m.

Solution

The expected values of mean spacing are given by μ_{XL} in equation 5.13. Inserting $\lambda = 1/0.26 = 3.846 \, \text{m}^{-1}$ and the three values of sampling line lengths L gives

(i)   when L = 1.0 m, $\lambda L = 3.846 \, \text{m}^{-1}$ and $\mu_{XL} = 0.238 \, \text{m}$
(ii) when L = 2.0 m, $\lambda L = 7.692 \, \text{m}^{-1}$ and $\mu_{XL} = 0.259 \, \text{m}$
(iii) when L = 3.0 m, $\lambda L = 11.538 \, \text{m}^{-1}$ and $\mu_{XL} = 0.260 \, \text{m}$.

The values of mean spacing determined by simulating 10 000 scanlines of lengths 1.0, 2.0 and 3.0 m for a discontinuity frequency of 3.846 m^{-1} were 0.194, 0.226 and 0.237 m respectively, for terminated sampling and were 0.206, 0.230 and 0.239 m, respectively, for augmented sampling.

This simple example shows that although short sampling lines tend to underestimate mean discontinuity spacing, this inaccuracy is only significant when the sampling line is very short indeed. The crucial term in equation 5.13 is the product λL, which is the expected number of discontinuities along the scanline. If this product exceeds 5 then μ_{XL} will theoretically be more than 96% of the population mean; simulations show that in practice this value is likely to be closer to about 80%. If λL exceeds 10 then μ_{XL} will theoretically exceed 99.9% of the population mean or about 90% in practice. Clearly if the sampling line is long enough to intersect 5 or more discontinuities the inaccuracy will be small; if 10 or more discontinuities are intersected the accuracy will be acceptable for most practical applications. It is shown in the next sub-section that imprecision in the estimate of mean discontinuity spacing is a far more significant problem than inaccuracy caused by short sampling lines.

Example 5.5

Discontinuities were intersected at the following distances along a sampling line: 0.0, 1.36, 1.49, 2.06 and 2.85 m. Assuming a negative exponential distribution for total discontinuity spacings, determine the best estimate of mean discontinuity spacing for the population.

Solution
In this example 4 discontinuity spacings were observed along a sampling line 2.85 m long, giving an observed mean spacing of 0.7125 m. Inserting $\mu_{XL} = 0.7125$ m and $L = 2.85$ m into equation 5.13, and employing iterative techniques to solve for λ gives $\lambda = 1.261\,\mathrm{m}^{-1}$ and an estimated population mean spacing of 0.793 m. If the sampling line were extended, and intersected the next discontinuity at a distance of, say, 3.17 m the best estimate of population mean spacing would be 0.660 m. This dramatic oscillation in the best estimate of mean spacing reflects the problems of imprecision at these very small sample sizes.

Example 5.6

The conventional RQD determined from a 0.68 m run of borehole core was found to be 83%. Assuming a negative exponential distribution of discontinuity spacings, determine the best estimate of RQD for the population.

Solution
Inserting the conventional RQD threshold value $t = 0.1$ m, a sampling line length $L = 0.68$ m and $\mathrm{TRQD}_{0.1} = 83\%$ into equation 5.15, and solving iteratively for discontinuity frequency gives $\lambda = 7.19\,\mathrm{m}^{-1}$. Inserting this result into equation 5.7 for a long sampling line gives a theoretical RQD of 83.8% for the population. Simulation of 10 000 augmented scanlines of length 0.68 m at a frequency of $7.19\,\mathrm{m}^{-1}$ gives a mean RQD of 78.8%. This example shows that even very short sampling lines impart only a small bias to the RQD estimate. The precision of this small sample size will, however, be very poor.

Sen (1990) and Sadagh *et al.* (1990), addressing some of the uncertainties attached to the estimation of RQD for a rock mass, have proposed the concept of RQP and RQR, which are respectively the probability density and the cumulative probability distribution functions for the conventional RQD. The value of this concept is limited by the fact that RQD must be estimated over a finite length of borehole or scanline. Regularisation effects discussed in section 2.5 will ensure that the variance in RQP will be inversely proportional to the length of borehole or scanline selected.

Table 5.1 Intersection distances and mean spacings for a sampling line

Intersection distance m	Current mean discontinuity spacing m
0	—
0.144	0.144
0.261	0.131
0.293	0.098
0.613	0.153
1.079	0.216
1.098	0.183
1.139	0.163
1.238	0.155
1.248	0.139
⋮	⋮
37.766	0.128
37.774	0.127
38.094	0.128
38.098	0.127
38.202	0.127

5.4.2 Imprecision caused by small sample sizes

Table 5.1 shows the beginning and the end of a list of 300 computer-generated random intersection distances of discontinuities along a hypothetical sampling line. Adjacent to each intersection distance is given the current mean discontinuity spacing, found by equation B.1, for all spacings encountered to that point along the sampling line.

Figure 5.10 is a graph of current mean discontinuity spacing against intersection distance for the data summarised in Table 5.1. This graph shows that the mean discontinuity spacing estimated from a short sampling line, less than about 5 m in this case, varies dramatically. For example, a sampling line of approximately 1.5 m would give a mean spacing of 0.156 m, while a sampling line of 2.5 m would give a mean spacing of 0.125 m. This variability, which is usually termed imprecision, diminishes gradually as the sampling line becomes longer, until at about 30 m the mean value seems to settle down at 0.127 m. The population mean for this simulation was, in fact, 0.125 m. Figure 5.10 suggests that, if this were a real rock exposure, a sampling line length of about 20 m would probably be sufficient to estimate mean spacing with reasonable precision. The time spent collecting data for the additional 18 m or so of sampling line, plotted in Figure 5.10, would be better spent measuring discontinuity characteristics along an additional orthogonal scanline.

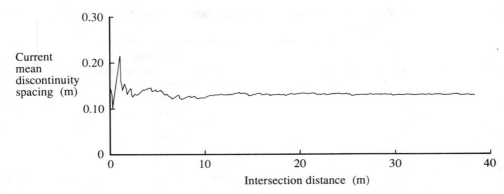

Figure 5.10 Graph of current mean discontinuity spacing against intersection distance for the computer-generated data in Table 5.1.

In order to determine the optimum sample size it is necessary to be able (i) to quantify precision in some way, (ii) to specify the required precision and (iii) to calculate the sample size that will give this precision. The problem of imprecision in a sample mean can be approached by assuming that the sample values come from a population that has some definite, but unknown, mean value μ_X and variance σ_X^2. The best estimate $\bar{X}$ of μ_X, based upon a sample size n, is given by equation B.1. The important basis for the quantitative analysis of precision is the central limit theorem. This theorem states that the mean values $\bar{X}$ of random samples of size n taken from a population that follows any distribution, with a mean μ_X and variance σ_x^2, will tend to be normally distributed with a mean μ_X and variance σ_X^2/n. This distribution is often called the sampling distribution of the mean; its standard deviation equation is termed the standard error of the mean. The normal distribution approximation improves with an increase in the sample size n of each of the samples, and becomes very good when n exceeds 30. Although a rigorous proof of the central limit theorem is relatively complex, and beyond the scope of this book, the theorem does tend to agree with intuitive ideas. The chance occurrence of extremely large or small values will have a greater influence on the mean when the sample size is small, and thereby lead to a higher variance than when the sample size is large. In the limit, when the sample size n is very large, all of the sample means will be very close to μ_X and the variance σ_X^2/n will approach zero.

In the context of discontinuity sampling, the population can be regarded as the complete set of all possible spacing measurements sampled in a specified way, in a given direction through a specified rock mass. If a number of different samples of discontinuity spacing, each of size n were obtained from scanlines in the same direction, it would be possible to plot a histogram of the various resulting mean spacing values $\bar{X}$. The central limit theorem

Table 5.2 Values of $\Phi(z)$ for the normal distribution

z	$\Phi(z)$
0.675	0.50
0.842	0.60
1.036	0.70
1.282	0.80
1.645	0.90
1.960	0.95
2.567	0.99
∞	1.00

predicts that such a histogram will, for large values of n, tend to have the characteristic bell shape of the normal distribution, irrespective of the distribution of discontinuity spacings in the population.

The properties of the normal distribution are well documented (see for example Smith, 1986). It is known that a proportion $\Phi(z)$ of the samples referred to above will yield a mean spacing within a range $\pm z\sqrt{\sigma_X^2/n}$ of the population mean μ_x, where z is the standard normal variable associated with a certain value of $\Phi(z)$. Selected values of z and $\Phi(z)$ obtained by numerical integration of the normal distribution function are listed in Table 5.2.

For a given sample of discontinuity spacings, the computed mean $\bar{X}$ has a $\Phi(z)$ probability (in other words there is $100\Phi(z)\%$ confidence) of lying within the range $\pm z\sqrt{\sigma_X^2/n}$ of the unknown population mean μ_x, as illustrated in Figure 5.11a. Hence, for this given sample, there is $100\Phi(z)\%$ confidence that μ_x lies within the range $\pm z\sqrt{\sigma_X^2/n}$ of $\bar{X}$, as illustrated in Figure 5.11b. This gives a direct measure of the precision, and hence the reliability, of the result. The value of σ_X^2 is unknown because it is the variance of the population. In practice, since variance is relatively insensitive to sample size, σ_X^2 may be taken to be equal to the variance S^2 of the sample, given by equation B.2. In this case the $\Phi(z)$ probability range becomes

$$\Phi(z) \text{ range} = \bar{X} \pm \frac{zS}{\sqrt{n}} \tag{5.16}$$

where S is the standard deviation of the sample and z is given in Table 5.2 for the required confidence level.

Example 5.7

The mean and standard deviation of 116 discontinuity spacing values were found to be 0.131 m and 0.154 m, respectively. Determine the range within which the population mean must lie, at the 90% confidence level.

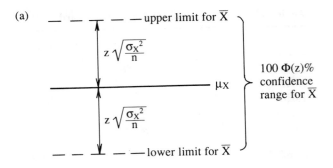

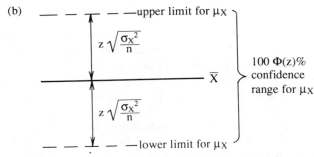

Figure 5.11   100 $\Phi(z)\%$ confidence ranges for (a) population mean μ_x and (b) sample mean $\overline{X}$.

Solution
Here $\Phi(z)\% = 90$ and so, from Table 5.2, $z = 1.645$. The $\Phi(z)$ probability range is given directly by equation 5.16. Setting $S = 0.154\,\mathrm{m}$ and $n = 116$ in this equation gives a range of $\pm0.0235\,\mathrm{m}$ centred on the estimated mean $\overline{X} = 0.131\,\mathrm{m}$. Hence there is 90% confidence that the true mean lies within the range 0.1075 to 0.1545 m.

The term '90% confidence' in the above example can be appreciated better by considering the possibility of collecting many similar samples of discontinuity spacing values at the same site, and computing the 90% confidence range for each. On average, we could expect that the true population mean would lie within this range for 90% of our samples, and outside the range for the other 10%. If we required a higher confidence level, say 95%, the associated range would have to be increased according to the values of z in Table 5.2. It is only possible to achieve 100% confidence by extending the range to infinity.

A valuable simplification of the above approach can be obtained if the discontinuity spacings follow the negative exponential distribution. Table B.1

shows that the mean and variance for this distribution are respectively $1/\lambda$ and $1/\lambda^2$. Consequently the mean and standard deviation are both equal to $1/\lambda$ in the theoretical distribution. For a large sample from a population of spacing values that obey a negative exponential distribution we could, therefore, expect the sample mean $\bar{X}$ and standard deviation S to be very nearly equal. Replacing S in equation 5.16 by $\bar{X}$ gives the $\Phi(z)$ probability range as

$$\Phi(z) \text{ range } = \bar{X} \pm \frac{z\bar{X}}{\sqrt{n}} \qquad (5.17)$$

or

$$\Phi(z) \text{ range } = \bar{X} \pm \varepsilon\bar{X} \qquad (5.18)$$

where ε is the allowable proportionate error, and

$$\varepsilon = \frac{z}{\sqrt{n}} \qquad (5.19)$$

or

$$n = \left(\frac{z}{\varepsilon}\right)^2 \qquad (5.20)$$

Equation 5.19 can be used to determine the error band-width given by a particular sample size for a value of z corresponding to the desired confidence level. Equation 5.20 can be used to compute the sample size required to achieve a given precision, by substituting the appropriate values of z and ε corresponding respectively to the desired confidence level and the acceptable error band-width.

Example 5.8

A sample of 128 discontinuity spacing values gave a mean spacing of 0.215 m. Assuming that the spacings obey a negative exponential distribution, determine the range within which the population mean must lie at the 80% confidence level. Determine what sample sizes would be required to give an allowable proportionate error of $\pm 10\%$ at the 90% and 95% confidence levels.

Solution
In the first part of this example $\Phi(z) = 0.80$ and so, from Table 5.2, $z = 1.282$. The proportionate error ε, from equation 5.19 for a sample size of 127, is 0.1138. The 80% confidence range, from equation 5.18 is therefore 0.1905 to 0.2395 m. In the second part of this example the allowable proportionate error is 10%, so $\varepsilon = 0.10$. At the 90% confidence level $\Phi(z) = 0.90$ and so $z = 1.645$, giving by equation 5.20 a required sample size of approximately 271. At

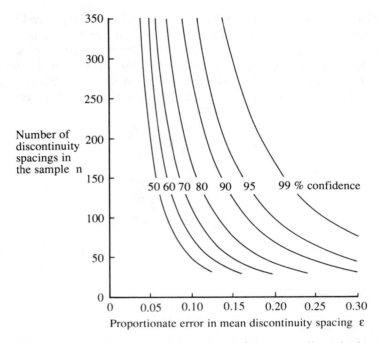

Figure 5.12 Sample number versus the precision of the mean discontinuity spacing estimate for a negative exponential distribution of spacings (after Priest and Hudson, 1981).

the 95% confidence level $\Phi(z) = 0.95$ and $z = 1.960$, giving a required sample size of approximately 384.

Priest and Hudson (1981) have produced curves, which are reproduced in Figure 5.12, and which summarise the relations in equation 5.20. This figure illustrates how the required sample size increases rapidly as the confidence level is increased and/or as the allowable proportionate error is reduced. For most practical applications an allowable proportionate error of 10% coupled with a 90 to 95% confidence level would require a sample size of about 300 to 400.

It must be emphasised that the theory explained in this sub-section is applicable to discontinuity spacing values only. If the input data are in terms of discontinuity frequency they must first be converted to mean spacings before computing the $\Phi(z)$ probability range. If necessary, the resulting discontinuity spacing range can be converted into frequency values simply by taking reciprocals. In Example 5.8, a discontinuity spacing range of 0.1905 to 0.2395 m about a mean spacing of 0.215 m corresponds to a frequency range of 5.248 to 4.176 m^{-1}, a result that is not symmetrical about the (mean) frequency of 4.651 m^{-1}. If desired, the discontinuity frequencies can be converted to RQD values by employing equation 5.7; this is illustrated in the final example of this chapter.

Example 5.9

A 4.65 m length of borehole core, logged to determine the conventional RQD gave a value of 53%. Assuming that the discontinuities are randomly located along the core, and ignoring end effects, determine the 95% confidence range for RQD. What additional length of borehole core from this rock mass unit would need to be sampled and logged in order to bring this 95% confidence range down to about ±7 RQD percentage points?

Solution
In the first part of this example, assuming that the discontinuity spacings obey a negative exponential distribution allows us to use equation 5.7 to determine (mean) frequency. Setting $RQD_{0.1} = 53\%$ and $t = 0.1$ m gives, by iterative solution, a λ of $15.84 \, m^{-1}$. This result indicates that a total of approximately 74 discontinuities were intersected by the 4.65 m length of core, giving a mean spacing of 0.063 m. Setting $\Phi(z) = 0.95$ in Table 5.2 gives $z = 1.960$, which when input to equation 5.19 with $n = 74$, gives a proportionate error $\varepsilon = 0.228$. This error corresponds to a 95% confidence range of 0.049 to 0.077 m in spacing, approximately 20.5 to $12.9 \, m^{-1}$ in frequency and, by equation 5.7, approximately 39 to 63% in terms of RQD. In other words, we can be 95% sure that the true RQD for this rock mass lies in the range 39 to 63%.

In the second part of this example, 7 percentage points below the observed value of 53% corresponds to an RQD of 46% at the lower end of the 95% confidence range. An RQD of 46% gives, by equation 5.7, a $\lambda = 18.10 \, m^{-1}$ and hence a mean spacing of 0.055 m. Taking the original mean spacing of 0.063 m indicates that this spacing at the lower end of the confidence range corresponds to a proportionate error $\varepsilon = (0.063 - 0.055)/0.063 \approx 0.127$. Inputting this value, together with $z = 1.960$ for the 95% confidence range, to equation 5.20 gives a required sample size of about 238. This sample size would require a borehole core length of approximately 15 m, or an additional length of 10.35 m. The upper limit of the 95% confidence range for this sample length will be less than 53 + 7% because of the asymmetrical nature of the RQD range, so the criterion will have been satisfied. In fact, for a sample size of 238 the upper limit is approximately 58.9%. Again it is interesting to note how dramatically the required length of borehole core has increased in order to achieve the narrower error band-width on RQD.

EXERCISES FOR CHAPTER 5

5.1

The conventional Rock Quality Designation (RQD) obtained from measurements along a 15 m length of borehole core from a jointed limestone rock mass was calculated to be 64.3%. Assuming that the discontinuity spacings obey the negative exponential distribution:

(i)   Estimate the discontinuity frequency along the axis of the borehole core.
(ii) Estimate the range within which the true value of RQD will lie at the 80% and at the 90% confidence levels.
(iii) Estimate the approximate number of pieces of core that are longer than 0.1 m and the number that are longer than 0.2 m.

5.2

A preliminary borehole investigation of a fractured sandstone rock mass produced 30 m of core, which contained 33 drilling breaks, 283 iron-stained joints and 38 other discontinuity features of uncertain origin.

(i)   Calculate the band-widths within which the true mean discontinuity spacing of the rock mass, in the direction of the borehole axis, lies at the 90% and 95% confidence levels.
(ii) What approximate additional length of borehole is required to provide a band-width of $\pm 8\%$ at the 95% confidence level?
(iii) It is proposed that fracture frequency will be calculated over 1 m lengths of the core produced during the main investigations. Assuming that the rock mass is statistically homogeneous, what approximate percentage of these 1 m lengths could be expected to contain more than 8 but less than 13 discontinuities?

5.3   (Also Chapter 4)

It is proposed that during tunnelling operations through a fractured rock mass, the rock quality should be evaluated by measuring RQD along a single vertical 2 m scanline set up at the exposed face. Any face with an RQD above 90%, measured using the conventional threshold value of 0.1 m, will be classified as 'very good' for the purposes of contractual payments. If the actual RQD for a given zone of the rock mass is 85% in a vertical direction, calculate the probability that the rock will be classified as 'very good' on the basis of a single vertical 2 m scanline.

5.4 (Also Chapter 4)

A rock mass is intersected by three sets of discontinuities with the following orientations and frequencies:

Discontinuity set	Dip direction/ dip angle	Normal frequency m^{-1}
1	006/36	2.7
2	292/63	3.5
3	170/44	1.9

The rock also contains a randomly orientated group of discontinuities with an effective isotropic frequency of $2.1\,\mathrm{m}^{-1}$. A site investigation borehole, driven through the rock mass along a line of trend/plunge 260/34, recovered 129 m of core, in runs of 1.5 m. Calculate the expected value of RQD for these core runs. If the measured value of RQD for the entire borehole is 84% estimate (i) the total number of additional discontinuities introduced during the drilling and sampling process, and (ii) the number of core runs that could be expected to contain less than 8 discontinuities.

Answers to these exercises are given on pages 461–2.

6

Discontinuity size

6.1 INTRODUCTION

Although it is relatively easy to specify the size of a discontinuity in terms of its surface area, size is one of the most difficult discontinuity properties to measure accurately. This is because only by completely dismantling a given rock mass is it possible to trace and to measure the complete area of each discontinuity. This has never been done satisfactorily for a rock mass. When studying the size of discontinuities it is desirable also to consider their shape. In a completely blocky rock mass, where all discontinuities terminate at other planar discontinuities, the shapes will take the form of complex polygons whose geometry is governed by the locations of the bounding discontinuities. It was noted in Chapter 5 that discontinuity occurrence is often random, leading to negative exponential distributions in spacing. It is reasonable to suppose, therefore, that the linear dimensions of discontinuities would also be of negative exponential form. Sampling difficulties have so far made it impossible to prove or disprove this hypothesis. In view of these sampling difficulties, a number of workers have adopted the simplifying assumption that discontinuities are circular, to provide a starting point for the analysis of size (Baecher *et al.*, 1977 and Warburton, 1980a).

Section 6.2 contains an analysis of discontinuity size based on the assumption that discontinuities are circular discs. All subsequent sections proceed on the assumption that linear traces produced by the intersection of planar discontinuities with a planar rock face form the target population, about which information is to be obtained by sampling. Section 6.3 contains an analysis of the size sampling bias imposed by scanline surveys, the semi-trace length distributions produced by scanline sampling and the curtailment of long semi-trace lengths at rock faces of limited extent. Section 6.4 presents a number of distribution independent and other methods for estimating mean trace length.

The next section contains a brief discussion of the trimming of very short semi-trace lengths. Section 6.6 examines the relation between linear discontinuity frequency, areal discontinuity frequency and size. Section 6.7 contains a brief summary of the theory presented in sections 6.3 and 6.5 with some comments on how this theory can be applied to the estimation of discontinuity size in practice. The chapter ends with a section explaining the generation of random fracture networks in three and two dimensions.

Some readers may find the mathematical developments in this chapter somewhat demanding. This mathematical complexity reflects the complex geometrical and probabilistic nature of discontinuity size and its analysis. It is hoped that the fairly detailed examples will help in the understanding of the main principles. It was noted in Chapter 1 that certain chapters will require considerable re-reading and cross-referencing; this point is particularly true for this chapter.

6.2 DISCONTINUITIES AS CIRCULAR DISCS

It is assumed here that discontinuities from a given set can be represented by circular discs of diameter s, distributed according to some probability density distribution c(s). The cumulative distribution of diameters C(s) is found from equation B.12 by introducing a dummy variable t and integrating between 0 and s, as follows

$$C(s) = \int_0^s c(t)dt$$

The area of each discontinuity is given by $a = \pi s^2/4$. The density distribution j(a) of discontinuity areas can be found from c(s) by substitution. As in earlier chapters the term P(event) is adopted to represent the probability associated with the event in parenthesis.

$$P(\text{given diameter} \leq s) = C(s)$$

now

$$s = 2\sqrt{(a/\pi)}$$

so

$$P(\text{given area} \leq \pi s^2/4) = C(s) = C(2\sqrt{(a/\pi)})$$

hence

$$j(a) = \frac{dC(2\sqrt{(a/\pi)})}{da} \tag{6.1}$$

Example 6.1

It is assumed that a given set of discontinuities can be represented by circular discs whose diameters s are distributed according to a negative exponential probability density distribution with a mean of $1/\lambda$. Obtain expressions (i) for the density distribution of discontinuity areas, and (ii) for mean discontinuity area.

Solution

(i) If the discontinuity diameters s obey a negative exponential distribution, their density distribution c(s) is, from Table B.1, given by

$$c(s) = \lambda e^{-\lambda s}$$

where in this case $1/\lambda$ is the mean diameter. By analogy with equation 5.3 the cumulative distribution C(s) of diameters is given by

$$C(s) = 1 - e^{-\lambda s}$$

Substituting $s = 2\sqrt{(a/\pi)}$ gives

$$C(2\sqrt{(a/\pi)}) = 1 - e^{-2\lambda\sqrt{(a/\pi)}}$$

Carrying out the differentiation in equation 6.1 gives

$$j(a) = \frac{\lambda\, e^{-2\lambda\sqrt{(a/\pi)}}}{\sqrt{a\pi}}$$

This is the probability density distribution of discontinuity areas.

(ii) The mean area μ_A is found from the density distribution j(a) by applying equation B.14, so that

$$\mu_A = \int_0^\infty aj(a)da$$

or

$$\mu_A = \int_0^\infty \frac{\lambda\, a\, e^{-2\lambda\sqrt{(a/\pi)}}}{\sqrt{a\pi}}$$

Here it is convenient to identify the constant

$$k = 2\lambda/\sqrt{\pi}$$

so that

$$\mu_A = \frac{k}{2}\int_0^\infty \sqrt{a}\, e^{-k\sqrt{a}}da$$

If we substitute $x = \sqrt{a}$ and note that $da = 2x\, dx$, then

$$\mu_A = k\int_0^\infty x^2\, e^{-kx}dx$$

This result is exactly similar to the expression for m_{X2} in Example B.2, so we can use the result given in equation B.20. Hence

$$\mu_A = k\left[\frac{-x^2e^{-kx}}{k} - \frac{2x\,e^{-kx}}{k^2} - \frac{2\,e^{-kx}}{k^3}\right]_0^\infty \qquad (6.2)$$

Inserting the limits gives

$$\mu_A = \frac{2}{k^2} = \frac{\pi}{2\lambda^2}$$

It is interesting to note that the above result gives a mean area that is twice the area calculated for a disc at the mean diameter $1/\lambda$.

The distribution of discontinuity areas can be found for any continuous form of c(s) by applying the principles set out in equation 6.1 and illustrated in the above example. Although it is possible to write down theoretical expressions for j(a) in this way, the sampling difficulties referred to in Chapter 2 make it almost impossible to determine j(a) and its parameters directly. The best, and most widely adopted sampling strategy for determining discontinuity size is based upon the measurement of the lengths of the traces produced where the discontinuities intersect a planar face.

Warburton (1980a) has provided a valuable analysis of the distributions of trace lengths produced by the intersections of parallel circular planar discs with a planar face. He assumed that the discontinuity centres obeyed a three-dimensional Poisson process with a volumetric frequency λ_v, and considered the linear traces, which are the chords of circular discs produced where such discs are intersected by a cutting plane whose normal makes an angle $(\pi/2) - \delta$ with the normal to the discontinuity set. By equation B.10 there is a probability c(s) ds that a randomly selected circular discontinuity will have a diameter in the range s to s + ds. In a unit volume of rock the total number of such discontinuities is λ_v c(s) ds. Of the discontinuities with diameters in the range s to s + ds only those whose centres lie within a distance $(s/2)\cos\delta$ on either side of the cutting plane can be intersected. If the cutting plane is large, with an area A_p, there will be a volume of rock given by $2A_p(s/2)\cos\delta$ within which the discontinuity centres must lie in order to intersect the cutting plane. Consequently, the average number, N_s, of discontinuities with diameters in the range s to s + ds intersecting a unit area of the cutting plane is given by

$$N_s = s\cos\delta\ \lambda_v\ c(s)\ ds \qquad (6.3)$$

The average number, N_a, of discontinuities with diameters in the range 0 to ∞ intersecting a unit area of the cutting plane is found by integrating equation 6.3 over the complete range of circle diameters.

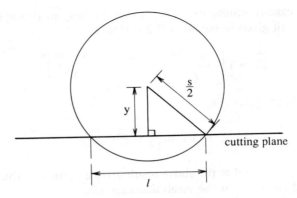

Figure 6.1 Discontinuity trace produced by a circular disc intersecting a cutting plane (after Warburton, 1980a).

Hence

$$N_a = \int_0^\infty \lambda_v \cos\delta \; s \; c(s) \; ds \qquad (6.4)$$

Now the mean diameter μ_s of the circular discontinuities is, from equation B.14, given by

$$\mu_s = \int_0^\infty s \; c(s) \; ds$$

so

$$N_a = \lambda_v \cos\delta \; \mu_s \qquad (6.5)$$

The value N_a is the expected number of traces per unit area of the cutting plane, produced by this particular set of parallel circular discontinuities. The ratio N_s/N_a gives the relative frequency of traces, which represent the chords of circles, produced by discontinuities with a diameter in the range s to s + ds. Combining equations 6.3 and 6.5 gives

$$\frac{N_s}{N_a} = \frac{s}{\mu_s} c(s) \; ds \qquad (6.6)$$

Hence, employing equation B.9, the probability density distribution k(s) of chords on the cutting plane, produced by discontinuities of diameter s is given by

$$k(s) = \frac{s}{\mu_s} c(s) \qquad (6.7)$$

This is the result obtained in equation 5 of Warburton (1980a).

Figure 6.1 after Warburton (1980a), illustrates the geometry of a typical circular discontinuity represented by a disc of radius s/2 which, by its inter-section with the cutting plane produces a chord of length l located at a perpendicular distance y from the centre of the circle. It is assumed that the discontinuity is located randomly relative to the cutting plane; this means that the distance y will be distributed uniformly in the range 0 to s/2 with a constant density of 2/s. Of these circular discs that have diameters in the range s to s + ds and are intersected by the cutting plane there will, therefore, be a proportion 2 dy/s that also have their centres in the range y to y + dy from the cutting plane. Multiplying this proportion by the relative frequency given by equation 6.6 gives the proportion P_{sy}, of the total number of traces that have parent disc diameters in the range s to s + ds **and** centre locations in the range y to y + dy, as follows

$$P_{sy} = \frac{2}{\mu_s} c(s) \, ds \, dy \qquad (6.8)$$

Simple application of Pythagoras' theorem to the geometry in Figure 6.1 gives

$$y = \frac{1}{2} \sqrt{s^2 - l^2}$$

hence

$$dy = \frac{-l \, dl}{2\sqrt{s^2 - l^2}}$$

Here the negative sign simply means that l decreases as y increases. Taking the absolute value and substituting for dy in equation 6.8 gives the proportion, P_l, of the total number of traces that have parent disc diameters in the range s to s + ds **and** chord lengths in the range l to l + dl , as follows

$$P_{sl} = \frac{1}{\mu_s} c(s) \, ds \, \frac{l \, dl}{\sqrt{s^2 - l^2}} \qquad (6.9)$$

A chord length in the range l to l + dl could be produced by a circular disc that has a diameter greater than l. Consequently, the proportion, P_{sl}, of the total number of chords that have lengths in the range l to l + dl is found by integrating equation 6.9 between the limits l and ∞, as follows

$$P_l = \frac{l \, dl}{\mu_s} \int_l^{\infty} \frac{c(s) \, ds}{\sqrt{s^2 - l^2}}$$

This gives the probability density distribution of complete trace lengths $f(l)$ over the entire area of the cutting plane as

$$f(l) = \frac{l}{\mu_s} \int_l^{\infty} \frac{c(s) \, ds}{\sqrt{s^2 - l^2}} \qquad (l \le s) \qquad (6.10)$$

This is the result obtained in equation 9 of Warburton (1980a). Warburton emphasises that his derivation of this equation was adapted from work originally done by Wicksell (1925 and 1926). In theory, if it is assumed that discontinuities are randomly located circular discs, it is possible, by measuring the complete trace lengths exposed at a cutting plane, and by applying equation 6.10, to determine the distribution of the disc diameters. This is not, in general, a straightforward procedure since it involves numerical integration of a function that displays a singularity at the lower limit of integration. Warburton (1980a) suggested the following trigonometrical substitution to render this integration more tractable.

$$f(l) = \frac{l}{\mu_s} \int_0^{\frac{\pi}{2}} c\left(\frac{l}{\cos m}\right) \frac{dm}{\cos m} \qquad (6.11)$$

It is important to note that the term $\left(\dfrac{l}{\cos m}\right)$ in the above expression must obey any range limitations imposed on the function c(s). For example in Example 6.2, s must lie in the range 0 to a limiting maximum value s_m.

Example 6.2

It is assumed that a given set of discontinuities can be represented by randomly-located, parallel circular discs whose diameters s are distributed according to a uniform probability density distribution in the range 0 to s_m. Obtain an expression for the probability density distribution of complete trace lengths on a plane cutting through the discontinuities.

Solution
If the discontinuity diameters s obey a uniform distribution in the range 0 to s_m, their density distribution c(s) is, from Table B.1, given by

$$c(s) = \frac{1}{s_m} \qquad 0 \leqslant s \leqslant s_m$$

where the mean diameter $\mu_s = s_m/2$. Substituting $c(s) = 1/s_m$ and $\mu_s = s_m/2$ into equation 6.10, and inserting the parameter s_m as the upper limit of integration gives the probability density distribution $f(l)$ of trace lengths on the cutting plane as

$$f(l) = \frac{2l}{s_m^2} \int_l^{s_m} \frac{ds}{\sqrt{s^2 - l^2}}$$

hence

$$f(l) = \frac{2l}{s_m^2} \left[\ln\left(s + \sqrt{s^2 - l^2}\right) \right]_l^{s_m}$$

so

$$f(l) = \frac{2l}{s_m^2}[\ln(s_m + \sqrt{s_m^2 - l^2}) - \ln l] \qquad 0 \leqslant l \leqslant s_m$$

For example, taking $\mu_s = 5.0\,$m for $l = 1.0\,$m, $f(l) = 0.060\,$m^{-1}, which is the result obtained by the numerical integration of equations 6.10 and 6.11. It is worth noting that the above expression exhibits a singularity when $l = 0$ and that $f(l) = 0$ when $l = s_m$. This latter property is caused by the negligible probability of a given discontinuity of diameter s_m being cut along one of its diameters.

Warburton (1980a) went on to apply a similar approach to that explained above to derive expressions giving the distribution of trace lengths, $g(l)$ that would be obtained by scanline sampling on the cutting plane. Here it is necessary to consider the second moment, m_{s2} of the disc diameter distribution, where, by equation B.15

$$m_{s2} = \int_0^\infty s^2 c(s)\,ds$$

The expression for $g(l)$ is as follows

$$g(l) = \frac{4l^2}{\pi\,m_{s2}} \int_l^\infty \frac{c(s)\,ds}{\sqrt{s^2 - l^2}} \qquad (6.12)$$

Equation 6.12 is the result obtained in equation 27 of Warburton (1980a). In a subsequent paper Warburton (1980b) extended his analysis to include parallelogram shaped discontinuities, as a first step towards the analysis of more complex polygons. Although based upon a similar approach to that described above, the results are inevitably more complex since more parameters are required to describe the geometry of a parallelogram than a circle. Moreover, there is no evidence, at this stage, to suggest that a parallelogram shape is more realistic than a circle.

6.3 DISCONTINUITIES AS LINEAR TRACES

In view of the difficulties in developing a model for discontinuity shape, a number of authors have preferred to treat the problem in an entirely two-dimensional way (Cruden, 1977; Priest and Hudson, 1981; and Pahl, 1981). Here the approach is to regard the linear traces produced by the intersection of planar discontinuities with a planar rock face as the target population, about which information is to be obtained by sampling. The data collection method adopted can be based either upon scanline or window sampling over the rock face. Whichever method is adopted, the most important difficulties are related to any sampling bias imposed by the chosen sampling method and the

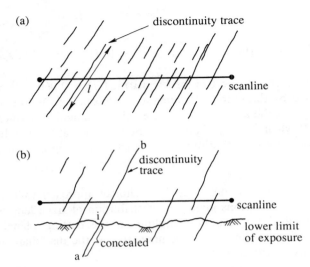

Figure 6.2 Discontinuities intersecting a scanline on a planar face (after Priest and Hudson 1981).

measurement of discontinuities that extend beyond the limits of the rock face. One method of overcoming these difficulties, summarised in sections 6.3.1 to 6.3.3, has been developed by Priest and Hudson (1981) for analysing trace length data obtained from scanline surveys.

6.3.1 Sampling bias imposed by scanline surveys

Figure 6.2(a) shows a diagrammatic representation of a scanline set up on an extensive planar rock face intersected by a set of discontinuities that, being of various limited sizes produce traces of various lengths. Priest and Hudson (1981) noted that the scanline sampling process itself introduces a bias since the scanline will tend to intersect preferentially the longer traces. They assumed that the probability density distribution of the complete traces over the entire rock face is given by f(l), as defined for circular discs in equation 6.10. If the scanline is located randomly with respect to a set of parallel discontinuity traces then the probability of the scanline intersecting a given trace is directly proportional to the length of that trace. Hence, applying equation B.10, the probability that the scanline intersects a trace with a length in the range l to $l + dl$ is given by $k l$ f(l) dl, where k is a constant.

The probability density distribution, g(l), of trace lengths intersected by the scanline is therefore given by

$$g(l) = k l \ f(l)$$

The density distribution $g(l)$ for circular discs has been given previously in equation 6.12. Now, since $g(l)$ is a probability density distribution, applying equation B.11 gives

$$\int_0^\infty g(l) \, dl = 1$$

or

$$k \int_0^\infty l \, f(l) \, dl = 1$$

but

$$\int_0^\infty l \, f(l) \, dl = \mu_L$$

where μ_L is the mean trace length for the entire face, hence

$$k = 1/\mu_L$$

and

$$g(l) = \frac{l \, f(l)}{\mu_L} \qquad (6.13)$$

Combination of equations 6.10 and 6.12 shows that, for circular discs, the derivations obtained by Warburton (1980a) give the result

$$g(l) = \frac{4l \, \mu_s \, f(l)}{\pi \, m_{s2}}$$

Warburton (1980a) also demonstrated that, for circular discs, the mean μ_L of $f(l)$ is given by

$$\mu_L = \frac{\pi \, m_{s2}}{4\mu_s}$$

Combination of these results confirms that equation 6.13 is consistent with the derivations obtained by Warburton. Equation 6.13 also shows how the distribution of trace lengths sampled by a scanline is biased by the preferential sampling of the longer trace lengths.

Example 6.3

It is assumed that the density distribution $f(l)$, of complete trace lengths for a given discontinuity set over an entire rock face could be either (i) negative exponential, (ii) uniform or (iii) triangular, as defined in Table B.1. Obtain for each, expressions for $g(l)$ the density distribution, and μ_{gL} the mean value, of complete trace lengths sampled by a scanline across the rock face.

(i) If f(*l*) is negative exponential then

$$f(l) = \frac{e^{-(l/\mu_L)}}{\mu_L}$$

where μ_L is the mean of f(*l*).

Hence by equation 6.13

$$g(l) = \frac{l\, e^{-(l/\mu_L)}}{(\mu_L)^2}$$

Applying equation B.14 gives the mean of g(*l*), μ_{gL} as

$$\mu_{gL} = \int_0^\infty l\, g(l)\, dl$$

so

$$\mu_{gL} = \left(\frac{1}{\mu_L}\right)^2 \int_0^\infty l^2 e^{-(l/\mu_L)} dl$$

Utilising the result in equation B.20 of Example B.2(i) gives

$$\mu_{gL} = 2\mu_L$$

(ii) If f(*l*) is uniform then

$$f(l) = 1/l_m \qquad 0 \leqslant l \leqslant l_m$$

where the mean trace length $\mu_L = l_m/2$. Hence by equation 6.13

$$g(l) = \frac{2l}{l_m^2} \qquad 0 \leqslant l \leqslant l_m$$

Again, applying equation B.14 gives the mean of g(*l*), μ_{gL} as

$$\mu_{gL} = \int_0^{l_m} 2\left(\frac{l}{l_m}\right)^2 dl \qquad 0 \leqslant l \leqslant l_m$$

so

$$\mu_{gL} = \frac{2l_m}{3} = \frac{4\mu_L}{3}$$

(iii) If f(*l*) is triangular then

$$f(l) = \frac{2(l_m - l)}{l_m^2} \qquad 0 \leqslant l \leqslant l_m$$

where the mean trace length $\mu_L = l_m/3$. Again, by equation 6.13

$$g(l) = \frac{6l(l_m - l)}{l_m^3}$$

(a)

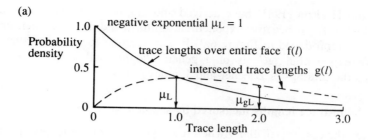

(b)

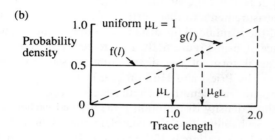

(c)

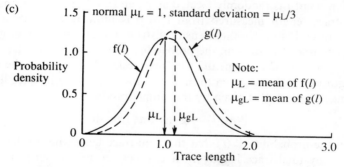

Figure 6.3 Probability density distributions of trace lengths over entire face f(l) and intersected trace lengths g(l) when f(l) is (a) negative exponential, (b) uniform and (c) normal (after Priest and Hudson, 1981).

Applying equation B.14 gives the mean of g(l), μ_{gL} as

$$\mu_{gL} = \int_0^{l_m} \frac{6l^2(l_m - l)}{l_m^{\,3}}\, dl \qquad 0 \leqslant l \leqslant l_m$$

so

$$\mu_{gL} = \frac{l_m}{2} = \frac{3\mu_L}{2}$$

Priest and Hudson (1981) have derived and graphed the distributional forms for g(l) when f(l) is negative exponential, uniform and normal. Their graphical results are reproduced in Figure 6.3. It is interesting to note that when f(l) is negative exponential, g(l) is of a general 'lognormal' shape; a result that confirms the findings of Baecher and Lanney (1978).

6.3.2   Semi-trace lengths measured by scanline surveys

It is often the case, particularly when the exposure is of limited extent, that the scanline is located towards the edge of the exposure. This location usually restricts trace length measurements to that portion of the trace length lying on one side or the other of the scanline. This distance, from the intersection point i to the end of the trace at b in Figure 6.2b, is here referred to as the **semi-trace length**. The general form of the distribution of sampled semi-trace lengths h(l) was obtained by Priest and Hudson (1981) as follows.

The intersected complete trace length in Figure 6.2b, given by the distance ab = m, has a probability density distribution g(m) derived earlier and given in equation 6.13. The probability that the complete trace length lies in the range m to m + dm is, by equation B.10, g(m) dm. It is assumed that the intersection point i is randomly located along ab in Figure 6.2b. Consequently the semi-trace length measured from i to b is uniformly distributed in the range 0 to m with a probability density distribution of 1/m. Hence, given that the complete trace length is m, the probability that the semi-trace length lies in the range l to l + dl is (1/m) dl. The probability P(m, l) that the complete trace length lies in the range m to m + dm **and** that the semi-trace length lies in the range l to l + dl is given by the simple product

$$P(m, l) = g(m) \ dm(1/m) \, dl$$

To obtain the probability P (l) that the semi-trace length lies in the range l to l + dl for any total trace length m, it is necessary to sum all P(m, l) for all possible values of m. Since m must always be greater than l, it is necessary to integrate the above result with respect to m between l and ∞, hence

$$P(l) = \int_l^\infty \left(\frac{1}{m}\right) dl \ g(m) \ dm$$

so, applying equation B.10, the distribution of sampled semi-trace lengths is given by

$$h(l) = \int_l^\infty \left(\frac{1}{m}\right) g(m) \ dm \tag{6.14}$$

Replacing l in equation 6.13 by m gives

$$g(m) = \frac{m \ f(m)}{\mu_L}$$

where μ_L is the mean of the complete trace length distribution f(m). Hence

$$h(l) = \int_l^\infty \frac{f(m)\ dm}{\mu_L} \tag{6.15}$$

or

$$h(l) = \frac{1 - F(l)}{\mu_L} \tag{6.16}$$

where $F(l)$ is the cumulative distribution of f(m), given by equation B.12 as follows

$$F(l) = \int_0^l f(m)\ dm$$

Equation 6.15 gives the theoretical probability density distribution of the semi-trace lengths sampled by the scanline. It is important to note that μ_L in equation 6.16 is the mean of the complete trace lengths sampled over the entire rock face, and not the mean of h(l).

Example 6.4

Obtain expressions for h(l), the theoretical density distribution of semi-trace lengths sampled by a scanline, for the three distributions of complete trace lengths in Example 6.3 and in each case determine the mean, μ_{hL}, of h(l).

Solution
(i) In this case we use the dummy variable m to represent complete trace lengths sampled over the entire face. Hence, if the density distribution f(m) of complete trace lengths is negative exponential then

$$f(m) = \frac{e^{-(m/\mu_L)}}{\mu_L}$$

where μ_L is the mean of f(m). Applying equation B.12

$$F(l) = \int_0^l f(m)\ dm$$

so

$$F(l) = \int_0^l \frac{e^{-(m/\mu_L)}}{\mu_L}\ dm = 1 - e^{-(l/\mu_L)}$$

hence, by equation 6.16

$$h(l) = \frac{e^{-(l/\mu_L)}}{\mu_L}$$

In this case, then, f(m) and h(l) are identical, both being negative exponential. This result is consistent with the assumptions made by Cruden (1977) in his analysis of discontinuity spacings. The above analysis becomes the proof referred to in section 5.2.

(ii) If f(m) is uniform then

$$f(m) = 1/l_m \qquad 0 \leqslant m \leqslant l_m$$

where the mean trace length $\mu_L = l_m/2$. Applying equation B.12 gives

$$F(l) = \int_0^l \frac{1}{l_m} \, dm \qquad 0 \leqslant l \leqslant l_m$$

so

$$F(l) = \frac{l}{l_m}$$

hence by equation 6.16

$$h(l) = \frac{3}{l_m} - \frac{6l}{l_m^2} + \frac{3l^2}{l_m^3} \qquad 0 \leqslant l \leqslant l_m$$

which is the triangular distribution in Table B.1. Applying equation B.14 gives the mean of h(l), μ_{hL} as

$$\mu_{hL} = \int_0^{l_m} l \, h(l) \, dl$$

so

$$\mu_{hL} = \frac{2}{l_m^2} \int_0^{l_m} (l_m \, l) - (l_m)^2 \, dl$$

which, by analogy with Example B.2(iii) gives

$$\mu_{hL} = \frac{l_m}{3} = \frac{2\mu_L}{3}$$

(iii) If f(m) is triangular then

$$f(m) = \frac{2(l_m - m)}{l_m^2} \qquad 0 \leqslant m \leqslant l_m$$

where the mean trace length $\mu_L = l_m/3$. Applying equation B.12 gives

$$F(l) = \frac{2}{l_m^2} \int_0^l (l_m - m) \, dm = \frac{2l}{l_m} - \frac{l^2}{l_m^2}$$

hence by equation 6.16

$$h(l) = \frac{3}{l_m} - \frac{6l}{l_m^2} + \frac{3l^2}{l_m^3} \qquad 0 \le l \le l_m$$

Again, applying equation B.14 gives the mean of $h(l)$, μ_{hL} as

$$\mu_{hL} = \int_0^{l_m} \frac{3l}{l_m} - \frac{6l^2}{l_m^2} + \frac{3l^3}{l_m^3} \, dl \qquad 0 \le l \le l_m$$

so $\mu_{hL} = l_m/4 = 3\mu_L/4$.

It is worth commenting on the expected result in the above example, that for all distributions $\mu_{hL} = \mu_{gL}/2$, i.e. the mean semi-trace length is half the mean complete trace length. Priest and Hudson (1981) have derived and graphed the distributional forms for $h(l)$ when $f(m)$ is negative exponential, uniform and normal. Their graphical results, reproduced in Figure 6.4, serve to illustrate the results obtained in Example 6.4(i) and (ii). The adoption of semi-trace length measurements as a basis for estimating mean trace length has been confirmed by Zhang and Liao (1990) who also provide instructive case studies of the estimation of confidence bounds.

6.3.3 Curtailment of long semi-trace lengths measured by scanline surveys

If a rock exposure is of limited extent there will be some maximum observable value, c_m, for semi-trace length, as illustrated in Figure 6.5. Since c_m can vary with distance along the scanline it is usually convenient to apply one or more arbitrary cut-off levels c that are less than c_m. The imposition of cut-offs in this way is here referred to as 'curtailment'; although the number of semi-traces that are longer than c may be known, no information is available concerning their true lengths. The statistical term 'censoring' is reserved for situations where a sample is terminated above or below a given level and the number of values lost is **known**. The statistical term 'truncation' is reserved for situations where a sample is terminated above or below a given level and the number of values lost is **unknown**. In this and subsequent sections the term 'curtailment' will be used to cover both censoring and truncation of values **larger** than a specified value; the term 'trimming' will be used to cover both censoring and truncation of values **smaller** than a specified value. Information concerning the number of curtailed or trimmed values is only used in certain cases. The probability density distribution, $i(l)$, of semi-trace lengths curtailed above a level c can be found directly from the distribution $h(l)$ of semi-trace

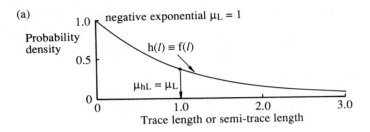

(a)

1.0 negative exponential $\mu_L = 1$

Probability density

$h(l) \equiv f(l)$

0.5

$\mu_{hL} = \mu_L$

0   1.0   2.0   3.0

Trace length or semi-trace length

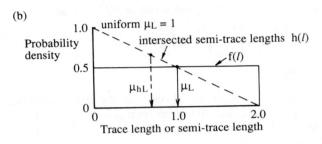

(b)

1.0 uniform $\mu_L = 1$

Probability density

intersected semi-trace lengths $h(l)$

$f(l)$

0.5

μ_{hL} μ_L

0   1.0   2.0

Trace length or semi-trace length

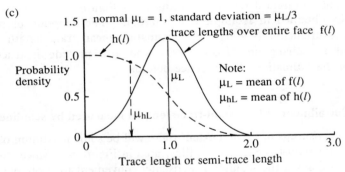

(c)

1.5 normal $\mu_L = 1$, standard deviation $= \mu_L/3$

trace lengths over entire face $f(l)$

$h(l)$

1.0

Probability density

μ_L

Note:
μ_L = mean of $f(l)$
μ_{hL} = mean of $h(l)$

0.5

μ_{hL}

0   1.0   2.0   3.0

Trace length or semi-trace length

Figure 6.4 Probability density distributions of trace lengths over entire face $f(l)$ and semi-trace lengths $h(l)$ when $f(l)$ is (a) negative exponential, (b) uniform and (c) normal (after Priest and Hudson, 1981).

lengths, noting that $i(l) = 0$ when $l > c$. This curtailment at a value of $l = c$ reduces the area under the $h(l)$ density curve from unity to

$$\int_0^c h(l)\,dl = H(c)$$

The density $i(l)$ is obtained, therefore, by dividing $h(l)$ by the constant $H(c)$, hence

$$i(l) = \frac{h(l)}{H(c)} \qquad l \leqslant c \qquad (6.17)$$

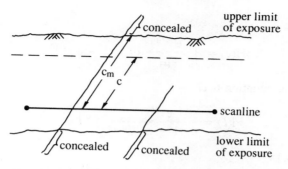

Figure 6.5 Curtailed semi-trace lengths (after Priest and Hudson, 1981).

The mean value μ_{iL} of $i(l)$ is given by

$$\mu_{iL} = \int_0^c \frac{l \, h(l) \, dl}{H(c)} \qquad (6.18)$$

The theoretical mean μ_{iL} can be estimated at a rock exposure by calculating the mean semi-trace length for those discontinuities that have a semi-trace length less than c. Equation 6.18 can then be used to determine the mean trace length μ_L for the entire rock face. This approach is only feasible if the forms of the trace length, or semi-trace length, distributions are known, or can be estimated with reasonable accuracy. This problem is discussed further in section 6.7. The complex problem of curtailment at progressively varying values of c is discussed by Baecher (1980).

Example 6.5

Obtain expressions for $i(l)$, the density distribution of semi-trace lengths curtailed above a level c, for the three distributions of complete trace lengths in Examples 6.3 and 6.4. In each case determine the mean μ_{iL}, of $i(l)$.

Solution
(i) If the density distribution of complete trace lengths is negative exponential then, by Example 6.4(i)

$$h(l) = \frac{e^{-(l/\mu_L)}}{\mu_L}$$

now, by equation B.12

$$H(c) = \int_0^c h(l) \, dl$$

so, in this case

$$H(c) = \int_0^c \frac{e^{-(l/\mu_L)}}{\mu_L} \, dl = 1 - e^{-(c/\mu_L)}$$

hence, applying equation 6.17

$$i(l) = \frac{e^{-(l/\mu_L)}}{\mu_L(1 - e^{-(c/\mu_L)})} \qquad l \leqslant c$$

By equation 6.18

$$\mu_{iL} = \frac{1}{\mu_L(1 - e^{-(c/\mu_L)})} \int_0^c l e^{-(l/\mu_L)} \, dl$$

Utilising the result in equation B.19 of Example B.2(i) gives

$$\mu_{iL} = \mu_L - \frac{c \, e^{-(c/\mu_L)}}{1 - e^{-(c/\mu_L)}} \qquad (6.19)$$

If c is very large then $\mu_{iL} = \mu_{hL} = \mu_L$.

(ii) If the density distribution of complete trace lengths is uniform, then by Example 6.4(ii)

$$H(l) = \frac{2(l_m - l)}{l_m^2} \qquad 0 \leqslant l \leqslant l_m$$

where $\mu_L = l_m/2$ and $\mu_{hL} = l_m/3$. In this case

$$H(c) = \int_0^c \frac{2(l_m - l)}{l_m^2} \, dl$$

so

$$H(c) = \frac{2c}{l_m} - \frac{c^2}{l_m^2} \qquad 0 \leqslant c \leqslant l_m$$

hence applying equation 6.17

$$i(l) = \frac{l_m - l}{l_m c - \dfrac{c^2}{2}} \qquad 0 \leqslant l \leqslant c \leqslant l_m$$

By equation 6.18

$$\mu_{iL} = \frac{1}{l_m c - \dfrac{c^2}{2}} \int_0^c (l_m \, l) - l^2 \, dl$$

hence

$$\mu_{iL} = \frac{l_m c - \dfrac{2c^2}{3}}{2l_m - c}$$

or substituting $l_m = 2\mu_L$

$$\mu_{iL} = \frac{2c\left(\mu_L - \dfrac{c}{3}\right)}{4\mu_L - c} \qquad 0 \leqslant l \leqslant c \leqslant l_m \qquad (6.20)$$

Again, as c approaches its effective upper limit of l_m, then μ_{iL} approaches $l_m/3 = \mu_{hL} = 2\mu_L/3$.

(iii) If the density distribution of complete trace lengths is triangular, then by Example 6.4(iii)

$$h(l) = \frac{3}{l_m} - \frac{6l}{l_m{}^2} + \frac{3l^2}{l_m{}^3} \qquad 0 \leqslant l \leqslant l_m$$

where $\mu_L = l_m/3$ and $\mu_{hL} = l_m/4$. In this case

$$H(c) = \int_0^c \frac{3}{l_m} - \frac{6l}{l_m{}^2} + \frac{3l^2}{l_m{}^3} \, dl$$

so

$$H(c) = \frac{3c}{l_m} - \frac{3c^2}{l_m{}^2} + \frac{c^3}{l_m{}^3} \qquad 0 \leqslant c \leqslant l_m$$

hence, applying equation 6.17

$$i(l) = \frac{l_m{}^2 - 2l_m l + l^2}{l_m{}^2 c - l_m c^2 + \dfrac{c^3}{3}} \qquad 0 \leqslant l \leqslant c \leqslant l_m$$

By equation 6.18

$$\mu_{iL} = \frac{1}{l_m{}^2 c - l_m c^2 + \dfrac{c^3}{3}} \int_0^c l_m{}^2 l - 2l_m l^2 + l^3 \, dl$$

hence

$$\mu_{iL} = \frac{6l_m{}^2 c - 8l_m c^2 + 3c^3}{12(l_m{}^2 - l_m c) - 4c^2}$$

or, substituting $l_m = 3\mu_L$

$$\mu_{iL} = \frac{9\mu_L{}^2c - 4\mu_L c^2 + \frac{1}{2}c^3}{18\mu_L{}^2 - 6\mu_L c + \frac{2}{3}c^2} \qquad 0 \leqslant l \leqslant c \leqslant l_m \qquad (6.21)$$

Again, as c approaches its effective upper limit l_m, then μ_{iL} approaches $l_m/4 = \mu_{hL} = 3\mu_L/4$.

Example 6.6

A set of parallel planar discontinuities intersects a planar rock face of limited extent to produce parallel linear traces of various finite lengths. A scanline sample of discontinuities from this set revealed that the mean semi-trace length for those discontinuities with a semi-trace length of less than 5.0 m, was 1.87 m. Use the solutions obtained in Example 6.5 to estimate the mean trace length for the complete discontinuity traces.

Solution
Here c = 5.0 m and $\mu_{iL} = 1.87$ m. Putting these values into equations 6.19, 6.20 and 6.21, and solving for μ_L gives mean trace lengths of 3.18, 2.90 and 2.93 m for negative exponential, uniform and triangular trace length distributions respectively. Other theoretical solutions are inadmissible since they are either negative or violate the range constraints. The fairly good agreement between these three results reflects the fact that μ_{iL}, and hence μ_L, is significantly smaller than the curtailment level c. If the ratio μ_{iL}/c exceeds about 0.4 then μ_L tends to be larger than c and the computed value of μ_L varies significantly with the type of trace length distribution that has been assumed. For example, if c = 3.0 m and $\mu_{iL} = 1.31$ m the three values of mean trace length μ_L are 3.91, 2.72 and 3.10 m for negative exponential, uniform and triangular trace length distributions, respectively.

An alternative approach to estimating mean trace length can be developed by considering the numerical proportion of discontinuities that have a semi-trace length less than c. If the total sample size for a given discontinuity set is n, and a number r of these have a semi-trace length less than c then, for large n, the proportion r/n provides the best estimate of H(c) in equation 6.18. Utilising the result in Example 6.5(i), for a negative exponential distribution of complete trace lengths

$$H(c) = 1 - e^{-(c/\mu_L)}$$

hence

$$\frac{r}{n} = 1 - e^{-(c/\mu_L)} \qquad (6.22)$$

or

$$\mu_L = \frac{c}{-\ln\left(1 - \frac{r}{n}\right)} \tag{6.23}$$

For a uniform distribution of trace lengths, utilising the result in Example 6.5(ii)

$$H(c) = \frac{2c}{l_m} - \frac{c^2}{l_m^2} \qquad 0 \leqslant c \leqslant l_m$$

hence

$$\frac{r}{n} = \frac{2c}{l_m} - \frac{c^2}{l_m^2} \qquad 0 \leqslant c \leqslant l_m$$

or, substituting $l_m = 2\mu_L$

$$\mu_L = \frac{c/2}{1 \pm \sqrt{1 - \frac{r}{n}}} \tag{6.24}$$

Since μ_L approaches ∞ as r approaches 0, the negative sign provides the required root of the quadratic.

For a triangular distribution of trace lengths, utilising the result in Example 6.5(iii)

$$H(c) = \frac{3c}{l_m} - \frac{3c^2}{l_m^2} + \frac{c^3}{l_m^3} \qquad 0 \leqslant c \leqslant l_m$$

Hence, substituting $l_m = 3\mu_L$

$$\frac{r}{n} = \frac{c}{\mu_L} - \frac{c^2}{3\mu_L^2} + \frac{c^3}{27\mu_L^3} \tag{6.25}$$

In this case it is convenient to leave the result in the form of equation 6.25; the mean trace length μ_L is found by solving the cubic expression and taking the valid solution $0 \leqslant (r/n) \leqslant 1.0$.

In obtaining the results given in equations 6.23 and 6.24, Priest and Hudson (1981) noted that μ_L could be determined graphically. In the case of a negative exponential distribution of trace lengths, a graph of c against $-\ln(1 - (r/n))$ will, theoretically, be a straight line with a slope of μ_L. In the case of a uniform distribution of trace lengths, a graph of c against $2 - 2\sqrt{(1 - (r/n))}$ will, theoretically, be a straight line with a slope of μ_L. The data in Table 6.1, from a case study presented by Priest and Hudson (1981), plotted in Figure 6.6 illustrate the graphical estimation of mean trace length, assuming a negative exponential distribution.

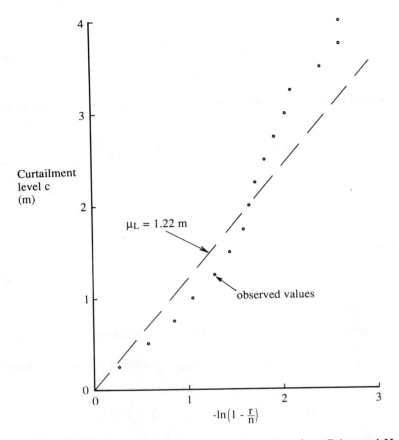

Figure 6.6 Graphical estimation of mean trace length, data from Priest and Hudson (1981).

A further simplification of the expression in equation 6.19 can be obtained by utilising equation 6.22 to substitute for $e^{-(c/\mu_L)}$. By equation 6.22

$$e^{-(c/\mu_L)} = 1 - \frac{r}{n}$$

Substituting this into equation 6.19 gives

$$\mu_L = \mu_{iL} + c\left(\frac{n}{r} - 1\right) \tag{6.26}$$

The result in equation 6.26 was previously presented in a slightly different form by Cruden (1977).

Table 6.1 Data for the graphical estimation of mean trace length (data from Priest and Hudson, 1981)

$c(m)$	r	$-\ln\left(1 - \left(\dfrac{r}{n}\right)\right)$	$\dfrac{nc}{r}$
0.25	28	0.261	1.089
0.50	53	0.570	1.151
0.75	70	0.853	1.307
1.00	79	1.043	1.544
1.25	88	1.278	1.733
1.50	93	1.437	1.968
1.75	97	1.585	2.201
2.0	98	1.626	2.490
2.25	100	1.713	2.745
2.50	102	1.808	2.990
2.75	104	1.914	3.226
3.00	106	2.031	3.453
3.25	107	2.096	3.706
3.50	111	2.406	3.847
3.75	113	2.607	4.049
4.00	113	2.607	4.319

Example 6.7

A scanline sample of the discontinuity set in Example 6.6 revealed that, out of a total sample size of 263 discontinuities, 212 had a semi-trace length of less than 5.0 m. Use the solutions obtained in equations 6.23 to 6.26 to estimate the mean trace length for the complete discontinuity traces.

Solution
In this example n = 263, r = 212 and c = 5.0 m. Equations 6.23, 6.24 and 6.25 give mean trace length values of 3.05, 4.47 and 3.96 for negative exponential, uniform and triangular trace length distributions, respectively. Inputting the value of $\mu_{iL} = 1.87$ m from Example 6.6 into equation 6.26 gives a mean trace length of 3.07 m. If these had been real field measurements, the relatively good agreement between the values found from equations 6.19, 6.23 and 6.26 could be taken to indicate that the trace length distribution was of negative exponential form.

Although it may be possible to deduce the form of the trace length distribution by examining a histogram of the curtailed semi-trace lengths, the distribution dependent methods described above must be used with some care when determining mean trace length. It should be noted also, that the 'ncr' methods outlined above are not generally as accurate as methods based on the calculation of the mean curtailed semi-trace length μ_{iL}. Distribution independent methods, which do not require any assumptions concerning the form of the trace length distribution are discussed in the next section.

6.4 DISTRIBUTION INDEPENDENT AND OTHER METHODS FOR ESTIMATING MEAN TRACE LENGTH

Methods for estimating mean trace length that do not depend upon a knowledge of the trace length distribution have been developed by Pahl (1981) and Bray (1982). A relatively simple distribution independent method can, however, be developed from the analysis given in the previous section. Returning to equation 6.16, it can be seen that as l approaches zero, $F(l)$ also approaches zero and so, in the limit as l approaches 0,

$$h(l) = \frac{1}{\mu_L} \qquad \text{as } l \to 0$$

Consequently, if a histogram of semi-trace lengths is constructed, its intercept with the frequency axis provides an estimate of $1/\mu_L$. This result is demonstrated for negative exponential, uniform and normal distributions of $f(l)$ in Figure 6.4. The histogram in Figure 6.7, based upon the values in Table 6.1 illustrates the approach when applied to real data. The best fit curve sketched for the histogram intersects the frequency axis at $N(l) \approx 32$. Applying equation B.6,

$$h(l) = \frac{N(l)}{n\Delta}$$

where $N(l)$ is the numerical frequency, Δ is the class interval and n is the sample size. In this case $\Delta = 0.25$ and $n = 122$, hence in the limit as l approaches 0

$$\mu_L = \frac{1}{h(l)} \approx 0.95 \,\text{m}$$

Although this result agrees reasonably well with the value $\mu_L = 1.22 \,\text{m}$ based upon a graphical analysis of the same data in Figure 6.6, it should be noted that the result is sensitive to the assumed shape of the best fit curve. In this case, since the assumed curve intersects the frequency axis at a flat angle, a small change in its shape will produce a significant change in the computed value of μ_L. Here different interpretations of the histogram shape could yield values of μ_L anywhere in the range 0.8 to 1.2 m.

Bray (1982) extended the above method by considering the cumulative distribution of $h(l)$ in the region where l is close to zero. Again $F(l)$ in

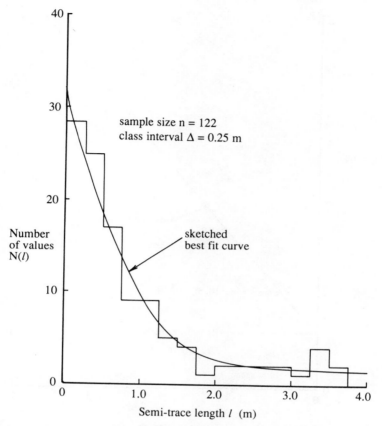

Figure 6.7   Histogram of semi-trace lengths, data from Priest and Hudson (1981).

equation 6.16 will be close to zero, and so, in the limit as l approaches 0, the cumulative distribution $H(c)$ is given by

$$H(c) = \int_0^c h(l)\, dl = \int_0^c \frac{dl}{\mu_L} = \frac{c}{\mu_L} \qquad \text{as } l \to 0$$

It was noted earlier that if the total sample size for a given discontinuity set is n, and a number r of these have a semi-trace length less than c then the proportion r/n provides the best estimate of $H(c)$. Hence, in the limit as l approaches 0

$$\mu_L = \frac{nc}{r} \tag{6.27}$$

The limiting value can be found by plotting a graph of nc/r against c for a range of curtailment levels c and extrapolating the resulting curve to give the

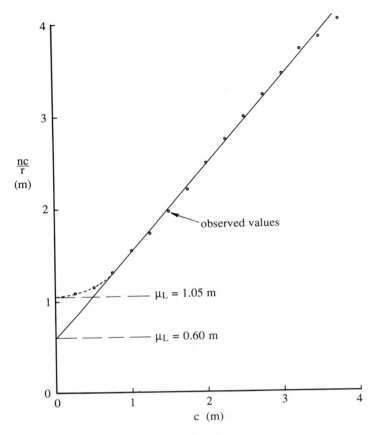

Figure 6.8 Distribution independent estimation of mean trace length, data from Priest and Hudson (1981).

value of nc/r when c = 0. The graph in Figure 6.8, based upon the data in Table 6.1, illustrates this construction. The difficulty in applying this method is deciding how much influence the data points for small values of c should have on the curve. This difficulty arises because as c approaches the limiting value of zero, r becomes small, so that a small change in r produces wide fluctuations in the ratio nc/r. In Figure 6.8, if the graph is curved to pass through the data points for c = 0.5 and 0.25 m, the intercept gives a mean trace length of approximately 1.05 m. If these two data points are ignored, a linear extrapolation gives a mean trace length of only 0.6 m. In this case the former value is closer to estimates found by the other methods described earlier.

The theoretical form, J(c), of the graph of nc/r against c can be found for any continuous distribution by replacing r/n by the appropriate expression for H(c), so that

$$J(c) = \frac{c}{H(c)} \qquad (6.28)$$

Utilising the results in Example 6.5 gives, for a negative exponential distribution of complete trace lengths

$$J(c) = \frac{c}{1 - e^{-(c/\mu_L)}} \qquad (6.29)$$

If the trace lengths are uniform, then

$$J(c) = \frac{\mu_L^2}{\mu_L - \left(\frac{c}{4}\right)} \qquad (6.30)$$

finally if the trace lengths obey a triangular distribution

$$J(c) = \frac{\mu_L^3}{\mu_L^2 - \left(\frac{c\,\mu_L}{3}\right) + \left(\frac{c^2}{27}\right)} \qquad (6.31)$$

It is clear from equations 6.29 to 6.31 that in each case as c approaches zero, J(c) approaches μ_L. The graphs of J(c) given by equations 6.29 to 6.31 are plotted in Figure 6.9 for $\mu_L = 1.0$ and for c in the range 3 down to values approaching zero.

Pahl (1981) presented an alternative distribution independent approach to the estimation of mean trace length. His method is based upon the categorisation of randomly located discontinuities that intersect a vertical, rectangular planar rock face window of height h and width w, and whose traces make an angle ϕ with the vertical, as shown in Figure 6.10. It is necessary to recognise three classes of discontinuities that intersect the face window as follows:

(i)   A discontinuity is said to be **contained** within the face window if it intersects the face and has **both** ends visible in the face window.
(ii) A discontinuity is said to **dissect** the face window if it intersects the face and has **one** end visible in the window. The other end is obscured by extending beyond the limits of the face window.
(iii) A discontinuity is said to **transect** the face window if it intersects the face but has **neither** end visible in the window. Both ends are obscured by extending beyond the limits of the face window.

If the numbers of discontinuities contained within, dissecting and transecting a given face are n_c, n_d and n_t, respectively, then the total number of discontinuities n that **intersect** the face window in some way is

$$n = n_c + n_d + n_t$$

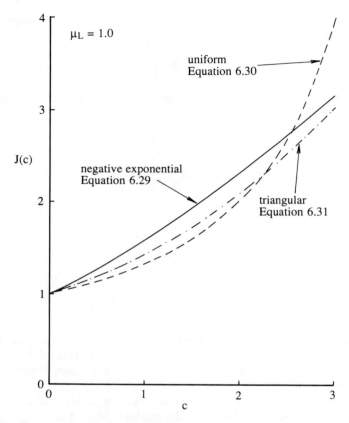

Figure 6.9 Graphs of the function J(c) for various trace length distributions.

It is now possible to define the ratios

$$\theta_c = \frac{n_c}{n} \quad \text{and} \quad \theta_t = \frac{n_t}{n}$$

Since contained and transecting discontinuities are a subset of those intersecting the face, $n \geq (n_c + n_t)$ and the ratios θ_c and θ_t must always be less than or equal to unity. Pahl (1981) has derived the following expression for mean trace length μ_L

$$\mu_L = \frac{w\,h(1 - \theta_c + \theta_t)}{(w\cos\phi + h\sin\phi)(1 + \theta_c - \theta_t)} \tag{6.32}$$

Although the approach in equation 6.32 is both rigorous and easy to implement, it does rely on the discontinuities being grouped into a parallel, or

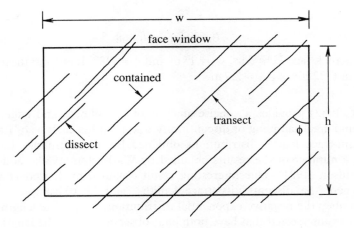

Figure 6.10 Discontinuities intersecting a vertical rock face (after Pahl, 1981).

nearly parallel, set. The method also relies on the face being well exposed, so that both ends of all contained discontinuities and one end of all dissecting discontinuities can be observed. It is interesting to note that if all discontinuities transect the face window then $n_c = 0$ and $n_t = n$; this gives $\theta_c = 0$ and $\theta_t = 1$ defining a theoretically infinite mean trace length. Conversely if all discontinuities are contained within the face window then $n_c = n$ and $n_t = 0$; this gives $\theta_c = 1$, $\theta_t = 0$ and a theoretical mean trace length of zero. Pahl (1981), noting these extreme values, commented that they can never occur in practice since it is assumed that the discontinuities are distributed randomly with respect to the face window. Kulatilake and Wu (1984c) have adopted a similar approach to Pahl, to derive a distribution dependent model for the density of discontinuity traces in sampling windows.

Example 6.8

A vertical rock face 5 m high and 15 m wide is intersected by a parallel planar set of discontinuities producing traces that are inclined at 38° to the vertical. Of the 235 traces observed to intersect the face, 87 are contained within and 16 transect the rectangular area specified above. Use Pahl's method to estimate the mean trace length for the discontinuity set.

Solution
In this case $n = 235$, $n_c = 87$ and $n_t = 16$, hence

$$\theta_c = n_c/n = 0.370$$

and

$$\theta_t = n_t/n = 0.068$$

For this rock face $H = 5\,m$, $w = 15\,m$ and $\phi = 38°$. Inputting these values to equation 6.32 gives $\mu_L = 2.7\,m$.

Laslett (1982) provides a concise analysis of curtailment and edge effects in linear and areal sampling of discontinuity traces. In his analysis of trace length and semi-trace length distributions obtained by line sampling, Laslett confirmed a number of the results obtained by Warburton (1980a) and by Priest and Hudson (1981). One interesting result obtained by Laslett concerns the case where the discontinuity trace lengths, and hence sampled semi-trace lengths obey the negative exponential distribution. If x_i is the length of the ith of n traces intersected that have both ends observable, y_j is the length of the jth of m traces that have one end observable and z_k is the length of the kth of p traces that have no ends observable, the best estimate of the mean trace length μ_L is given by

$$\mu_L = \frac{\sum_{i=1}^{n} x_i + \sum_{j=1}^{m} y_j + \sum_{k=1}^{p} z_k}{2n + m} \tag{6.33}$$

Laslett commented that the mean trace length estimated in this way gives consistent results even when there is variability in the values of x_i, y_j and z_k within a sample.

6.5 TRIMMING OF SHORT DISCONTINUITY TRACES

When dealing with the subject of discontinuity size it is necessary to comment briefly upon the problem of 'trimming' of short traces. A number of workers feel that at certain rock exposures it is impractical to record and to measure discontinuity traces that have a trace length below a certain threshold value t; this approach is here referred to as trimming. If all discontinuity traces below this threshold level are consistently ignored the resulting trace length data will also be truncated at the level t. The process of trimming of short traces is directly analogous to the curtailment of long traces, except that in most cases an unknown number of values are omitted, with lengths between 0 and t instead of a known number between c and ∞. The probability density distribution, $i(l)$, of semi-trace lengths trimmed below a level t and curtailed above a level c can be found directly from the distribution $h(l)$ of semi-trace lengths given in equations 6.15 and 6.16. Trimming and curtailment reduce the area under the $h(l)$ density curve from unity to

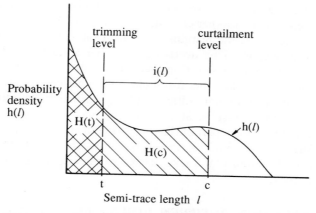

Figure 6.11   Trimming and curtailment of the semi-trace length distribution.

$$\int_t^c h(l) \, dl$$

now

$$\int_t^c h(l) \, dl = \int_0^c h(l) \, dl - \int_0^t h(l) \, dl = H(c) - H(t)$$

A graphical representation of the above expression is presented in Figure 6.11. The density $i(l)$ is obtained, therefore, by dividing $h(l)$ by the constant $H(c) - H(t)$, hence

$$i(l) = \frac{h(l)}{H(c) - H(t)} \qquad t \leqslant l \leqslant c \tag{6.34}$$

Warburton (1980b) used this general approach when correcting for trimming in his derivations of the probability densities of observed trace lengths. It is interesting to note that, when discussing the implications for geological surveys, Warburton emphasised that the trimming threshold should be set at a constant value that is as low as practicable. This approach is recommended because any determination of the distribution of discontinuity size must be based entirely upon the observed distribution of trace lengths; the more completely the latter is known, the less ambiguity there is in estimating the diagnostic parameters.

The topic of trimming of short discontinuity traces is an extremely complex one. It could, for example, be argued that any distribution of discontinuity trace lengths must, in theory, be continuous down to values of $l = 0$. If the frequency of trace lengths below the threshold level is significant, as is the case with the negative exponential distribution, then any method for estimating mean trace length based upon counting discontinuities, such as that proposed by Pahl (1981), becomes sensitive to the threshold level and must also become distribution dependent. Another complication, analysed by Pahl (1981) and by Laslett (1982), occurs at the margins of an areal sample where trimming and curtailment can overlap. This overlap means that a trace length that is in reality longer than the trimming threshold can be obscured to the extent that its observed length is below this threshold. One final complication concerns the geological nature of discontinuities that have a diameter close to zero. Such discontinuities, which must be at the scale of micro-cracking between and within mineral grains, form part of the rock material and make no contribution to the rock structure. It could be argued, therefore, that the discontinuity size population is itself trimmed at a level related to the size of the mineral grains that form the rock.

6.6 THE RELATION BETWEEN LINEAR FREQUENCY, AREAL FREQUENCY AND SIZE

Before leaving the topic of discontinuity size it is worth noting the relation between linear frequency, areal frequency and size developed by Priest and Samaniego (1983). Consider a single set of parallel discontinuity traces with an areal frequency λ_a discontinuity centres per unit area of rock face, and mean trace length μ_L. Figure 6.12 shows a rectangular sample area, of side lengths x by y orientated with the sides of length y normal to the discontinuity traces. It is assumed that x and y are very large compared with μ_L, so that edge effects are negligible. The expected summed length of discontinuity traces in the sample area is given by λ_a xy μ_L. A sampling line of length y across the sample area, normal to the discontinuity set will observe a discontinuity frequency λ given by the expected number of intersections divided by the length y. The expected number of intersections along the scanline is given by the summed length of discontinuity traces divided by the width x, hence

$$\lambda = \frac{\lambda_a \, xy \, \mu_L}{xy} = \lambda_a \mu_L \qquad (6.35)$$

The relation between the average number of intersections and the average line length has been considered from a stereological point of view by Underwood (1967). He found that for a totally random line (i.e. discontinuity) orientation, an estimate of the average total length of traces per unit area is given by $\pi\lambda/2$, where λ is the linear discontinuity frequency derived above. The expected average total length of traces per unit area is given by $\lambda_a\mu_L$, hence

$$\lambda_a\mu_L = \frac{\pi\lambda}{2}$$

so

$$\lambda = \frac{2\lambda_a\mu_L}{\pi} \qquad (6.36)$$

Equation 6.35 is applicable for perfectly parallel discontinuities, and equation 6.36 for totally random orientations. It is reasonable to expect, therefore, that discontinuities showing some variability about a preferred orientation will have a discontinuity frequency given by

$$\frac{2\lambda_a\mu_L}{\pi} \leq \lambda \leq \lambda_a\mu_L$$

The hypotheses presented in equations 6.35 and 6.36 were tested by Priest and Samaniego (1983) by means of computer simulations. They found that graphs of $\lambda_a\mu_L$ against λ for a number of different trace length distributions were indeed linear with slopes that were in general agreement with the predictions of the equations. This simple linear relation between $\lambda_a\mu_L$ and λ provides a basis for analysing the complex relation between discontinuity frequency and discontinuity size in three dimensions.

6.7 THE PRACTICAL DETERMINATION OF DISCONTINUITY SIZE

At this stage it is appropriate to draw together the theory developed earlier in the chapter and to give some indication as to how this theory can be applied to the determination of discontinuity size in practice. Applying equation 6.10 it has been shown that circular discs of diameter s with a probability density distribution c(s) and a mean diameter μ_s produce, by their intersection with the free face shown in Figure 6.13a, discontinuity traces of length l and a probability density distribution f(l) as follows

$$f(l) = \frac{l}{\mu_s} \int_l^\infty \frac{c(s)\ ds}{\sqrt{s^2 - l^2}} \qquad (l \leq s) \qquad (6.37)$$

Applying equation 6.13, discontinuity traces of length l, a probability density distribution f(l) and mean trace length μ_L distributed over a complete rock face produce, by their intersection with the linear scanline in Figure 6.13b, discontinuity traces of length l and a probability density distribution g(l) as follows

$$g(l) = \frac{l\ f(l)}{\mu_L} \qquad (6.38)$$

Applying equation 6.14, discontinuity traces of length m and a probability density distribution g(m) intersected by the scanline in Figure 6.13b produce semi-traces of length l and a probability density distribution h(l) as follows

$$h(l) = \int_l^\infty \left(\frac{1}{m}\right) g(m)\ dm \qquad (6.39)$$

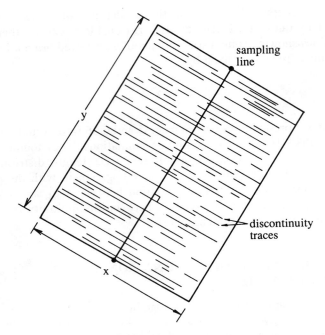

Figure 6.12 The relation between linear discontinuity frequency, areal frequency and size (after Priest and Samaniego, 1983).

Finally, applying equation 6.34, discontinuity semi-traces of length l and a probability density distribution $h(l)$ trimmed at length t and curtailed at length c, as shown in Figure 6.13c, produce a probability density distribution $i(l)$ as follows

$$i(l) = \frac{h(l)}{\displaystyle\int_{t}^{c} h(l)\,dl} \qquad (t \leq l \leq c) \qquad (6.40)$$

The distribution $i(l)$ of trimmed and curtailed semi-trace lengths is observed by scanline sampling. An example of such an observed distribution is presented as a histogram of curtailed semi-trace lengths in Figure 6.14.

Figure 6.13 (a) Circular discs of diameter distribution c(s) intersecting a face to produce trace lengths of distribution $f(l)$.

 (b) Traces of distribution $f(l)$ intersected by a scanline to produce traces of distribution $g(l)$ and semi-traces of distribution $h(l)$.

 (c) Semi-traces of distribution $h(l)$ trimmed at t and curtailed at c to produce the observed semi-trace distribution $i(l)$.

(a)

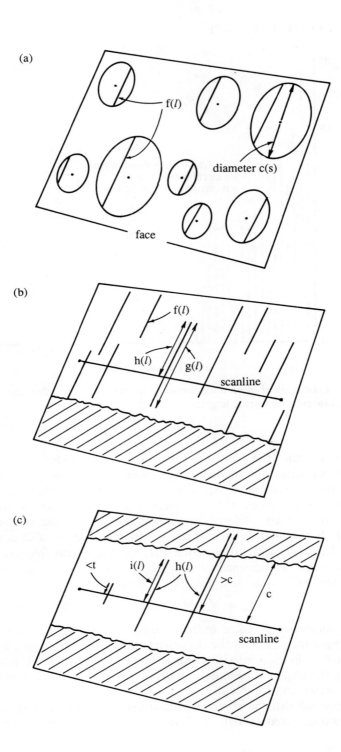

f(*l*)

diameter c(s)

face

(b)

f(*l*)

h(*l*)   g(*l*)

scanline

(c)

<t   i(*l*)   h(*l*)

>c

c

scanline

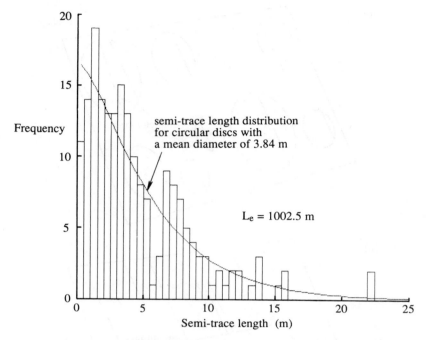

Figure 6.14   Estimation of mean discontinuity diameter by fitting a distribution to the histogram of observed semi-trace lengths.

If it assumed that the observed semi-traces were produced by circular discontinuities intersecting the rock face, it is necessary to assume a form and parameters for c(s) then apply equations 6.37 to 6.40 to predict the form of i(l). The result is compared with the observed distribution then the form and parameters for c(s) are adjusted to achieve the best fit for the observed distribution. If the observed semi-trace length frequency in a class interval centred on l is $N_o(l)$ and, by equation B.7, the theoretical frequency for a sample size n and a class interval Δ is $N_t(l) = n \, \Delta \, i(l)$, then a sensitive measure of the 'badness' of fit is given by

$$L_e = \sum l(N_o(l) - N_t(l))^2$$

where the summation is taken over all class intervals. The error term L_e, which is simply the square of the deviations multiplied by the trace length at the mid-point of the class interval summed for all class intervals, is minimised by adjusting the form and parameters for c(s). Various candidate distributions for c(s) are presented in Table B.1.

If it is assumed that the observed semi-traces were produced by sampling linear traces distributed over the rock face, it is necessary to assume a form and parameters for f(l) then apply equations 6.38 to 6.40 to predict the form of i(l). The result is compared with the observed distribution then, as before, the form and parameters for f(l) are adjusted to achieve the best fit. Again the parameter L_e provides a sensitive measure of the badness of fit.

The above methods have been implemented in an interactive graphics program CANDIS, which allows the user to view the observed histogram of sampled semi-trace lengths and then to superimpose the fitted distribution i(l) derived from the distribution and parameters assumed for c(s) or f(l) as appropriate. The user also monitors the parameter L_e as the optimisation proceeds, seeking the minimum value which will be associated with the best fit. Figure 6.14 shows the theoretical distribution of semi-trace lengths generated by assuming that the traces were produced by circular discontinuities conforming to the negative exponential distribution with a mean diameter of 3.84 m. The observed distribution of semi-trace lengths in this figure was generated by taking random values from a lognormal distribution with a mean of 5.14 m and a standard deviation of 4.91 m. In this case the minimum value of the parameter L_e is 1002.5 m, which is taken to indicate the best fit for the 'observed' distribution.

6.8   GENERATION OF RANDOM FRACTURE NETWORKS

The aim in the generation of random fracture networks is to produce one or more graphical or numerical *realisations* of fracture geometry, in two or three dimensions, that reflect(s) the characteristics of a population of real fractures sampled in a given rock mass. Chapters 1 to 5, and the earlier portion of this chapter, have dealt with the sampling and characterisation of the primary geometrical properties of discontinuities: orientation, frequency, spacing and size. One further property, discontinuity aperture, is examined in Chapter 11. In these chapters it is shown that discontinuity properties can be characterised by relatively simple statistical distributions governed by one or two controlling parameters. It is these distributions that provide the basis for producing a random realisation. Among the first to develop this concept were Hudson and La Pointe (1980), Long (1983) and Priest and Samaniego (1983) for fluid flow modelling, and Priest and Samaniego (1988) for the analysis of block stability.

The following input properties are required for the generation of a random network:

1. The number of discontinuity sets that have an identifiable mean orientation and distribution of orientations (Chapter 3).
2. The mean orientation, the type of orientation distribution and the associated parameters for each set (Chapter 3 and Appendix B).
3. The frequency of each set, expressed in terms of the mean number of discontinuity centres per unit volume of rock, or, in a two-dimensional study, per unit area of the plane of analysis. Alternatively, discontinuity

frequency can be expressed as an observed frequency for the set along a line of specified orientation. It may also be necessary to specify the isotropic frequency of any random frequency component in the discontinuity network (Chapter 4).

4. The distribution pattern for the discontinuity centres within the generation space. This pattern may be random, and therefore governed by a one- two- or three-dimensional Poisson process or may exhibit some spatial variability (Chapters 2, 4 and 5).

5. The shape, mean size, the type of the size distribution and the associated parameters for each set. For two-dimensional studies it is the mean trace length and the trace length distribution in the plane of analysis that is required (Chapter 6).

6. The mean aperture, the type of the aperture distribution and the associated parameters for each set (Chapter 11).

The following assumptions concerning the above discontinuity characteristics are made for the purposes of this section:

1. There are a finite number of identifiable discontinuity sets.
2. The orientation within each set can be characterised by the Fisher distribution controlled by Fisher's constant.
3. The frequency of each set can be characterised in terms of an areal or volumetric frequency, or by a known, or observed, frequency along a line of some specified orientation.
4. Discontinuity occurrence is random in one, two or three dimensions.
5. Discontinuities are circular discs in three dimensions and linear traces in two dimensions, with distributions of diameter and length, respectively, that can be characterised by continuous functions such as the uniform, negative exponential, normal and lognormal distributions.
6. Discontinuity aperture can be characterised by continuous functions such as the uniform, negative exponential, normal and lognormal distributions, but is constant for any given discontinuity. In other words the walls are smooth and parallel.

The above assumptions have been adopted to generate fairly realistic representations of a range of fracture networks while at the same time providing computational simplicity.

6.8.1   Networks in three dimensions

Although the generation of networks in three dimensions is relatively straightforward, the field determination of the discontinuity parameters that control the generation process is relatively complex. In particular, it is necessary to have information about the volumetric frequency, size and shape of the discontinuities. The first step in the generation process is to define a generation space in terms of three coordinate ranges $x_{g1} < x_{g2}$, $y_{g1} < y_{g2}$, $z_{g1} < z_{g2}$ along a local set of Cartesian axes. The generation then proceeds set by set. Random Poisson coordinates x_r, y_r, z_r for the centre of the first discontinuity from set 1 are generated from three random variables $R^i_{U,1}$, $R^{i+1}_{U,1}$ and $R^{i+2}_{U,1}$ from a uniform distribution in the range 0 to 1 as follows

$$x_r = x_{g1} + R^i_{U,1}(x_{g2} - x_{g1})$$
$$y_r = y_{g1} + R^{i+1}_{U,1}(y_{g2} - y_{g1})$$
$$z_r = z_{g1} + R^{i+2}_{U,1}(z_{g2} - z_{g1})$$

Section B.4 contains algorithms for generating random values from a range of distributions. A random orientation for the discontinuity is obtained by first generating a random deviation angle θ_r from the mean set normal. This random angle is taken to be a random value from a Fisher distribution governed by the appropriate Fisher's constant for the set (see Chapter 3 and Appendix B). This one-dimensional angle must be converted to three dimensions by rotating the generated normal about the mean set normal through a random angle taken from a uniform distribution in the range 0 to 2π. The simplest starting point for this rotation is the vertical plane through the mean set normal.

Random values for discontinuity diameter and aperture are generated from the appropriate parent distributions by means of the algorithms given in section B.4. The location, orientation, diameter and aperture of each generated discontinuity are stored in a large realisation file which can be drawn upon for future analysis or for producing a graphical representation. An illustration of part of a three-dimensional realisation, from Long *et al.* (1985), is presented in Figure 6.15a.

Generation proceeds for the first discontinuity set until the required number of discontinuity centres per unit volume of the generation space have been produced. An alternative way of controlling discontinuity frequency is to sample the generated frequency along scanlines constructed through the generation space. Generation continues until the observed frequency for the set along one or more scanlines reaches the required value, or reaches the value observed in the real rock mass. This latter method has the advantage of simultaneously taking into account volumetric density and size during the generation process.

Discontinuities from other sets, controlled by different parameters, are generated in the same way until the required number of sets have been produced. An additional, totally random component of discontinuity orientation can be generated by taking random deviation angles θ_r from a vertical mean set normal. This deviation angle is taken to be a random value from a uniform distribution in the range 0 to $\pi/2$ at a random azimuth in the range 0 to 2π.

The generation methods outlined above usually work very well. There are,

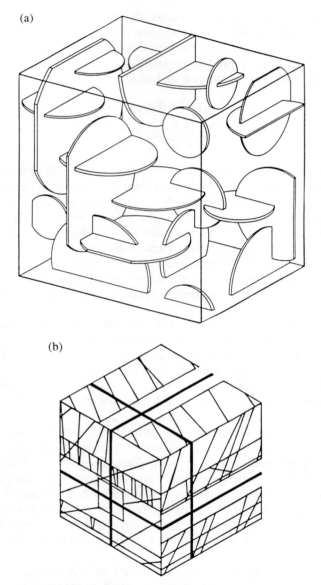

(a)

(b)

Figure 6.15 Random realisations of discontinuity networks.

(a) Three-dimensional random realisation of circular discontinuities (from Long *et al.*, 1985).

(b) Three-dimensional discontinuity network adjacent to an underground opening (from Heliot, 1988).

(c) Two-dimensional random realisation of discontinuity traces containing 1592 discontinuities and 29 184 intersections (from Priest and Samaniego, 1988).

(c)

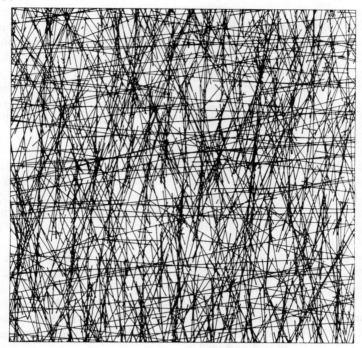

however, a number of areas where the resulting realisation can be unsatisfactory. The first of these deficiencies occurs when attempting to generate discontinuities that are bedding planes. In reality bedding planes do not usually intersect each other. The above generation algorithm will always produce intersecting bedding planes, even when Fisher's constant is large. This problem can be overcome by inputting a very high value of Fisher's constant for bedding plane features and thereby producing almost parallel planes. For example a Fisher's constant of 10 000 will ensure that only 1 in about 440 of the generated discontinuities will deviate from the mean normal by more than 2°. A second difficulty with the above generation methods is that, in their present form, they are unable to produce discontinuities with rock bridges. This difficulty can be overcome by generating random zones of rock bridge within a previously generated discontinuity.

Whether the final realisation is to be used for the analysis of block stability or for the analysis of fluid flow it is important to be aware of boundary effects, exhibited as a reduction in discontinuity frequency towards the edge of the realisation space. This phenomenon can be explained as follows: consider an element of volume close to the boundary of a given generation space, and assume that this element contains portions of, say, 8 discontinuities. If the same realisation, with the same seed values, were run again but with a larger generation space, our element of volume would probably contain portions of more than 8 discontinuities. These extra discontinuities have their centres in the enlarged generation space but extend back into the original generation space. This effect is smaller for elements of volume that are further away from the original boundary. The rate of decline in this effect depends upon the adopted statistical distributions for discontinuity size, and their parameters. Boundary effects force us to reject any model that incorporates discontinuities of infinite size, since if all discontinuities are of infinite size then all points within any random realisation must contain an infinite number of discontinuities — the space becomes all fractures and no rock. Boundary effects can be avoided by the simple expedient of analysing a volume that is smaller than, and at the centre of, the generation volume. Samaniego and Priest (1984) suggest that a ratio of generation volume/analysis volume in excess of about 4 minimises boundary effects. Overcoming boundary effects in this way dramatically increases the computational overheads associated with the generation and analysis of random realisations.

Heliot (1988) has developed a powerful computer language BGL (Block Generation Language) to facilitate the generation of three-dimensional block realisations. In essence the method is based upon two simple processes: the splitting of blocks to create discontinuities and the removal of one or more blocks to simulate excavation. An example of a three-dimensional realisation from Heliot (1988), showing discontinuities adjacent to an underground excavation is reproduced in Figure 6.15b.

6.8.2 Networks in two dimensions

The generation of networks in two dimensions proceeds in much the same way as networks in three dimensions. In many cases the plane of generation is the plane of a rock face that has been examined in the field to determine discontinuity characteristics. If scanline sampling techniques have been adopted, three-dimensional discontinuity orientation data will have been collected but information on discontinuity size will probably be restricted to measurements of trace length. The realisation seeks to create a two-dimensional network that reflects the properties of the observed two-dimensional discontinuity pattern One approach is to generate a three-dimensional discontinuity network as explained in the previous section, and then to introduce a cutting plane of the appropriate size and orientation to generate the required two-dimensional realisation. This approach, which requires assumptions to be made about the three-dimensional frequency, size and shape of discontinuities, may not always generate a two-dimensional realisation that reflects the observed pattern. An alternative approach is to use the trace length data observed at a particular rock face as the basis for the generation process, as explained below.

As in the three-dimensional case, the first step in the generation process is to define a generation space in terms of two coordinate ranges $x_{g1} < x_{g2}$, $y_{g1} < y_{g2}$ along a local set of Cartesian axes. The generation then proceeds set by set. Random Poisson coordinates x_r, y_r for the mid point of the first discontinuity from set 1 are generated from two random variables $R^i_{U,1}$ and $R^{i+1}_{U,1}$ from a uniform distribution in the range 0 to 1 as follows

$$x_r = x_{g1} + R^i_{U,1}(x_{g2} - x_{g1})$$
$$y_r = y_{g1} + R^{i+1}_{U,1}(y_{g2} - y_{g1})$$

A random value for the orientation of the discontinuity is generated in exactly the same way as for a three-dimensional realisation. The line of intersection between the generation plane and the discontinuity plane gives the orientation of the discontinuity trace. Random values of discontinuity trace length and aperture are then generated from the appropriate parent distributions in the usual way.

For block stability studies it is necessary to extend each discontinuity back into the rock mass to permit the analysis of three-dimensional block geometry. Priest and Samaniego (1988) achieved this by assuming that a discontinuity trace, of length l, is a chord of a circular discontinuity of radius r that has its centre at a distance y from the rock face. This distance y is measured at right angles to the trace in the plane of the discontinuity as shown in Figure 6.1. By simple geometry

$$r = \sqrt{\left(\frac{l}{2}\right)^2 + y^2}$$

The offset y is assumed to be a random uniform variable in the range $-kl$ to $+kl$, with negative values indicating that the discontinuity centre lies in free air. The parameter k was selected following recommendations by Lamas (1986) who showed that a value of $k = 0.5\sqrt{3}$ would give a maximum discontinuity radius equal to the trace length l. Lamas noted that for a given trace length l, and a uniform distribution of the offset y, the distribution of radii r would be of exponential shape within the range $l/2$ to l. Priest and Samaniego commented that this simple size/shape model had the advantages of (i) preserving the observed trace length distribution for the rock face and (ii) forcing a strong correlation between discontinuity trace length and radius. For example, a generated trace length $l = 2.654$ m would require an offset value y to be selected from a uniform distribution in the range -2.298 to 2.298 m. A random value of, say, $y = -0.832$ m from this distribution would give a discontinuity radius of 1.566 m and place the discontinuity centre in free air (and therefore excavated) leaving the minor segment with a chord depth of only 0.734 m within the rock mass. Priest and Samaniego concluded that more sophisticated models of discontinuity geometry are not justified until more is known about discontinuity size and shape in real rock masses.

As in the three-dimensional case, generation proceeds for each discontinuity set until the required number of discontinuity centres per unit area of the generation space have been produced or until the observed frequency for the set along one or more scanlines reaches the required value. As before, the geometrical parameters for each generated discontinuity are stored in a large realisation file which can be drawn upon for future analysis or for producing a graphical representation such as the example in Figure 6.15c from Priest and Samaniego (1988), which contains 1592 discontinuity traces and 29 184 intersections. The comments in the previous section concerning intersecting bedding planes, rock bridges and boundary effects are directly applicable to two-dimensional realisations.

EXERCISES FOR CHAPTER 6

6.1

A particular discontinuity set can be represented by circular discs whose diameters s are distributed according to the triangular distribution up to a maximum diameter s_m. Obtain expressions for the cumulative distribution $F(a)$ and the probability density distribution $j(a)$ of discontinuity areas a. If $s_m = 10\,m$ calculate the expected percentage of discontinuities that will have areas less than $20\,m^2$.

6.2

A scanline sample of the complete traces from a particular discontinuity set exposed at an extensive rock face gave a mean trace length μ_{gL} of $4.8\,m$. Estimate the mean trace length μ_L for the complete traces sampled over the entire face on the assumption that the complete traces obey the following density distributions (i) negative exponential, (ii) uniform and (iii) triangular.

6.3

A scanline sample of the semi-traces from a particular discontinuity set exposed at an extensive rock face gave a mean trace length μ_{hL} of $2.4\,m$. Estimate the mean trace length μ_L for the complete traces sampled over the entire face on the assumption that the complete traces obey the following density distributions (i) negative exponential, (ii) uniform and (iii) triangular.

6.4

A set of parallel planar discontinuities intersects a planar rock face of limited extent to produce parallel linear traces of various finite lengths. A scanline sample of discontinuities from this set revealed that the mean semi-trace length for those discontinuities with a semi-trace length of less than 8.5 m, was 3.26 m. Use the solutions obtained in Example 6.5 to estimate the mean trace length for the complete discontinuity traces, adopting negative exponential, uniform and triangular distributions for these complete trace lengths.

6.5

A scanline sample of a particular discontinuity set revealed that, out of a total sample size of 119 discontinuities, 107 had a semi-trace length less than 8.5 m. Estimate the mean trace length for the complete discontinuity traces on the assumption that the complete traces obey the following density distributions (i) negative exponential, (ii) uniform and (iii) triangular. Compare your results with those obtained in Exercise 6.4.

6.6

The figure below shows a diagrammatic three-dimensional view of a 60 m high rock slope intersected by planar discontinuities with the following dip directions/dip angles:

Faults forming
  the slope face   150/60 at a horizontal spacing of 15 m
Inclined joints   150/40
Vertical joints   240/90

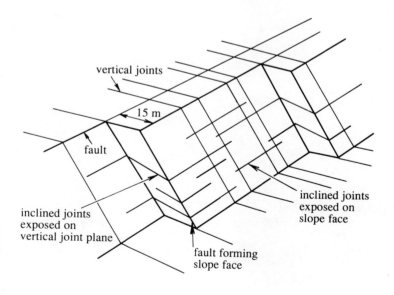

vertical joints

15 m

fault

inclined joints
exposed on
vertical joint plane

fault forming
slope face

inclined joints
exposed on
slope face

The traces of the inclined joints on the slope face were found to obey the negative exponential distribution with a mean trace length of 20 m. It is observed that on a given segment of the slope, a total of n inclined joints exhibit traces on the slope face that extend the full distance between the two vertical joints. Calculate the probability that none of these n inclined joints will extend from the slope face as far as the next fault for values of n = 1, 2 and 3.

Answers to these exercises are given on page 462.

7

Stresses on discontinuities

7.1 INTRODUCTION

Measurement of *in situ* stresses forms an increasingly important part in the rock investigation stage of the design of underground openings. Over-coring techniques now make it feasible to determine the three-dimensional state of stress to an acceptable degree of accuracy, both in terms of magnitude and orientation. The relatively complex, three-dimensional, nature of the problem can make the visualisation, interpretation and application of stress measurement data a daunting task. A key aspect in the application of stress measurement data is the transformation of stress from one set of coordinate axes to another, for example from the global coordinate system of a mine to a local system that allows the calculation of normal and shear stresses in the plane of a major fault zone or some other discontinuity. In the Author's experience, the difficulties that rock mechanics engineers have with stress transformation problems, although partly related to the tensorial nature of stress, are mainly linked to difficulties in defining three-dimensional Cartesian coordinate axes and correctly interpreting the associated sign conventions. The aim of this chapter is to present a simple, practical method for three-dimensional stress transformation, based partly upon hemispherical projection techniques and partly upon analytical methods. A brief review of the theoretical background to stress analysis is presented in Appendix E for those who are not familiar with this topic. All readers are, however, strongly urged to consult this Appendix to acquaint themselves with the sign conventions and with the stress analysis equations adopted in this chapter.

The first part of this chapter contains an explanation of how coordinate axes can be represented on a hemispherical projection and how angular measurements from the projection can be used for stress transformation. Later sections contain examples to illustrate applications of the method for stress transformation and for the determination of stresses on an inclined discontinuity plane.

7.2 GRAPHICAL REPRESENTATION OF THREE-DIMENSIONAL STRESS

Hemispherical projection methods are graphical techniques for representing and analysing three-dimensional orientation data in two dimensions on a sheet of paper. Most of the mathematical expressions for stress analysis and stress transformation, presented in Appendix E, contain three-dimensional orientation data in the form of direction cosines. Not only can hemispherical projection methods help with the visualisation of these orientation data they can also assist in the analysis process itself. The fundamentals of hemispherical projection are explained in Chapters 1 to 3 of Priest (1985) and are also summarised in Appendix A. The remaining sections of this chapter proceed on the assumption that the reader is familiar with these fundamentals.

The orientation of any line, such as one of the Cartesian coordinate axes in Figure 1.2, can be defined unambiguously in terms of the trend α and plunge β, as defined in section 1.2. The global Cartesian axes adopted in this chapter are the same as those used elsewhere in this book as follows:

x axis: horizontal to the north, trend/plunge 000/00
y axis: horizontal to the east, trend/plunge 090/00
z axis: vertical downwards, trend/plunge 000/90

Strictly speaking, although the trend of the z axis is not defined, it is convenient to assign it an arbitrary trend of zero. This set of axes is, of course, the same as the right handed system in Figure 1.2. In this xyz Cartesian system a directed line of length L (L > 0), trend α_l and plunge β_l has components l_x, l_y and l_z as follows

$$l_x = L \cos \alpha_l \cos \beta_l$$
$$l_y = L \sin \alpha_l \cos \beta_l \qquad (7.1)$$
$$l_z = L \sin \beta_l$$

If L is of unit value the components given above are the direction cosines of the l axis in the xyz system. The inverse forms of equations 7.1 are given by equations 1.3 to 1.5 and Table 1.1, by replacing u_x, u_y and u_z in these equations by l_x, l_y and l_z, respectively.

If the lower hemisphere, equal angle projection system of Priest (1985) is adopted then the orientation of any line with a downward direction (i.e. a positive value of plunge) can be plotted in the usual way. In this chapter we are concerned with plotting the orientations of coordinate axes, so any co-ordinate axis whose positive end has a downward plunge can be plotted. Any axis whose positive direction is upwards (i.e. it has a negative plunge) cannot be plotted on the lower hemisphere. Since it is inadvisable to mix upper and lower hemisphere projections the option that will be adopted here is to plot instead the negative direction of such axes, taking care to label them appropriately. For example, if the positive end of the n axis is directed upwards with a trend $228/-34$, the negative end will have a trend of $228 - 180 = 048°$ and a downward plunge of $+34°$, allowing it to be plotted in the usual way on the lower hemisphere, but labelled '$-n$'. A horizontal axis always plots on the perimeter of the projection at the point defined by the trend direction of its positive end. For the purposes of the subsequent analysis, a horizontal axis plotted in this way is taken to be directed downwards.

It is often the case that a local set of coordinate axes needs to be defined by reference to the orientation of some geological feature or engineering structure. To guarantee the precision of subsequent calculations it is necessary to ensure that an exactly orthogonal set of coordinate axes, of the correct handedness, is defined. A simple application of vector algebra can assist with this, as illustrated below.

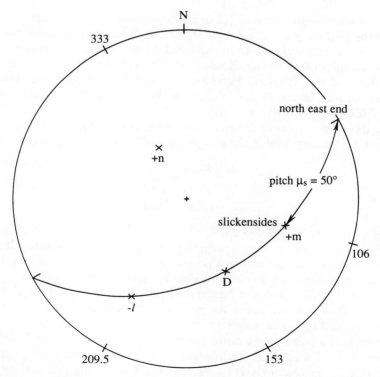

Figure 7.1 Lower hemisphere projection of coordinate axes for a shear surface with slickensides.

Suppose a planar shear surface of dip direction/dip angle $\alpha_d/\beta_d = 153/38$ exhibits slickensides that have a pitch μ_s of 50° from the north-east end of the strike line of the shear surface, as shown on the lower hemisphere projection in Figure 7.1. The aim is to specify a coordinate axis system that has one axis (l) completing the right handed orthogonal set, another axis (m) parallel to the slickensides, with the third axis (n) along the normal to the shear surface. Here we will adopt the global Cartesian axes defined earlier, and accept the orientation of the shear zone as a datum. The n coordinate axis, which is the normal to the shear zone, has a trend/plunge 333/52 calculated from the dip direction and dip angle of the plane by equations 1.1 and 1.2. Application of equation 7.1 for a unit vector gives the direction cosines of this axis as $n_x = 0.549$, $n_y = -0.280$ and $n_z = 0.788$. The trend/plunge α_s/β_s of the slickensides can be found from simple trigonometry as follows

$$\alpha_s = \alpha_d \pm \arctan\left(\frac{1}{\tan \mu_s \cos\beta_d}\right) \qquad 0 \leqslant \alpha_s \leqslant 360° \qquad (7.2)$$

$$\beta_s = \arcsin (\sin \mu_s \sin \beta_d) \qquad (7.3)$$

The sign adopted in equation 7.2 depends on the end of the strike line from which the angle of pitch μ_s has been measured. If the measurement end of the strike line is 90° **clockwise** from the trend α_d of the line of maximum dip of the plane, then the +ve sign is taken; if the strike line is 90° **anti-clockwise** then the −ve sign is taken. Equations 7.2 and 7.3 give the trend/plunge of the slickensides as 106.20°/28.14°, giving, by equation 7.1, direction cosines $m_x = -0.246$, $m_y = 0.847$ and $m_z = 0.472$.

The direction cosines of the l axis can be found from the direction cosines of the m and n axes by finding the components of their vector product as follows

$$l_x = m_y n_z - m_z n_y$$
$$l_y = m_z n_x - m_x n_z \qquad (7.4)$$
$$l_z = m_x n_y - m_y n_x$$

giving $l_x = 0.799$, $l_y = 0.453$ and $l_z = -0.396$. Equations 1.4 and 1.5 give the trend/plunge of the l axis as 029.53°/−23.32°, which completes the right handed system. Because in this case the positive end of the l axis is directed upwards it is necessary to plot the negative end of the axis, of trend/plunge 209.53°/+23.32° on the lower hemisphere projection in Figure 7.1.

The method outlined above for generating orthogonal coordinate axes can also be applied to engineering structures. The independent input data are the orientation of a plane whose normal forms one of the axes and the pitch angle in that plane of a line that forms another of the axes. The orientation of the third axis is, by equations 7.2 to 7.4, dependent on the orientations of the other two. Depending on how the axes are labelled it is possible to generate a left handed coordinate system by this method. In this case, reversal of any one

Table 7.1 Interpretation of angular measurements on a lower hemisphere projection

Direction of positive end of coordinate axis		Sign of the coordinate axis plotted on a LHP		δ_{lx} when δ_i is measured internally between the l and x axes on a LHP
l	x	l	x	
down	down	+ve	+ve	$\delta_{lx} = \delta_i$
up	up	−ve	−ve	$\delta_{lx} = \delta_i$
up	down	−ve	+ve	$\delta_{lx} = 180° - \delta_i$
down	up	+ve	−ve	$\delta_{lx} = 180° - \delta_i$

of the axes will change the handedness of the system. The simplest way of generating an exactly orthogonal coordinate system linked to the orientation of a plane is, of course, to select the strike, the line of maximum dip and the normal to the plane. The orientations of the axes in this case can be found directly from the orientation of the plane, following the methods explained in Chapter 1, expressed in equations 1.1 and 1.2, and illustrated later in this chapter.

The direction cosines in rotation matrices such as equation E.2 are found by taking the cosines of the angles measured between the **positive** ends of pairs of coordinate axes. If both axes, for example l and x, have downward directed positive ends, and therefore both plot on the lower hemisphere projection (LHP), then the angle between them can be measured in the usual way. This is done by placing the pair of axes on the same great circle and then counting the **internal** angle δ_i between them; this angle will always lie between 0 and 180°. The term 'internal' is adopted to describe an angle that is counted along a great circle between two points without crossing the perimeter of the projection, as explained in Appendix A. In this case the direction angle δ_{lx} is equal to δ_i and the direction cosine l_x is cos δ_{lx}. The same approach is used if both axes have upward directed positive ends; in this case δ_i is the internal angle between the negative ends of the coordinate axes plotted on the lower hemisphere projection and again δ_{lx} equals δ_i. If one of the axes is directed downwards and the other is directed upwards then the internal angle δ_i is measured from the positive end of one to the negative end of the other; in this case $\delta_{lx} = 180° - \delta_i$. A horizontal axis is taken to be directed downwards if it is plotted on the perimeter of the projection at an azimuth corresponding to its trend direction. These simple rules are summarised in Table 7.1 by reference to the specific example of l and x axes; the rules can, of course, be applied to any pair of axes such as m to x, n to x, l to y etc. The strict application of these rules for measuring angles is crucial to the methods presented in subsequent sections of this chapter.

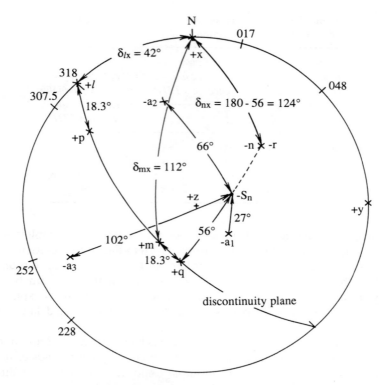

Figure 7.2 Lower hemisphere projection illustrating the determination of the resultant stress and peak shear stress for an inclined discontinuity plane, Example 7.1.

Alternatively, the direction cosine l_x can be calculated directly from the following expression

$$l_x = (\cos(\alpha_l - \alpha_x) \cos \beta_l \cos \beta_x) + (\sin \beta_l \sin \beta_x) \qquad (7.5)$$

Where α_l, β_l are the trend, plunge of the positive end of the l axis, and α_x, β_x are the trend, plunge of the positive end of the x axis.

Equation 7.5 can also be used to check that a given coordinate system has orthogonal axes. The representation and analysis of coordinate axes on a hemispherical projection is best illustrated by an example.

Example 7.1 (Figures 7.2 to 7.5)

Stress measurement coupled with numerical modelling of a rock mass adjacent to a proposed underground opening indicate that the state of stress $[\sigma]$ at a particular location, expressed as components in the global geographical xyz coordinate system defined earlier and in Appendix E, is as follows: $\sigma_{xx} = 17.4$,

$\sigma_{yy} = 11.8$, $\sigma_{zz} = 33.5$, $\sigma_{xy} = -5.2$, $\sigma_{yz} = 8.7$ and $\sigma_{zx} = -6.3\,\text{MPa}$. It is known that there is a major planar discontinuity passing through this location. The line of maximum dip of this discontinuity is known to have a trend $228°$ and plunge $56°$, i.e. the discontinuity has a dip direction/dip angle 228/56. Calculate the normal stress across the discontinuity and the shear stresses along the line of maximum dip and the strike of the discontinuity plane.

Solution

Figure 7.2 shows the positive ends of the xyz axes plotted on a lower hemisphere equal angle projection. The local *lmn* system is defined as follows: *l* is the strike of the discontinuity plane of trend/plunge 318/00; m is the line of maximum dip of the discontinuity 228/56; to complete the right handed system we must select the upward normal n of trend/plunge 228/−34. The positive ends of the *l*, m axes are plotted in Figure 7.2. It is only possible, however, to plot the negative end of the n axis on the lower hemisphere projection; this negative end has a trend/plunge 048/34. The direction angles between the xyz and *lmn* axes can be determined by measuring the internal angles on the projection and then applying the rules in Table 7.1. For example, for the *l* and x axes $\delta_{lx} = \delta_i = 42°$ so $l_x = 0.74$; for the m and x axes $\delta_{mx} = \delta_i = 112°$ (to the nearest degree) so $m_x = -0.37$; for the n and x axes $\delta_i = 56°$ (to the nearest degree), however, since in this case the measurement is from $-n$ to $+x$ the angle $\delta_{nx} = 180 - 56$ giving $n_x = -0.56$. The complete rotation matrix [**R**] in equations E.2, E.4 and E.6 can be determined in this way, taking care to note the signs of the axes between which the internal angles are measured. In cases such as this, where the global xyz axes are the geographical axes defined earlier, the rotation matrix can be determined by applying equations 7.1 to the *l*, m and n axes in turn, taking each to be of unit length. This approach gives the following rotation matrix, correct to 3 significant figures:

$$[\mathbf{R}] = \begin{bmatrix} l_x = 0.743 & l_y = -0.669 & l_z = 0 \\ m_x = -0.374 & m_y = -0.416 & m_z = 0.829 \\ n_x = -0.555 & n_y = -0.616 & n_z = -0.559 \end{bmatrix}$$

Introduction of the terms of this rotation matrix and the xyz stress tensor [σ] into equations E.2, E.4 and E.6 gives the following rotated stresses for the *lmn* system: $\sigma_{ll} = 20.06$, $\sigma_{mm} = 23.80$, $\sigma_{nn} = 18.84$, $\sigma_{lm} = -9.96$, $\sigma_{mn} = -12.14$, $\sigma_{nl} = 4.02\,\text{MPa}$. Interpretation of the signs of the three normal stresses is simple; they are all compressive. The shear stresses, however, require some careful thought. Figure 7.3 shows a three-dimensional sketch of the discontinuity plane that defines the *lmn* axes. Since the n axis is directed upwards the small cubic stress element appears on the upper side of the discontinuity plane. Following the sign convention in Figure E.2 for stress directions, the positive directions for the shear stresses $\sigma_{nm} = \sigma_{mn}$ and $\sigma_{nl} = \sigma_{ln}$ on the origin-n face have been sketched in. In this case σ_{mn} is negative $(-12.14\,\text{MPa})$ so the shear stress acting along the line of maximum dip of the

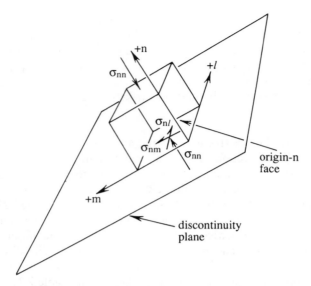

Figure 7.3   Three-dimensional sketch of a cubic stress element on an inclined discontinuity plane.

discontinuity plane is tending to shear the origin-n face, which forms the **lower** face of the discontinuity, **upwards** relative to the obverse-n face which forms the **upper** face of the discontinuity. The shear stress σ_{nl} acting along the strike of the discontinuity plane is positive (4.02 MPa) so the lower face of the discontinuity has a tendency to shear towards the north-east quadrant relative to the upper face. It must be emphasised that these senses of shear apply only to the shear stresses, they do not imply that slip actually occurs in these directions; shear displacement by slip can only occur if the shear strength of the discontinuity is exceeded.

It is a straightforward matter to determine the principal stresses from the xyz stress tensor $[\sigma]$, given at the start of the above example, by the direct application of equations E.7 to E.16 . The principal stresses are $\sigma_1 = 39.28$, $\sigma_2 = 15.72$ and $\sigma_3 = 7.71$ MPa. The direction cosines of the principal axes α_1, α_2 and α_3 relative to the xyz axes are found from equations E.18 to E.20 and are, respectively, for α_1 0.334, -0.341, -0.879, for α_2 -0.878, 0.227, -0.422 and for α_3 0.344, 0.912, -0.224. Equations 1.4 and 1.5 give the trend/plunge of the three principal axes α_1, α_2 and α_3 to the nearest degree, respectively, as follows 314/-61, 165/-25 and 069/-13. Each of these axes is directed upwards, so the negative end of each has been plotted on the lower hemisphere projection in Figure 7.2.

7.3   EXTREME STRESSES IN A PLANE

In the example discussed in the previous section, shear stresses were determined for the line of maximum dip and the strike direction of the discontinuity plane plotted in Figures 7.2 and 7.3; these stresses were $\sigma_{mn} = -12.14$ and $\sigma_{nl} = 4.02\,MPa$, respectively. If it is known that the discontinuity plane has an angle of friction of, say $30°$, and, from earlier calculations, that the normal stress across the plane is $\sigma_{nn} = 18.84\,MPa$ (compressive), the question that immediately presents itself is whether the discontinuity plane has sufficient shear strength to sustain these shear stresses. Adopting the Coulomb shear strength criterion, discussed in Chapter 9, for zero cohesion gives a shear strength of $\sigma_{nn} \tan \phi = 10.88\,MPa$. Although the discontinuity can sustain the strike shear stress, it clearly cannot sustain the shear stress along the line of maximum dip calculated in the above example. If slip does occur, however, it will not necessarily develop along the line of maximum dip; slip will occur along the direction of maximum shear stress in the discontinuity plane. Aswegen (1990) presents an instructive account of shear displacements along faults in the Witwatersrand quartzites of the Welkom gold field in South Africa. Shear displacement, which was generally associated with extensive stoping in the region of the faults, was estimated to be in the order of 150 to 410 mm and was usually linked to major seismic events. There are several ways of determining the orientation, magnitude and sign of the maximum shear stress in a given plane. Three of these methods are presented below, by reference to the example presented in the previous section.

7.3.1   Graphical construction for extreme stresses

The first method for determining the extreme shear stresses is partly graphical. Figure 7.4 shows a view of the origin-n face of the discontinuity plane. The view is along the n axis looking **upwards** towards the underside of the discontinuity plane, so the trend/plunge of the line of sight is $228/-34$, the $+l$ axis runs to the right along the strike of the discontinuity plane and the $+m$ axis runs down along the line of maximum dip. The l and m axes have been graduated to indicate values of the shear stresses σ_{nl} and σ_{mn}, respectively. The state of shear stress in the discontinuity plane is represented by a point at coordinates $\sigma_{nl} = 4.02$ and $\sigma_{mn} = -12.14\,MPa$. The vector drawn to this point in Figure 7.4 gives the magnitude and direction of the maximum shear stress in the discontinuity plane. This peak shear stress is directed upwards along a line inclined at approximately $18.3°$ from the line of maximum dip of the discontinuity plane.

It is helpful to express the peak shear stress in terms of a second set of local coordinate axes p aligned at right angles to, and q aligned parallel to the peak shear stress axis, as shown in Figure 7.4. The r axis is directed upwards along the normal to the discontinuity plane to complete the right handed system.

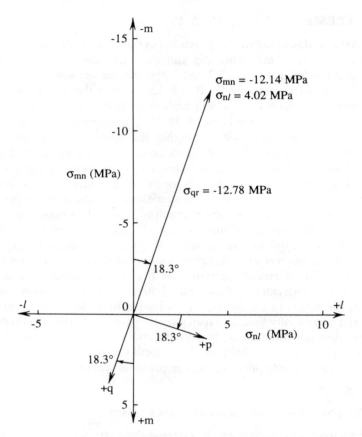

Figure 7.4 Shear stresses on the origin-n face of a cubic stress element on an inclined discontinuity plane, Example 7.1.

Defining p_l, p_m, q_l and q_m as the direction cosines of the p, q axes relative to the l, m axes allows us to write general vector transformation expressions for shear stresses in the discontinuity plane, relative to the pqr system as follows

$$\sigma_{pr} = \sigma_{mn}\, p_m + \sigma_{nl}\, p_l \tag{7.6}$$

$$\sigma_{qr} = \sigma_{mn}\, q_m + \sigma_{nl}\, q_l \tag{7.7}$$

Vector, rather than tensor, transformation is used here because the axis of rotation is normal to the plane on which the stress components act. The direction cosines are $p_l = \cos 18.3° = 0.949$, $p_m = \cos(90° - 18.3°) = 0.314$, $q_l = -0.314$ and $q_m = 0.949$, giving the result $\sigma_{pr} = 0$ and $\sigma_{qr} = -12.78$ MPa. The stress σ_{qr} is the peak shear stress in the discontinuity plane. Applying our sign convention in Appendix E for shear stresses confirms that σ_{qr} is negative in the pqr coordinate system since it acts on the origin-r face and is directed towards the negative end of the q axis as shown in Figure 7.4. The minimum shear stress σ_{pr} is zero; this will always be the case. The magnitude of the peak shear stress in the discontinuity plane can, of course, be found from simple trigonometry, as follows

$$|\sigma_{qr}| = \sqrt{\sigma_{nl}^2 + \sigma_{mn}^2} \qquad (7.8)$$

The positive directions of the p and q axes have been plotted on the lower hemisphere projection in Figure 7.2. Clearly the discontinuity plane, which in this case has a shear strength of 10.88 MPa, cannot sustain the peak shear stress of 12.78 MPa, so slip will occur in a direction that translates the lower face of the discontinuity plane upwards along the q axis relative to the upper face of the discontinuity plane. Slip will cease when there has been a redistribution of stresses in the surrounding rock material sufficient to regain static equilibrium.

In practice, once any pair of shear stress components has been determined for a given plane, the construction of a simple shear stress vector diagram, such as the one in Figure 7.4, permits the determination of the orientation and value of the peak and zero shear stresses for that plane. In doing this, care must be taken with the following points: (i) note whether the stresses are being plotted for an origin or an obverse face, (ii) operate with consistent handedness of axes (usually right handed) and (iii) measure direction cosines between the positive ends of pairs of axes.

7.3.2 Resultant stress method

Jaeger and Cook (1979) outline an alternative approach for determining the peak shear stresses for a given plane. This method is based upon determining, from the principal stresses, the resultant stress S acting across the plane. Pursuing the earlier example, the magnitude of the resultant stress S_n for the discontinuity plane, which has the n axis as its normal, is given by

$$|S_n| = \sqrt{(n_1\sigma_1)^2 + (n_2\sigma_2)^2 + (n_3\sigma_3)^2} \qquad (7.9)$$

where n_1, n_2 and n_3 are the direction cosines for the n axis relative to the major, intermediate and minor principal axes a_1, a_2 and a_3 respectively. The direction cosines s_1, s_2 and s_3 of this resultant stress relative to the three principal axes are, following Jaeger and Cook, respectively

$$s_1 = \frac{n_1\sigma_1}{|S_n|} \qquad s_2 = \frac{n_2\sigma_2}{|S_n|} \qquad s_3 = \frac{n_3\sigma_3}{|S_n|} \qquad (7.10)$$

Taking the principal axes determined earlier, and either applying equation 7.5 or measuring the angles directly from the projection in Figure 7.2 gives $n_1 = 0.516$, $n_2 = 0.583$ and $n_3 = -0.628$ for the current example. Hence $|S_n| = 22.77$ MPa, $s_1 = 0.891$ (27°), $s_2 = 0.402$ (66°) and $s_3 = -0.212$ (102°), the associated direction angles being given in parentheses to the nearest degree. The negative direction of the S_n axis lies at a point on the projection that makes an angle of 27° with $-a_1$, 66° with $-a_2$, and 102° with $-a_3$ measured internally along great circles in the usual way, as shown in Figure 7.2. This is the negative end of S_n because internal angles are measured from the **negative** ends of each of the principal axes. The resulting point, labelled $-S_n$ has a trend/plunge 072/65 (to the nearest degree) so the positive end S_n has a trend/plunge 252/−65.

The normal stress σ_{nn} on the discontinuity plane can be found by applying the stress transformation equations E.6, replacing σ_x by σ_1, σ_y by σ_2, σ_z by σ_3, n_x by n_1, n_y by n_2 and n_z by n_3. Noting that shear stresses are zero on the principal planes gives

$$\sigma_{nn} = \sigma_1(n_1)^2 + \sigma_2(n_2)^2 + \sigma_3(n_3)^2 \tag{7.11}$$

Although the magnitude and orientation of the resultant stress S_n have been determined, equation 7.9 gives no indication of its sign, i.e. whether it is compressive or tensile across the plane. The simplest way of establishing the sign of S_n is to note that it will always have the same sign as the normal stress given by equation 7.11. In the current example σ_{nn} by equation 7.11 is 18.84 MPa (compressive) so S_n is also compressive. The peak shear stress in the discontinuity plane is co-planar with S_n and the normal to the discontinuity plane, labelled $-r$ in Figure 7.2. The great circle passing through $-S_n$ and $-r$ defines, by its intersection with the discontinuity plane, the orientation $+q$ of the peak shear stress. The line $+p$ of zero shear stress in the discontinuity plane lies 90° from $+q$ forming a right handed coordinate system as before. The value of the peak shear stress σ_{qr} is given by

$$\sigma_{qr} = S_n s_q \tag{7.12}$$

where S_n is +22.77 MPa and s_q is the direction cosine for the S_n and q axes. In the current example the internal angle between the $-S_n$ and $+q$ axes is 56° (to the nearest degree) so in this case s_q is $\cos(180° - 56°) = -0.56$, giving $\sigma_{qr} = -12.73$ MPa, which, allowing for the approximation in measuring angles from the projection, is the same as the earlier result.

7.3.3 Alternative resultant stress method

A third method for determining the extreme stresses in a plane has been outlined by Goodman (1976). This method is based on determining the resultant stress S_n on a plane from the components of shear stress and normal stress for the plane. The lmn coordinate system, defined earlier, is a local system with l along the strike, m along the line of maximum dip and n along the normal to the discontinuity plane. Only the three components of stress with a subscript 'n' in the lmn system need to be considered when determining the magnitude of S_n as follows

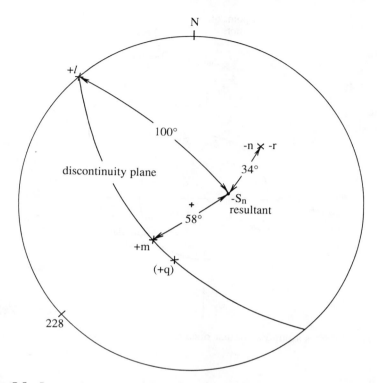

N

+*l*

100°

discontinuity plane

-n ✕ -r

34°

-S$_n$
resultant

+
58°

+m

(+q)

228

Figure 7.5 Lower hemisphere projection illustrating an alternative method for determining the resultant stress on an inclined discontinuity plane, Example 7.1.

$$|S_n| = \sqrt{\sigma_{nn}^2 + \sigma_{mn}^2 + \sigma_{nl}^2} \qquad (7.13)$$

As before, the sign of S_n is the same as that of σ_{nn}. The direction cosines s_l, s_m and s_n of S_n relative to the *l*mn system are, respectively

$$s_l = \frac{\sigma_{nl}}{S_n} \qquad s_m = \frac{\sigma_{mn}}{S_n} \qquad s_n = \frac{\sigma_{nn}}{S_n} \qquad (7.14)$$

In the current example, equations 7.13 and 7.14 give $S_n = 22.77\,\text{MPa}$, $s_l = 0.176\ (80°)$, $s_m = -0.533\ (122°)$ and $s_n = 0.827\ (34°)$, the associated direction angles being given in parentheses to the nearest degree. The discontinuity plane and *l*mn axes are re-plotted in Figure 7.5. Because it is the negative end of the n axis that is plotted on the lower hemisphere projection in Figure 7.5, the direction angle counted internally on the projection from this axis to the positive end of S_n is $180 - 34 = 146°$. There is no orientation on the lower hemisphere projection that, counting internal angles, is simultaneously 80°

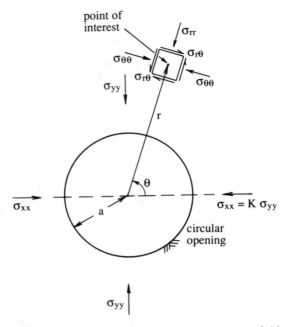

Figure 7.6 Stresses around a circular opening in a biaxial stress field.

from $+l$, 122° from $+m$ and 146° from $-n$ so the positive end of S_n cannot be plotted. Instead it is necessary to plot the negative end of S_n, which plots at an internal angle of $180 - 80 = 100°$ from $+l$, an angle of $180 - 122 = 58°$ from $+m$ and 34° from $-n$, as shown in Figure 7.5. The orientation of $-S_n$ agrees with that determined earlier from the analysis of principal stresses. Having established the orientation, magnitude and sign of the resultant stress on the discontinuity plane, the procedure described earlier can be used to determine the extreme stresses for the plane.

7.4 TWO-DIMENSIONAL ANALYSIS OF STRESSES ON A DISCONTINUITY ADJACENT TO A CIRCULAR OPENING

The analysis in the previous section provides a general method for determining the peak shear stresses in any inclined plane in a three-dimensional stress field. Brady and Brown (1985) present a valuable special case of this analysis. They considered the state of stress on an inclined discontinuity whose strike runs parallel to the axis of a cylindrical opening. This approach, which is essentially a two-dimensional analysis, permits the application of the Kirsch equations for determining the state of stress in the rock adjacent to the opening, and permits the application of two-dimensional stress transformation equations for determining the normal and shear stresses on the inclined discontinuity plane. In this way it is possible to identify those regions of the discontinuity surface that do not have sufficient strength to sustain the predicted continuum stress distribution.

Figure 7.6 shows a circular opening of radius 'a' created in a continuum with remote field stresses σ_{yy} and σ_{xx} which are taken to be principal stresses. For the purposes of the following analysis it is convenient to replace σ_{xx} by $K\sigma_{yy}$ where the remote principal stress ratio $K = \sigma_{xx}/\sigma_{yy}$, can be less than or greater than unity. Adopting polar coordinates originating from the centre of the circular opening in Figure 7.6 allows us to specify in two dimensions the location of a point of interest in terms of the anti-clockwise polar angle of rotation θ from the σ_{xx} axis, and the distance r along a radial axis from the centre of the opening. The state of stress at the point defined by polar coordinates r, θ is given by the radial stress σ_{rr}, the tangential stress $\sigma_{\theta\theta}$ and the associated shear stress $\sigma_{r\theta}$, as shown in Figure 7.6.

Assuming that the material around the opening is a homogeneous, isotropic elastic continuum subject to conditions of simple plane strain, as defined by Brady and Brown, for the plane of the diagram in Figure 7.6, allows us to adopt the Kirsch equations which give the final values of σ_{rr}, $\sigma_{\theta\theta}$ and $\sigma_{r\theta}$ following creation of the opening as follows

$$\sigma_{rr} = \frac{\sigma_{yy}}{2}\left[(1 + K)\left(1 - \frac{a^2}{r^2}\right) - (1 - K)\left(1 - \frac{4a^2}{r^2} + \frac{3a^4}{r^4}\right)\cos 2\theta\right]$$

$$\sigma_{\theta\theta} = \frac{\sigma_{yy}}{2}\left[(1 + K)\left(1 + \frac{a^2}{r^2}\right) + (1 - K)\left(1 + \frac{3a^4}{r^4}\right)\cos 2\theta\right] \qquad (7.15)$$

$$\sigma_{r\theta} = \frac{\sigma_{yy}}{2}\left[(1 - K)\left(1 + \frac{2a^2}{r^2} - \frac{3a^4}{r^4}\right)\sin 2\theta\right]$$

For completeness, the radial displacement increment u_r (+ve away from opening) and the tangential displacement increment u_θ (+ve anticlockwise) induced by excavation of the circular opening in an elastic continuum under plane stress with a shear modulus G and a Poisson's ratio v are, correcting the minor error, given by

$$u_r = \frac{-\sigma_{yy}a^2}{4Gr}\left[(1 + K) - (1 - K)\left((4 - 4v) - \frac{a^2}{r^2}\right)\cos 2\theta\right]$$

$$u_\theta = \frac{-\sigma_{yy}a^2}{4Gr}\left[(1 - K)\left((2 - 4v) + \frac{a^2}{r^2}\right)\sin 2\theta\right] \qquad (7.16)$$

Brady and Brown present special cases of the general Kirsch equations listed above. In particular, at the boundary of the circular opening r = a and so $\sigma_{rr} = \sigma_{r\theta} = 0$, which is the expected result for a traction-free surface. In a hydrostatic remote stress field K = 1 and so $\sigma_{r\theta} = u_\theta = 0$, and σ_{rr}, $\sigma_{\theta\theta}$, u_r become independent of θ.

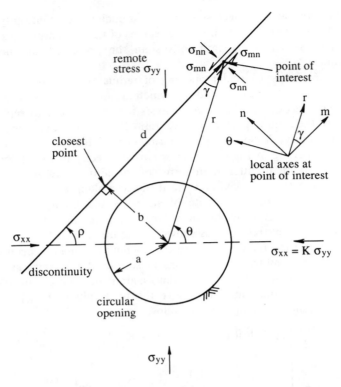

Figure 7.7 Single discontinuity plane adjacent to a circular opening in a biaxial stress field.

Consider now a planar discontinuity with a strike running parallel to the axis of the cylindrical opening, inclined at an angle ρ to the σ_{xx} axis and located, at its closest point, at distance b from the centre of the circular opening, as shown in Figure 7.7. A point of interest located at a distance d measured along the discontinuity from its closest point to the circular opening will, from simple geometry, be at a radial distance r from the centre of the opening given by

$$r = \sqrt{b^2 + d^2} \tag{7.17}$$

The angle γ between the discontinuity and the radial line drawn to the point of interest is given by

$$\gamma = \text{arc tan}\left(\frac{b}{d}\right) \tag{7.18}$$

(see equation 1.4 for quadrant interpretation.)

The polar angle θ is now given by

$$\theta = \rho + \gamma \qquad (7.19)$$

The inset in Figure 7.7 shows two sets of local coordinate axes at the point of interest on the discontinuity. The axes r and θ are, respectively, radial and tangential to the circular opening; the axes m and n are, respectively, parallel and normal to the discontinuity. The state of stress $[\sigma]$ at the point of interest, relative to the r, θ axes is given by

$$[\sigma] = \begin{bmatrix} \sigma_{rr} & \sigma_{r\theta} \\ \sigma_{r\theta} & \sigma_{\theta\theta} \end{bmatrix} \qquad (7.20)$$

The terms in $[\sigma]$ are given by the Kirsch equations.

The state of stress $[\sigma^*]$ at the same point of interest, but expressed relative to the m, n axes is given by

$$[\sigma^*] = \begin{bmatrix} \sigma_{mm} & \sigma_{mn} \\ \sigma_{mn} & \sigma_{nn} \end{bmatrix} \qquad (7.21)$$

In this case, since we are concerned about the possibility of local slip along the discontinuity, it is the normal and shear stress terms σ_{nn} and σ_{mn} in $[\sigma^*]$ that are of primary interest.

The two-dimensional version of equation E.2, giving the rotation matrix $[\mathbf{R}]$ for the m, n system relative to the r, θ system, is as follows

$$[\mathbf{R}] = \begin{bmatrix} m_r & m_\theta \\ n_r & n_\theta \end{bmatrix} \qquad (7.22)$$

The direction cosines in the rotation matrix, found by inspecting the local axes at the point of interest, are functions of the angle γ as follows

$$\begin{aligned}
m_r &= \cos\gamma \\
m_\theta &= \cos(90° + \gamma) = -\sin\gamma \\
n_r &= \cos(90° - \gamma) = \sin\gamma \\
n_\theta &= \cos\gamma
\end{aligned} \qquad (7.23)$$

Writing down the transpose of $[\mathbf{R}]$, implementing the matrix multiplication in equation E.4 and applying the substitutions in equation 7.23 gives the following expressions for σ_{nn} and σ_{mn}

$$\begin{aligned}
\sigma_{nn} &= \sigma_{rr}\sin^2\gamma + \sigma_{\theta\theta}\cos^2\gamma + 2\sigma_{r\theta}\sin\gamma\cos\gamma \\
\sigma_{mn} &= \sigma_{rr}\cos\gamma\sin\gamma - \sigma_{\theta\theta}\sin\gamma\cos\gamma + \sigma_{r\theta}(\cos^2\gamma - \sin^2\gamma)
\end{aligned} \qquad (7.24)$$

Equations 7.15, 7.17, 7.18, 7.19 and 7.24 make it possible to compute the stress condition adjacent to a circular opening and then to apply two-dimensional stress transformation to determine the shear and normal stresses at any point on a discontinuity of any orientation and location relative to the circular opening. Whether the discontinuity can support the computed stress

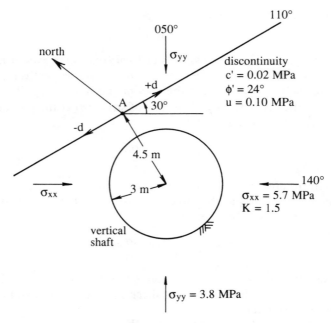

Figure 7.8 Vertical shaft adjacent to a vertical discontinuity in a biaxial stress field, Example 7.2.

state depends upon its shear strength τ_f. The Coulomb criterion, discussed in Chapter 9, gives τ_f as follows

$$\tau_f = c' + (\sigma_{nn} - u) \tan \phi' \qquad (7.25)$$

where σ_{nn} is the normal stress and u is the water pressure in the discontinuity. The parameters c' and ϕ' are, respectively, the cohesion and the angle of friction for the discontinuity under conditions of effective stress. If σ_{mn} tends to exceed τ_f at any point then slip must occur along the discontinuity; this will lead to a redistribution of the computed continuum stress distribution. The nature of this redistribution depends upon the extent and upon the direction of slip. These ideas are illustrated in the following example.

Example 7.2 (Figures 7.8 and 7.9)

A 3 m radius vertical shaft is to be excavated through a sandstone horizon in which the remote horizontal principal field stresses are 3.8 MPa along a line of trend 050° and 5.7 MPa along a line of trend 140°. A vertical discontinuity of strike 110° is, at its closest point A, located a distance of 1.5 m from the shaft

Table for Example 7.2

d m	r m	θ Deg	σ_{rr} MPa	$\sigma_{\theta\theta}$ MPa	$\sigma_{r\theta}$ MPa	σ_{nn} MPa	σ_{mn} MPa	τ_f MPa
−2	4.92	144.0	2.966	6.100	1.201	2.591	0.358	1.129
−1	4.61	132.5	2.751	6.888	1.239	2.421	−0.246	1.053
0	4.50	120.0	2.727	7.618	1.066	2.727	−1.066	1.190
1	4.61	107.5	2.860	7.960	0.712	3.401	−1.725	1.490
2	4.92	96.0	3.053	7.826	0.264	4.037	−1.948	1.773

wall on the northern side of the shaft, and therefore 4.5 m from the shaft centre as shown in Figure 7.8. The discontinuity has Coulomb shear strength parameters c' = 0.02 MPa, φ' = 24° and carries a water pressure of 0.10 MPa in the sandstone horizon. Identify, in terms of the distance d measured from A, the region of the discontinuity that will be unable to sustain the continuum stress distribution predicted by the Kirsch equations.

Solution
In this example we take σ_{yy} = 3.8 MPa and σ_{xx} = 5.7 MPa, which gives K = 1.5. The shaft radius a = 3 m and the shortest distance b between the shaft centre and the discontinuity is 4.5 m. The angle ρ between the discontinuity and the σ_{xx} direction is 30°. Taking values of d = −2, −1, 0, 1 and 2 m and applying equations 7.15, 7.17, 7.18, 7.19, 7.24 and 7.25 gives the tabulated values for r, θ and for σ_{rr}, $\sigma_{\theta\theta}$, $\sigma_{r\theta}$, σ_{nn}, σ_{mn} and τ_f in MPa.

Figure 7.9 shows a graph of shear strength τ_f and the absolute value of shear stress σ_{mn} plotted against d in the range −4 to 4 m. This graph shows that the non-hydrostatic stress field has produced an asymmetrical variation in shear strength and shear stress along the discontinuity, with shear stress changing sign at d ≈ −1.4 m. The magnitude of shear stress exceeds shear strength for values of d in the approximate range 0.2 to 2.75 m, with shear failure occurring under negative shear stress in this region. Reference to Figure 7.8 shows that negative shear stress causes rock on the shaft side of the discontinuity to slide towards point A. This movement will cause a redistribution of the continuum stress values which will in turn lead to a higher tangential stress in this region between the discontinuity and the shaft.

A stress field that has been modified by local slip along a discontinuity cannot readily be described by a simple closed form solution, such as the Kirsch equations. Moreover, if there is a second discontinuity in the region of the opening there will be a complex interaction between the discontinuities which can only be modelled adequately by applying numerical methods. The topic of

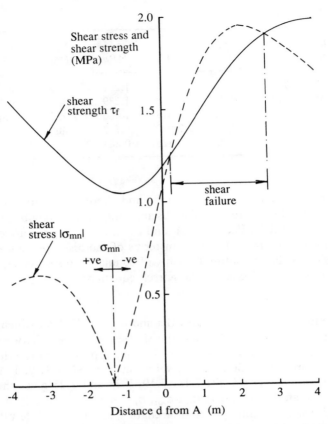

Figure 7.9 Variation of shear strength and shear stress with distance along the vertical discontinuity in Example 7.2.

slip along discontinuities will be considered again in Chapters 9 and 10 in the context of its influence on the strength and deformability of rock masses.

EXERCISES FOR CHAPTER 7 AND APPENDIX E

7.1

The stress state in a planar orebody of dip direction/dip angle 215/37 is to be measured in a borehole driven in the plane of the orebody and with a pitch of 44° measured from the north-west end of the strike line. Determine the trend and plunge of the positive ends of the following axes in a right-handed Cartesian coordinates system: *l* completes the right-handed system, *m* down-

ward along the borehole axis, and n upward along the normal to the plane of
the orebody.

7.2

The principal stresses in the rock mass adjacent to the orebody in Exercise 7.1
are known to have the following values: σ_1 18.4 MPa compressive, trend/
plunge 025/00; σ_2 13.3 MPa compressive, trend/plunge 115/00; and σ_3
9.1 MPa compressive, vertical. Determine the stress state in the l, m, n
Cartesian coordinate system determined in Exercise 7.1.

7.3

Stress measurements utilising the CSIRO Hollow Inclusion cell indicate that
the principal stresses near a thin, weak, mineralised zone adjacent to an open
stope have the following magnitudes and orientations (given as trend/plunge
to the nearest degree): σ_1 = 32 MPa compressive, orientation 190/53; σ_2 =
19 MPa compressive, orientation 308/20; σ_3 = 6 MPa compressive, orientation
050/30. Drilling investigations indicate that the mineralised zone is planar with
a dip direction/dip angle 260/60, an angle of friction of 30° and negligible
cohesion. Utilising three-dimensional stress transformations, calculate:

(i)   the normal stress across the mineralised zone,
(ii) the shear stresses in the mineralised zone along its strike direction and
      along its line of maximum dip, and
(iii) the orientation and value of the peak shear stress in the plane of the
      mineralised zone.

Does the mineralised zone have sufficient strength to sustain this stress state?

7.4

Stress measurement and numerical modelling of the rock adjacent to a proposed
stope development indicate that the state of stress [σ] at a particular location,
expressed as components relative to the global geographical Cartesian coordinate system: x horizontal north, y horizontal east and z vertical down are
σ_{xx} = 28.8, σ_{yy} = 11.4, σ_{zz} = 7.5, σ_{xy} = 4.5, σ_{yz} = −9.2, and σ_{zx} = −5.0 MPa.
Bedding planes within the rock mass are known to have a dip direction/dip
angle of 150/25, to possess zero cohesion and an angle of friction of 40°.
Calculate for this particular location:

(i) the values (but not the orientations) of the three principal stresses,
(ii) the normal stress, the shear stress along the line of maximum dip and the
     shear stress along the strike of the bedding plane,

(iii) the peak shear stress in the plane of the bedding, and
(iv) the factor of safety against slip along the bedding.

7.5

A 5 m diameter horizontal tunnel is to be excavated through a siltstone horizon along a line of trend 345°. Two of the remote principal field stresses, which lie in a plane normal to the tunnel axis, are 4.8 MPa along a line of trend/plunge 075/00 and 3.0 MPa in the vertical direction. A planar discontinuity of dip direction/dip angle 255/20 passes beneath the tunnel and, at its closest point A, is located a distance of 3.3 m from the tunnel axis. The discontinuity has Coulomb shear strength parameters $c' = 0.03$ MPa, $\phi' = 30°$ and carries a water pressure of 0.05 MPa in the siltstone horizon. Identify, in terms of the distance d measured from A, the region of the discontinuity that will be unable to sustain the continuum stress distribution predicted by the Kirsch equations.

Answers to these exercises are give on pages 462–3.

8

Analysis of
rigid blocks

8.1 INTRODUCTION

One of the most obvious and direct consequences of the presence of discontinuities in a rock mass is the creation of discrete blocks of rock, which can range in volume from a few cubic millimetres to many cubic metres. Those blocks that lie adjacent to an existing, or a planned, free rock face have the potential to fall, to slide or to topple from the face. In most civil engineering and mining situations, block instability of this nature is both dangerous and economically undesirable. Moreover, the removal of blocks adjacent to the face creates new free faces which allow the progressive loosening and dislodgement of deeper-seated blocks.

Since the *in situ* stresses close to a free face are usually low, the most important agents controlling the stability of near-surface rock blocks are their self weight, water pressures in the fractures, seismic effects and external forces created by foundations and rock support measures. In most cases we are concerned about the gross stability of a block rather than internal deformation and failure of the block. For this reason the approach is usually termed 'rigid block analysis'. An important precursor to rigid block analysis is the determination of kinematic feasibility. A given block is kinematically feasible if it is '. . . physically capable of being removed from the rock mass without disturbing the adjacent rock' (Priest, 1985). Kinematic feasibility is therefore assessed on the basis of a given block's **potential** to move and not upon an analysis of the forces that may cause this movement. Clearly it is only necessary to analyse the mechanical stability of kinematically feasible blocks.

The analysis of rigid blocks is essentially a problem of three-dimensional geometry, topology and mechanics. To make this analysis tractable it is usually

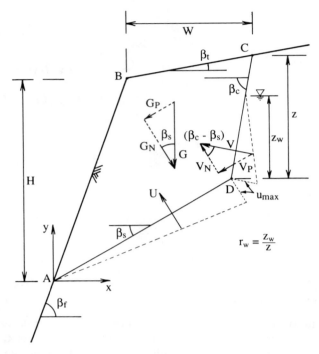

Figure 8.1   Geometry of single plane sliding mechanism.

necessary to make a number of simplifications concerning the geometry of the discontinuity network and the geometry of the resulting blocks. It is the aim of this chapter to present an introduction to the analysis of the stability of rigid blocks created by discontinuities at overhanging and at non-overhanging rock faces. An important tool in this analysis is the technique of hemispherical projection described by Priest (1985) and summarised in Appendix A. Those who wish to pursue the subject of rigid block analysis in more depth are directed to the comprehensive texts of Warburton (1981) and Goodman and Shi (1985). Discrete element methods and other numerical modelling techniques for blocky rock masses will be considered briefly in Chapter 10, and will not be discussed in this chapter.

8.2   TWO-DIMENSIONAL SINGLE PLANE SLIDING

A dramatic simplification of the analysis can be achieved when discontinuity orientations permit an essentially two-dimensional approach. Figure 8.1 illustrates a more generalised form of the classic single plane sliding mechanism discussed by Hoek and Bray (1981). The geometrical prerequisites and other assumptions for the analysis of this mechanism are as follows:

1. The rock face, AB, the sliding plane, AD, the top of the slope, BC and, if present, the tension crack, CD, strike within about 20° of each other and intersect to form a kinematically feasible block of known geometry, that could if unstable slide along the planar discontinuity AD.
2. The angles of dip of the rock face, the sliding plane, the top of the slope and the tension crack are respectively β_f, β_s, β_t and β_c, respectively. These angles must take values that create a kinematically feasible block. In general this latter requirement imposes the following range stipulations: $0 \leqslant \beta_s \leqslant \beta_f \leqslant 90°$, $-90° \leqslant \beta_t \leqslant \beta_c \leqslant 90°$. The vertical distance between the crest of the slope and the point where the sliding plane daylights on the slope face is H. The horizontal distance between the crest of the slope and the point where the tension crack daylights at the top of the slope is W, as illustrated in Figure 8.1.
3. The tension crack, of vertical depth z, contains water to a vertical depth z_w, as illustrated in Figure 8.1. The ratio of the distances $z_w/z = r_w$. The maximum water pressure at the base of the tension crack is $u_{max} = \gamma_w z_w$, where γ_w is the unit weight of water. This water pressure also acts within the sliding plane AD, decaying linearly to zero at the rock face.
4. The only forces acting on the block are its vertical weight of magnitude G, the force U due to water pressure on the plane of sliding, and the force V due to water pressure in the tension crack.
5. The failure mechanism is assumed to be translational sliding along AD. Moment equilibrium and the associated mechanisms of rotation and toppling are not considered. This latter stipulation, which makes the tacit assumption that G, U and V act through a common point, is rarely satisfied in practice.
6. The shear strength S_f (force) of the sliding plane is assumed to be governed by the Coulomb criterion with effective shear strength parameters c' and ϕ', such that

$$S_f = c'A_s + N'\tan \phi' \tag{8.1}$$

where A_s is the area of the sliding plane and N' is the effective normal force on the sliding plane.

There are two stages in the analysis of this mechanism; the first is essentially geometrical, the second deals with the analysis of forces.

8.2.1 Geometrical analysis

Geometrical analysis is usually the most complicated aspect of the analysis of rigid block failures. The following method has the advantages of utilising data that can be measured directly on site, of being general in its application, and lending itself to solution by spread-sheet methods. An x,y coordinate system has been set up with its origin at point A, the toe of the block. It is convenient to define an intermediate geometrical parameter M as follows

$$M = H (\cot \beta_f - \cot \beta_c) + W (1 - \tan \beta_t \cot \beta_c) \qquad (8.2)$$

The x,y coordinates of the four corners A,B,C and D are as follows:

$$x_A = 0 \quad y_A = 0$$
$$x_B = H \cot \beta_f \quad y_B = H$$
$$x_C = W + H \cot \beta_f \quad y_C = H + W \tan \beta_t$$
$$x_D = \frac{M}{1 - \tan \beta_s \cot \beta_c} \quad y_D = \frac{M}{\cot \beta_s - \cot \beta_c} \qquad (8.3)$$

The length l_{AD} of the sliding plane is given by

$$l_{AD} = \frac{M}{\cos \beta_s - \sin \beta_s \cot \beta_c} \qquad (8.4)$$

The length l_{CD} of the tension crack is

$$l_{CD} = \frac{(y_C - y_D)}{\sin \beta_C} $$

though this value is not used explicitly in the following analysis.

The cross-sectional area R of the quadrilateral ABCD is found by applying the trapezoidal rule and noting that $x_A = y_A = 0$, to give the following result

$$R = 0.5[x_C (y_B - y_D) + y_C (x_D - x_B)] \qquad (8.5)$$

8.2.2 Analysis of forces

The analysis of forces commences with the assumption that we consider the stability of a unit slice of rock measured normal to the plane of the cross-section in Figure 8.1. Although the block may be extensive along the crest of the slope it is assumed that vertical joints, or some other features, serve to release the block and allow it to slide without significant lateral constraint, as illustrated in Figure 1.7. For a rock material of unit weight γ the weight of this unit slice is given by

$$G = R\gamma \qquad (8.6)$$

The vertical depth of water in the tension crack is

$$z_w = r_w(y_C - y_D) \qquad (8.7)$$

The maximum water pressure u_{max} at the base of the tension crack and in the sliding plane is given by

$$u_{max} = \gamma_w z_w \qquad (8.8)$$

Table 8.1 Components of forces G, U and V in Fig. 8.1 that are parallel to and normal to the sliding plane AD

Force	Parallel component	Normal component
G	$G_P = G \sin \beta_s$	$G_N = G \cos \beta_s$
U	$U_P = 0$	$U_N = -U$
V	$V_P = V \sin (\beta_c - \beta_s)$	$V_N = -V \cos (\beta_c - \beta_s)$

where γ_w is the unit weight of water. The hydraulic forces U due to water pressure in the sliding plane and V due to water pressure in the tension crack are found from the areas of their respective triangular pressure distributions applied to the unit slice of rock, to give

$$U = \tfrac{1}{2} u_{max} \, l_{AD} \quad \text{and} \quad V = \tfrac{1}{2} u_{max} \, z_w \cosec \beta_c \tag{8.9}$$

In this analysis it is assumed that the block, if unstable, will fail by sliding along plane AD. It is convenient, therefore, to analyse the forces G,U and V to determine (i) the components that lie parallel to the sliding plane, and thereby activate or restrain sliding, and (ii) the components that are normal to the sliding plane and thereby contribute to frictional strength. These parallel and normal components are given in Table 8.1, adopting the sign convention that forces tending to activate sliding or to compress the sliding plane are positive.

One measure of the stability of the block is the ratio of the shear strength forces S_f on the sliding plane to the sum of the forces that tend to cause sliding. This ratio, which is usually termed the factor of safety F, is, from equation 8.1 and Table 8.1, given by

$$F = \frac{c' l_{AD} + (G_N + U_N + V_N) \tan \phi'}{G_P + U_P + V_P} \tag{8.10}$$

Equation 8.10 carries the implicit notion that the effective normal force on the sliding plane is controlled by the effect of forces, such as V, that act on the block some distance away from the sliding plane. This notion, which goes beyond the concept of effective stress in soil mechanics, is only feasible where the block has sufficient strength to transmit the effect of the remote forces to the sliding plane. Although it is beyond the scope of this section, it is a relatively simple matter to include the effects of other forces, such as those produced by rock bolts or seismic accelerations, in this analysis.

The input data for a single plane sliding analysis are the angles β_f, β_s, β_t and β_c, the dimensions H and W, the tension crack water depth ratio r_w, the unit weights γ and γ_w, and the shear strength parameters c' and ϕ'. The factor of safety of the block against single plane sliding can be determined by inputting

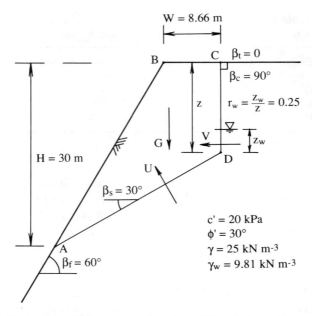

W = 8.66 m

B

C $\beta_t = 0$

$\beta_c = 90°$

z

$r_w = \dfrac{z_w}{z} = 0.25$

G

V

z_w

H = 30 m

D

U

$\beta_s = 30°$

c' = 20 kPa

$\phi' = 30°$

$\gamma = 25$ kN m⁻³

A

$\beta_f = 60°$

$\gamma_w = 9.81$ kN m⁻³

Figure 8.2 Single plane sliding mechanism for a 60° rock slope, Example 8.1.

these parameters to equations 8.2 to 8.10 and to the equations in Table 8.1. It is a relatively straightforward matter to implement the above analysis on a spread-sheet. This approach provides the additional benefit of facilitating a study of the sensitivity of the factor of safety to the variation of such parameters as β_s, r_w, c' and ϕ'. The following example provides a simple illustration.

Example 8.1 (Figures 8.2 and 8.3)

Figure 8.2 shows a cross-section through a 60° rock slope with a horizontal top. The rock mass is cut by a discontinuity dipping at 30° and a vertical tension crack which both strike parallel to the slope crest and intersect to form a kinematically feasible block ABCD as shown. The tension crack is located 8.66 m from the slope crest and contains water to a depth of 3.75 m. The discontinuity has shear strength parameters c' = 20 kPa and $\phi' = 30°$. The unit weights of the rock and water are, respectively, 25 kN m⁻³ and 9.8 kN m⁻³. Determine (i) the factor of safety of the block, and (ii) investigate the sensitivity of this factor of safety to changes in the tension crack water depth ratio in the range 0 to 1.0, to changes in c' in the range 0 to 40 kPa, changes in ϕ' in the range 28 to 36° and to changes in discontinuity dip in the range 28 to 36°.

Solution

(i) Geometrical analysis of the block by equations 8.2 to 8.3 gives the co-ordinates of the corners $x_A = 0$, $y_A = 0$, $x_B = 17.32$, $y_B = 30$, $x_C = 25.98$, $y_C = 30$, $x_D = 25.98$ and $y_D = 15$ m. Equations 8.4 to 8.6 give the length of the sliding plane $l_{AD} = 30$ m, the cross-sectional area of the block $R = 324.76$ m^2 and the weight of the block $G = 8119.0$ kN. Inputting the depth of water in the tension crack $z_w = 3.75$ m to equations 8.8 and 8.9 gives the maximum water pressure $u_{max} = 36.75$ kPa and hydraulic forces $U = 551.25$ kN on the sliding plane and $V = 68.91$ kN in the tension crack. Determining the components of these forces by the equations in Table 8.1 and inputting the results together with the shear strength parameters to equation 8.10 gives a theoretical factor of safety of 1.049.

(ii) The computations were set up on a spread-sheet for the purposes of the sensitivity analysis. Only one of the four variable parameters was varied at a time while the others were kept at their default values of $r_w = 0.25$, $c' = 20$ kPa, $\phi' = 30°$ and $\beta_s = 30°$. Variation of β_s leads to a variation in the geometrical properties of the block; variation of the other parameters only causes a variation in the hydraulic forces or variation in the shear strength of the sliding plane. Figure 8.3 shows graphs of the theoretical factor of safety of the block for the four selected parameters as each is varied within the stipulated range. As would be expected, the factor of safety increases with increasing c' and ϕ', while decreasing sharply with increasing r_w and β_s. The variations are linear, or very nearly so, within the stipulated ranges.

The sensitivity analysis in the above example was presented primarily to illustrate computation procedures. In practice, sensitivity analyses provide a valuable insight into a potential failure mechanism where there is a degree of uncertainty or variability in the input parameters. Those parameters that are shown to have a major influence on block stability can either be investigated in more detail to give a more precise input value, or, if block stability is still unacceptable, they can be controlled by rock improvement measures such as drainage or reinforcement. Sensitivity analyses such as this are limited by the fact that it is only feasible to vary one parameter at a time; in reality all parameters will vary to some degree with time and location in a rock mass. This shortcoming can be addressed by adopting probabilistic methods that permit the simultaneous variation of all significant parameters. Approaches that achieve this, such as Monte Carlo simulation and first order second moment methods, are described by Priest and Brown (1983) and Smith (1986). Priest and Brown also tabulate what they regard as acceptable factors of safety for a variety of slope configurations in open pit mines. Their recommended values range from 1.3 for small temporary slopes, through 1.6 for longer term higher slopes, to 2.0 for permanent major slopes. Most civil engineering rock slopes would be classified as permanent major slopes. Priest and Brown also stipulated limits on the probabilities $P(F < 1.0)$ and $P(F < 1.5)$ that the

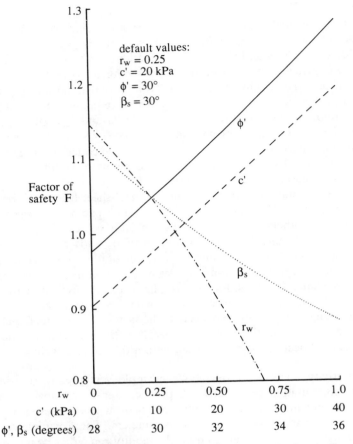

Figure 8.3 Sensitivity analysis for the single plane sliding mechanism in Example 8.1.

factor of safety of a given slope or mechanism falls below 1.0 and 1.5, respectively. These values are reproduced in Table 8.2.

8.3 TWO-DIMENSIONAL MULTIPLE PLANE SLIDING

Although discontinuities and free faces in a given rock mass may be orientated such that they form an essentially two-dimensional mechanism, it is often possible that additional discontinuities within an initially rigid block may permit internal slip and thereby enable multiple plane sliding. An example of such a mechanism is illustrated in Figure 8.4. In this figure it is assumed that there is a vertical load L bearing down on the surface AB; this causes the block ABD to slide along discontinuity AD which in turn forces the block BCD

Table 8.2 Acceptable values for factors of safety (after Priest and Brown, 1983)

Category of slope	Consequences of failure	Examples	Minimum Mean F	Maximum P(F < 1.0)	Maximum P(F < 1.5)
			Acceptable values		
1	Not serious	Individual benches, small* temporary slopes not adjacent to haulage roads.	1.3	0.1	0.2
2	Moderately serious	Any slope of a permanent or semipermanent nature	1.6	0.01	0.1
3	Very serious	Medium-sized and high slopes carrying major haulage roads or underlying permanent mine installations	2.0	0.003	0.05

* Small: height <50 m; Medium: height 50 to 150 m; High: height >150 m.

to slide along discontinuity CD. In this way the internal discontinuity BD permits simultaneous sliding on two planes. The mechanism in Figure 8.4 is not, however, strictly kinematically feasible because any downward vertical movement of block ABD will cause the block to lock up at point D. This difficulty can be overcome by assuming that localised crushing occurs in the region around point D sufficient to allow the mechanism to operate, as illustrated in the inset in Figure 8.4. In this case our task is to determine the load L required to overcome the shear strength of the discontinuities AD and CD and thereby to cause the mechanism to operate.

The analysis techniques presented in this section are based upon a course of lectures given by John Bray in 1983 in which he described methods for obtaining upper bound solutions for a range of geotechnical problems. The approach, summarised below, essentially applies the principles of static equilibrium to a relatively simple geometry in which slip on discontinuities is governed by a specified shear strength model. The approach consists of the following four steps:

1. Determine the geometries, weights and, if appropriate, the hydraulic forces acting on each separate block for a unit slice of rock. The methods described in the previous section can be applied here.
2. Draw a free body diagram for each of the blocks, inserting the known

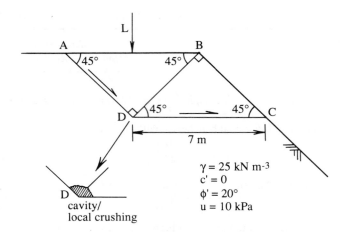

Figure 8.4   Multiple plane sliding mechanism, Example 8.2.

hydraulic forces, the unknown shear force reactions and the unknown effective normal force reactions.
3. Starting at the 'downstream' block set the shear reactions to the shear strengths of the sliding planes and apply the principles of static equilibrium to solve for the unknown effective normal reactions.
4. By transferring the computed effective normal reactions across interfacial discontinuities, work from block to block and hence determine the applied load required for limiting equilibrium.

It is important to bear in mind that, in general, only two equations of static equilibrium will be available for each block, for example those for vertical and horizontal forces. This fact restricts the number of unknown normal forces that can be solved to two per block. It is quite possible, therefore, to construct mechanisms for which there are insufficient equations to solve for the unknowns and which are therefore statically indeterminate. Another problem can occur when the orientations of the discontinuities and the angles of friction on the discontinuities cause the mechanism to 'lock up' such that block displacement does not occur, no matter how large the driving force. This latter problem is usually detected when solution of the equations of static equilibrium necessitates tensile normal reactions between a pair of blocks. The following simple example illustrates the general solution process for a mechanism that does not lock up.

Example 8.2 (Figures 8.4 and 8.5)

Figure 8.4 shows a cross-section through a rock slope that has a 45° face and a horizontal top. Discontinuities AD, BD and CD, which strike parallel to the

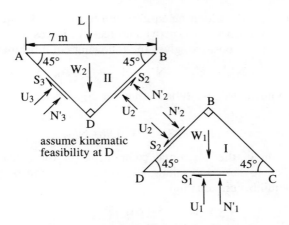

Figure 8.5 Free body diagram for the multiple plane sliding mechanism in Example 8.2.

slope crest, have Coulomb effective shear strength parameters $c' = 0$ and $\phi' = 20°$. The discontinuities, which form the double block failure mechanism illustrated, **each** carry a uniform water pressure of $10\,kPa$. Taking the unit weight of the rock to be $25\,kN\,m^{-3}$, and assuming kinematic feasibility at point D, calculate the maximum total vertical load L, per metre run of slope, that can be carried at the surface AB.

Solution

Figure 8.5 shows the free body diagrams for the blocks labelled I and II in this simple failure mechanism. The active force L and the weights of the two blocks W_1 and W_2 are vertical downwards. The hydraulic reaction forces U_1, U_2, U_3 and the effective normal reaction forces N'_1, N'_2, N'_3 have been drawn to indicate a compressive sense on the discontinuities. The mobilised shear reaction forces S_1, S_2, S_3 have been drawn to act against the block displacement direction indicated by the postulated mechanism.

The geometrical analysis is relatively straightforward in this case. The lengths of the block edges AB = CD = 7 m, while AD = BC = BD = 4.95 m. The area ABD = BCD = $12.25\,m^2$ giving, for a unit slice, block weights $W_1 = W_2 = 306.25\,kN$. Also, for a unit slice, the hydraulic forces are $U_1 = 70\,kN$ and $U_2 = U_3 = 49.5\,kN$.

We now consider block I, assuming that it is on the point of yield. If this is the case the shear reactions for this block must be given by

$$S_1 = N'_1 \tan \phi' = 0.364\,N'_1$$
$$S_2 = N'_2 \tan \phi' = 0.364\,N'_2$$

Applying the principles of limiting equilibrium to this block, equating the sum of the vertical components of the active and reactive forces to zero, and taking downward forces to be positive, gives the following equilibrium equation

$$W_1 - N'_1 - U_1 + (N'_2 + U_2 + S_2) \sin 45° = 0$$

Inputting the known values, substituting for S_1 and simplifying the above expression gives

$$N'_1 = 271.25 + 0.964 \, N'_2 \qquad (8.11)$$

Equating the sum of the horizontal components of the active and reactive forces for block I to zero, and taking left to right forces to be positive, gives the following equilibrium equation

$$(N'_2 + U_2 - S_2) \cos 45° - S_1 = 0$$

which, following substitution and simplification yields

$$N'_2 = 0.809 \, N'_1 - 77.78 \qquad (8.12)$$

Simultaneous solution of equations 8.11 and 8.12 gives the result $N'_1 = 892 \, kN$ and $N'_2 = 644 \, kN$.

We now consider block II. Both the geometry of this block and the forces acting on it are symmetrical about a vertical plane through point D, hence

$$N'_3 = N'_2 = 644 \, kN$$

The above result could have been obtained by considering the equilibrium of the horizontal components of forces for this block. If it is assumed that block II is also on the point of yield, the shear reactions must be given by

$$S_3 = S_2 = N'_2 \tan \phi' = 234.4 \, kN$$

Equating the sum of the vertical components of the active and reactive forces to zero, and taking downward forces to be positive, gives the following equilibrium equation

$$L_{eq} + W_2 - 2 \sin 45° \, (N'_2 + U_2 + S_2) = 0$$

The limiting equilibrium value of the vertical active load L_{eq} is the only unknown in the above expression, which can therefore be solved to give $L_{eq} = 1006 \, kN$ per metre run of slope. Values of L below this level will be stable with respect to the stipulated mechanism.

In the above example hydraulic pressures were considered explicitly as vectors acting normal to the discontinuities bounding the rigid blocks. If the blocks had been completely submerged in static water it would have been permissible to take account of water pressures simply by taking the submerged unit weight of the rock $\gamma' = \gamma - \gamma_w$ in the determination of the weight of a unit slice of each block. Although the analysis described above gives the limiting equilibrium load, or the collapse load, it provides no measure of the factor of safety of an identified rigid block mechanism. A factor of safety can be obtained, however, from the ratio of the limiting equilibrium active load L_{eq} to the actual load L_{act} as follows

$$F = \frac{L_{eq}}{L_{act}} \tag{8.13}$$

The above expression is not very helpful if L_{act} is close to zero. In such circumstances it is necessary to modify the limiting equilibrium approach to solve for the friction angle ϕ'_{eq} on the discontinuities required to achieve limiting equilibrium under the condition $L_{act} = 0$. If the actual value for the friction angle is ϕ'_{act} then the factor of safety is given by

$$F = \frac{\tan \phi'_{act}}{\tan \phi'_{eq}} \tag{8.14}$$

The limiting equilibrium methods outlined in this section are extremely powerful and can be applied to mechanisms that contain numerous blocks, as long as the mechanism does not lock up and subject to the requirement that the associated forces are statically determinate. The exercises at the end of this chapter illustrate the application of these methods to two-dimensional rigid block failure mechanisms in rock slopes and beneath foundations.

8.4 THREE-DIMENSIONAL SINGLE- AND DOUBLE-PLANE SLIDING OF TETRAHEDRAL BLOCKS

Most combinations of discontinuity orientation and rock face orientation do not satisfy the geometrical requirements that permit an essentially two-dimensional analysis. In most cases discontinuities do not strike parallel with the slope crest but instead are orientated in such a way that complex, multi-faceted block geometries are created adjacent to the rock face. Simulations show that the most common block geometry is the tetrahedron, formed by the mutual intersection of three discontinuities and the rock face, or by the intersection of two discontinuities, the top of a rock slope and the face, as shown in Figure 8.6. A full analysis of the kinematics and statics of three-dimensional block sliding is presented by Priest (1985). A compact algebraic analysis of this problem is given by Bray and Brown (1976). The aim of this section is to provide a simplified version of just one aspect of this analysis: single- and double-plane sliding of tetrahedral rock blocks. The following assumptions are made:

1. A tetrahedral block is formed by the mutual intersection of three discontinuity planes and a non-overhanging rock face, or by the mutual intersection of two discontinuity planes, the top of a rock slope and a non-overhanging face.

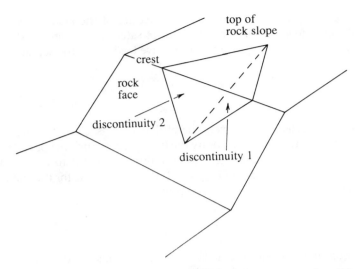

Figure 8.6 Tetrahedral block formed by the mutual intersection of two discontinuities, the face and the top of a rock slope.

2. Discontinuity planes 1 and 2, which are the potential sliding planes, have average water pressures, cohesions and angles of friction of u_1, c'_1, ϕ'_1 and u_2, c'_2, ϕ'_2 respectively. Discontinuity plane 3, which is not a sliding plane, carries an average water pressure u_3.
3. The geometrical properties of the block are known, in particular:
   (i)   the orientations of the four planes forming the block;
   (ii) the areas A_1, A_2 and A_3 of planes 1, 2 and 3 that form faces of the block;
   (iii) the volume V_b of the block.
4. For single plane sliding on either plane 1 or plane 2, the factor of safety is given by

$$F = \frac{c'A + |\mathbf{n}| \tan \phi'}{|\mathbf{s}|} \tag{8.15}$$

where A is the area of the sliding plane, c' and ϕ' are the shear strength parameters for the sliding plane, $|\mathbf{n}|$ is the magnitude of the compressive normal force on the sliding plane and $|\mathbf{s}|$ is the magnitude of the shear force in the direction of sliding.
5. For double plane sliding on planes 1 and 2

$$F = \frac{c'_1 A_1 + |\mathbf{n}_1| \tan \phi'_1 + c'_2 A_2 + |\mathbf{n}_2| \tan \phi'_2}{|\mathbf{s}|} \tag{8.16}$$

where $|\mathbf{n_1}|$ and $|\mathbf{n_2}|$ are the magnitudes of the compressive normal forces on planes 1 and 2, and $|\mathbf{s}|$ is the magnitude of the shear force along the line of intersection between planes 1 and 2.

6. The orientations and magnitudes of any additional forces acting on the block, due to foundation loads, rock support measures, seismic accelerations and other effects, are known.

If any of the discontinuity planes bounding the block carry water pressure it is necessary to identify which planes underlie and which planes overlie the block in order to establish the senses of the hydraulic forces acting on the block. It is assumed that plane 3, which may be a discontinuity or the top of the rock slope, always overlies the block so any hydraulic force on this plane must act **downwards** on to the block. It is possible that either plane 1 or plane 2 may also overlie the block; at least one of these planes must, however, underlie the block. The lower hemisphere projections in Figure 8.7 show two possible cases. In Figure 8.7a the portions of planes 1 and 2 that are involved in the block have been shaded. These portions can be identified by the fact that, together with the top of the slope, they form a spherical triangle that lies on the free air side of the non-overhanging rock face. In this figure the great circles of both planes present their convex side towards the spherical triangle that represents the block; this indicates that they both **underlie** the block and that their hydraulic forces will have an **upward** sense as they act upon the block. In Figure 8.7b plane 1 again presents its convex side towards the spherical triangle, however plane 2 presents its concave side. In this latter case, therefore, plane 2 **overlies** the block and its hydraulic force will have a **downward** sense as it acts upon the block. The simple rule is, therefore, that great circles that are convex towards the spherical triangle representing the block on a lower hemisphere projection underlie the block; those that present a concave side overlie the block.

The following step by step procedures for analysing block stability utilise the principles of hemispherical projection and the analysis of forces explained in Appendices A and D respectively.

1. The great circles and normals of discontinuities 1 and 2 (which are the potential sliding planes), plane 3 (which may be a discontinuity or the top of the rock slope) and the rock face (which is non-overhanging) are plotted on a lower hemisphere projection. Points representing the various forces acting on the block, including that due to gravitational acceleration, can also be plotted and labelled to indicate their magnitude and sense, though this is not essential at this stage.

2. The orientations, magnitudes and senses of the various forces acting on the block are listed. The force due to gravity acts vertically downwards of course, with a magnitude given by the weight of the block. The hydraulic force on each discontinuity plane acts along the normal to the plane, with a magnitude given by the product of average water pressure and the area of

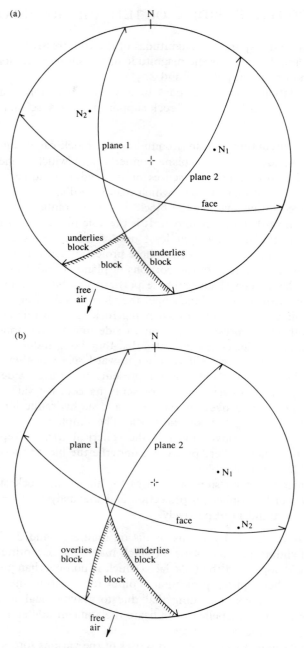

Figure 8.7 Lower hemisphere projections illustrating the geometrical relation between discontinuities and a tetrahedral block: (a) both discontinuity planes underlie the tetrahedral block; (b) one discontinuity underlies and the other overlies the tetrahedral block.

the block face. The sense of each hydraulic force is dictated by whether the discontinuity plane underlies or overlies the block, as discussed earlier. The orientations, magnitudes and senses of additional forces due to external factors, such as seismic acceleration and rock bolts, must also be listed.

3. The resultant r of all forces acting on the block is found by applying the methods explained in Appendix D.3, which essentially involve the following three steps: (i) determine the Cartesian components of all forces, (ii) sum these Cartesian components, and (iii) determine the orientation magnitude and sense of the resultant force from its Cartesian components. This resultant force is plotted on the lower hemisphere projection and labelled in the usual way.

4. It is assumed initially that the block, if unstable, will slide on planes 1 and 2 along their line of intersection. The orientation of this line of intersection can be found either by taking the cross-product of unit vectors normal to planes 1 and 2, as explained in section 4.4 and equations 4.20, or by identifying the point of intersection of the great circles of planes 1 and 2 on a lower hemisphere projection, as explained in Appendix A. It is now necessary to decompose the resultant force r into its components n_1 and n_2, normal to planes 1 and 2 respectively, and component s acting along the line of intersection. This decomposition can be done by the algebraic methods of Appendix D.4.1 or by the graphical methods explained in Appendix D.4.2. Double plane sliding can only occur if contact is maintained on planes 1 and 2 by virtue of compressive normal forces on both of these planes. A compressive normal component will have a **downward** sense if a given plane **underlies** the block; a compressive normal component will have an **upward** sense if a given plane **overlies** the block (readers are reminded that we are dealing with components not reactions in this case). If both planes are subject to compressive normal forces, the factor of safety against double plane sliding can be found by applying equation 8.16.

If it is found that one of the planes is predicted to carry a tensile normal force then, if the block is unstable, sliding is assumed to occur on the plane that is subject to compression while the other plane opens up. This assumption is based on the fact that discontinuities generally exhibit negligible tensile strength. In such cases it is necessary to discard the force components computed on the assumption of double plane sliding and to decompose r again, this time to find the component n normal to the sliding plane and the component s parallel to the sliding plane. The orientation of s is defined by the intersection between the sliding plane and the plane that contains r and n. The factor of safety for the single plane sliding mechanism is found from equation 8.15.

If it is found that both of the planes are subject to tensile normal forces, in theory, the block is predicted to burst out of the face by moving in the direction of **r** through free air. Although this mechanism can occur at an overhanging face when blocks fall under gravity, bursting can only develop at non-overhanging faces when there are very high water pressures, or other forces pushing the block upwards and out into free air. In most cases, blocks will fail by sliding before the water pressures have a chance to build up to levels that could induce bursting at a non-overhanging face.

Before proceeding with examples to illustrate the above methods it is worth noting that the category of block behaviour (double plane sliding, single plane sliding or translation through free air) and the plane(s) involved in sliding, can be deduced simply from the geometrical relation between the resultant force on the block and the planes that form the block, as depicted on an inclined hemisphere projection. The categorisation of block behaviour in this way, which does not require any force decomposition, is explained in Chapter 7 of Priest (1985). A full explanation of the determination of tetrahedral block geometry and factor of safety is given in Chapter 8 of Priest (1985).

Example 8.4 (Figure 8.8)

A non-overhanging planar rock slope of orientation (dip direction/dip angle) 230/60 and its top of orientation 225/05 are intersected by two extensive planar discontinuities of orientations (1) 203/47 and (2) 287/52, to form a kinematically feasible tetrahedral block 45.20 m^3 in volume. Geometrical analysis reveals that the triangular surface of the block formed by discontinuity (1) has an area of 41.15 m^2 and the surface formed by discontinuity (2) has an area of 20.43 m^2. A preliminary site investigation gave the following data:

Table for Example 8.4

Discontinuity	Cohesion kPa	Angle of friction Degrees	Mean water pressure kPa
1	10	40	5
2	20	35	15

Unit weight of rock $= 26\,\mathrm{kN\,m^{-3}}$

The foundations of a pylon to be sited on the block will exert a force of 180 kN downwards along a line of trend/plunge 168/70. Determine the resultant force on the block and hence calculate the factor of safety against sliding instability.

Solution
Figure 8.8 shows a lower hemisphere projection of the rock face, the two discontinuities and their normals. The top of the rock slope has not been plotted since it has no direct bearing on the mechanics of this problem. The

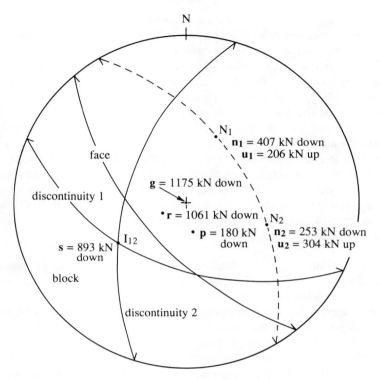

Figure 8.8   Stability analysis of a tetrahedral block, Example 8.4.

pylon foundation force **p** has been plotted and labelled in the usual way. In addition to this foundation force, there are three other forces acting upon the block. The block weight acts vertically downwards with a magnitude $\gamma V_b =$ 1175.2 kN. The other two forces are due to average water pressures of 5 and 15 kPa acting on discontinuities with areas of 41.15 and 20.43 m², which produce hydraulic forces of 205.75 and 304.45 kN, respectively, along the normals to the discontinuity planes. Figure 8.8 indicates that both of these planes underlie the block so these hydraulic forces both have an **upward** sense. The downward normal to discontinuity plane 1 has a trend/plunge 023/43, so, by equation D.5, the upward normal has a trend/plunge 203/−43. Similarly, the hydraulic force on discontinuity 2 has a trend/plunge 287/−38. The Cartesian components of the four forces can now be found by applying equations D.4. Summing these components and applying equations D.1 to D.3 gives the magnitude and trend/plunge of the resultant **r** as 1061.06 kN, 245.0/73.4, as plotted in Figure 8.8. The positive angle of plunge is indicative of a downward sense for this resultant.

Initially it is assumed that sliding instability will occur by double plane sliding, so the analysis proceeds with the decomposition of the resultant force **r** into its components $\mathbf{n}_1$ and $\mathbf{n}_2$, normal to planes 1 and 2, respectively, and component **s** acting along the line of intersection. As noted earlier this decomposition can be done by the algebraic methods of Appendix D.4.1 or by the graphical methods explained in Appendix D.4.2. Equations 4.20 give the trend/plunge of the line of intersection of the two discontinuities as 239.4/40.8. Taking the downward directed ends of the discontinuity normals and applying the algebraic decomposition methods of Appendix D.4.1 gives $|\mathbf{n}_1| = 406.68$, $|\mathbf{n}_2| = 252.66$ and $|\mathbf{s}| = 893.28\,\text{kN}$, all with a downward sense. Since the normal forces on both discontinuities act downwards, and are therefore compressive, equation 8.16 must be used to determine the factor of safety. Inputting the appropriate forces and shear strength parameters into this equation gives a factor of safety of approximately 1.5 against double plane sliding.

The factor of safety of 1.5, calculated in the above example, applies to the specific double plane sliding mechanism and indicates that this mechanism is in fact stable under the given conditions. If these conditions were changed, say, by an increase in the water pressures or by the application of an external force, it is possible that the block may become unstable. The mechanism of failure may be double or single plane sliding, depending on the geometrical and mechanical conditions that apply at failure. This important point is illustrated in the following example, which follows a similar format to the previous example.

Example 8.5 (Figure 8.9)

A non-overhanging planar rock slope of orientation (dip direction/dip angle) 134/65 and its top of orientation 122/11 are intersected by two extensive planar discontinuities of orientations (1) 065/74 and (2) 186/41, to form a kinematically feasible tetrahedral block $81.74\,\text{m}^3$ in volume. Geometrical analysis reveals that the triangular surface of the block formed by discontinuity (1) has an area of $34.39\,\text{m}^2$ and that the surface formed by discontinuity (2) has an area of $56.61\,\text{m}^2$. The preliminary site investigation gave the following data:

Table for Example 8.5

Discontinuity	Cohesion kPa	Angle of friction Degrees	Mean water pressure kPa
1	15	32	25
2	5	40	15

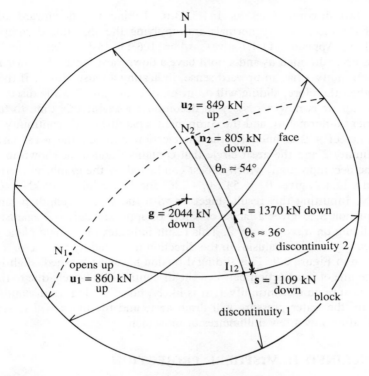

Figure 8.9 Stability analysis of a tetrahedral block, Example 8.5.

Unit weight of rock $= 25\,\mathrm{kN\,m^{-3}}$.

Determine the resultant force on the block and hence calculate the factor of safety against sliding instability.

Solution
Figure 8.9 shows a lower hemisphere projection of the rock face, the two discontinuities and their normals. The top of the rock slope has not been plotted. The block weight acts vertically downwards with a magnitude $\gamma V_b = 2043.5\,\mathrm{kN}$. Hydraulic forces of 859.75 and 849.15 kN act normal to discontinuity planes 1 and 2, respectively. Figure 8.9 indicates that both of these planes underlie the block so these hydraulic forces both have an **upward** sense. Applying the methods in Appendix D.3 gives the magnitude and trend/plunge of the resultant **r** as 1370.40 kN and 106.5/58.3, as plotted in Figure 8.9. As in the previous example, the positive angle of plunge is indicative of a downward sense for this resultant.

As before, it is initially assumed that sliding instability will occur by double plane sliding. Equations 4.20 give the trend/plunge of the line of intersection of the two discontinuities as 144.3/33.0. Taking the downward directed ends of the discontinuity normals and applying the algebraic decomposition methods of Appendix D.4.1 gives $|\mathbf{n_1}| = 106.11$, $|\mathbf{n_2}| = 781.15$ and $|\mathbf{s}| = 1112.28$ kN. Although $\mathbf{n_2}$ and $\mathbf{s}$ both have a downward sense, the normal force on discontinuity 1 has an upward sense, indicating a tensile force. If the block is unstable, therefore, sliding will occur on discontinuity 2 while discontinuity 1 opens up. It is now necessary to decompose $\mathbf{r}$ again, this time to find the component $\mathbf{n}$ normal to, and the component $\mathbf{s}$ parallel to, discontinuity 2. The orientation of $\mathbf{s}$ is defined by the intersection between the great circle for discontinuity 2 and the great circle that contains $\mathbf{r}$ and $\mathbf{n}$, as shown in Figure 8.9. The decomposition, which is best conducted by the graphical methods of Appendix D.4.2, gives $\theta_n \approx 54°$, $\theta_s \approx 36°$ and hence $|\mathbf{n}| \approx 805$ kN and $|\mathbf{s}| \approx 1109$ kN. Inputting this result, together with the shear strength parameters, into equation 8.15 gives a factor of safety of approximately 0.9 against single plane sliding on discontinuity 2. This result indicates that single plane sliding will occur by this mechanism, in the direction indicated by the vector $\mathbf{s}$ on the projection in Figure 8.9. This sliding direction has been 'pushed' slightly away from the line of intersection between the discontinuities largely due to the high water pressure on discontinuity 1. It is likely, however, that as discontinuity 1 opens up, the water pressure will drain away and the block will re-stabilise, perhaps after only a few millimetres of movement.

8.5   INCLINED HEMISPHERE PROJECTION

The analysis of sliding instability of tetrahedral blocks, presented in the previous section, made the assumption that a tetrahedral block was formed and that its geometrical properties were known. In practice, this information would have to be obtained by further analysis. An efficient way for determining the kinematic feasibility and the geometrical properties of tetrahedral blocks is the method of inclined hemisphere projection devised by Priest (1980) and described in detail in Chapters 7 and 8 of Priest (1985). Although the method is essentially graphical, being based on conventional stereographic projection, results are generally within 10% of those obtained by precise vectorial methods. The following paragraphs contain a brief summary of the principles and capabilities of inclined hemisphere projection; interested readers are advised to consult Priest (1985) for a more complete explanation and illustrative examples.

The normals and lines of maximum dip of all discontinuities and free faces at a particular location are first plotted on a lower hemisphere projection in the usual way. The normal to the main rock face is then rotated about the strike of the face in a direction, and by an amount, that takes it to the centre of the projection. All other data points are then rotated about the same axis, in the same direction and by the same amount as the main rock face. The great circles of all discontinuities and free faces are then plotted from their

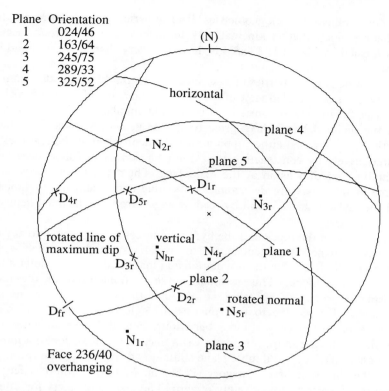

Plane Orientation
1 024/46
2 163/64
3 245/75
4 289/33
5 325/52

Figure 8.10 Inclined hemisphere projection for five discontinuity planes intersecting an overhanging rock face.

normals in the usual way and labelled carefully. The construction of inclined hemisphere projections can be fairly time-consuming, particularly where there are a large number of discontinuity sets involved or where the angle of rotation is large. To overcome this problem Priest (1983) has presented the vectorial equations required for the computer generation of inclined hemisphere projections.

The resulting inclined hemisphere projection has the important property that the plane of projection is parallel to the plane of the rock face. This property leads to the notion of kinematic congruence, which essentially means that the spherical triangles formed by the mutual intersection of discontinuities and free faces on the projection are geometrically analogous to the three faces forming the pyramidal portions of tetrahedral blocks on the rock mass side of the main free face. Figure 8.10, which presents the data in Exercise 8.4 at the end of this chapter, shows an inclined hemisphere projection of 5 discontinuity planes, which intersect to form 10 spherical triangles, corresponding to 10 different tetrahedral block geometries. Each spherical triangle corresponds to a tetrahedral block that is kinematically feasible at the main rock face. The block formed by planes 1, 3 and 4 is, however, very sharply tapered and is not significant for stability analysis.

The geometrical properties of a selected tetrahedral block are determined by constructing a scaled plan view of the block in the plane of the main rock face. This scaled plan view is constructed by tracing angular measurements directly from the inclined hemisphere projection. The geometrical scale for the construction can be based either upon a measurement taken at the real rock face, or alternatively by constructing the largest block that can fit between a particular limiting dimension at the main face. The areas of the faces and the volume of the block are determined by scaling angles and linear dimensions from the scaled plan view and by reading angles from the inclined hemisphere projection.

The weight of the block and the hydraulic forces acting normal to any of the four faces can now be calculated in the usual way, and combined with any other forces to determine the orientation and magnitude of the resultant force **r** acting on the block. This resultant force is transferred to the inclined hemisphere projection by taking it through the appropriate rotation. The orientation of **r** relative to the spherical triangle of its tetrahedral block is indicative of the category of block behaviour. Four different categories can be identified by taking simple angular measurements: (i) block does not move, (ii) single plane sliding, (iii) double plane sliding, and (iv) translation through free air in the direction of **r**. Category (i) has an infinite factor of safety while category (iv) has a factor of safety of zero. The factors of safety for categories (ii) and (iii) are determined by decomposing **r** on to the sliding plane(s) and then applying equation 8.15 or equation 8.16 as appropriate.

The Author has taught inclined hemisphere projection methods on a routine basis to final year mining engineering and civil engineering students for many years. The methods can be learned in a 2 to 3 hour lecture, supplemented by tutorial exercises. Although it is quicker to carry out block analyses by computer-based vectorial methods, inclined hemisphere projection methods give students a valuable insight into the geometrical and mechanical principles, while at the same time providing the capacity to conduct independent checks on computer calculations. Although Priest (1980) extended inclined hemisphere projection methods to consider simple polyhedral blocks, the methods become somewhat unwieldy for blocks with more than four faces. The methods described in the following section should be used for analysing these more complex blocks.

8.6 POLYHEDRAL BLOCKS

The work on rigid blocks in this chapter has so far been restricted to simple two-dimensional blocks and to tetrahedral blocks. In reality rock blocks can

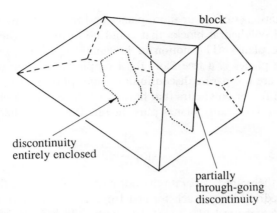

Figure 8.11 Complex polyhedral block that contains a partially through-going discontinuity and that also entirely encloses a small discontinuity.

be multi-faceted solids created by the mutual intersection of several discontinuities. These general polyhedral blocks may be entirely convex, or they may contain re-entrant corners which create a locally concave geometry. A walk over a waste rock dump of any mine or quarry in hard rock will reveal portions of polyhedral blocks that have been created by natural discontinuities but that have broken during excavation and transport. It is very rare to find an unbroken polyhedral block; indeed the author is not aware of any published systematic studies of the true geometries of *in situ* polyhedral blocks. The probable reason for this lack of information is that although it is possible to infer the geometry of a tetrahedral block from the orientation and location of discontinuities exposed at a rock face, it is impossible to do this for a polyhedral block with five or more faces. The geometrical shape of any polyhedral block with five or more faces is uniquely controlled by the orientation **and location** of discontinuities, which may or may not intersect the face. This geometry can only be determined by completely excavating the block; a process that destroys the object of investigation.

The difficulties raised in the above paragraph make it necessary to consider polyhedral blocks in a statistical or in a generic manner. As an example of the former approach, consider a three-dimensional random realisation of discontinuity planes, generated by the methods explained in Chapter 6. It is easy to imagine some sort of vectorial search routine that would identify, and then calculate the geometrical properties of all finite polyhedral blocks that are intersected by the free face(s). Many of these blocks will contain partially through-going discontinuities, and some may entirely enclose relatively small discontinuities, as shown in Figure 8.11. These complications make it difficult to identify simple explicit block geometries for stability analysis.

A generic approach, such as the one adopted by Goodman and Shi (1985), takes the orientations of four or more planes and then examines the kinematic feasibility of all polyhedral blocks that could be formed by the mutual intersection of these planes. The notion of kinematic feasibility requires that at least one of the planes is a free face. By a simple application of combination theory, if there are n separate discontinuity planes plus one free face there will be a total of t different polyhedra that have $(x+1)$ faces, each polyhedron being formed from x discontinuity planes plus the one free face, where

$$t = \frac{n!}{x!(n-x)!} \tag{8.17}$$

For example if there are 8 separate discontinuities, n = 8 and there will be 56 different tetrahedral blocks (each formed from x = 3 discontinuities plus the free face), 70 pentahedral blocks, 56 hexahedra, 28 heptahedra, 8 octahedra and 1 enneahedron. Whether any of these 219 possible blocks actually exists is not at issue here; it is their potential to exist and to cause instability that is being examined.

Whether a given polyhedron is a real block that has been surveyed on site, or a block that has been generated in a random realisation, or a generic block that has been identified by combining planes, it is necessary to determine its kinematic feasibility and identify the failure mechanism in order to calculate block stability. The author is aware of three different approaches that have been fully documented and comprehensively validated. The first, by Warburton (1981) involves a vectorial algorithm. The second method, by Goodman and Shi (1985) can be implemented graphically or vectorially. The third method, described by Lin et al. (1987) and by Lin and Fairhurst (1988) is an extension of the combinatorial topology concepts of solid geometry applied to the systematic identification of polyhedral blocks. Lin and Fairhurst (1988) describe algorithms to construct the paths of removable blocks and also outline procedures for creating computer graphics displays of the block system. The methods of Lin and co-workers are, in some respects, similar to those of Warburton. The methods of Warburton and the methods of Goodman and Shi are outlined in the following sections in order to illustrate the general principles of the two contrasting approaches.

8.6.1 Warburton's vectorial method

Warburton (1981) describes an efficient method for determining the kinematic feasibility and stability of arbitrary polyhedra. These polyhedra can have any number of vertices and can possess a locally concave geometry due to re-entrant surface features. The first step in the procedure assumes that the Cartesian coordinates of each of the block's vertices are known. A process of translation and rotation is then applied to determine the area of each face of the polyhedron. The volume of the block is then found by summing the

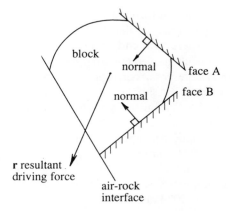

Figure 8.12 Two-dimensional diagrammatic illustration of Warburton's vectorial method for the kinematic analysis of polyhedral blocks.

volumes of pyramidal elements radiating from the origin of the coordinate system.

Warburton explains an ingenious vector-based algorithm for determining whether a given block is kinematically feasible and for identifying the potential movement direction. The algorithm assumes that the resultant driving force **r** has been determined, and that the block can move only by translation, not by rotation or toppling. For the purposes of understanding the algorithm we can assume that each of the fixed rock-to-rock interfaces bounding the block has been removed, leaving a shapeless mass exposed at one or more rock-to-air interfaces. The algorithm proceeds by introducing each of the fixed faces in turn and determining the restriction, if any, that the fixed face imposes on the potential movement direction. Figure 8.12 shows a simplified two-dimensional view of two general cases. The inward normal from fixed face A has a positive component in the direction of **r** and does not, therefore, influence the block movement direction. If all fixed faces were of type A the block would fail by translation through free air in the direction of **r**. The inward normal from fixed face B has a negative component in the direction of **r**. This face imposes a constraint on the movement direction, forcing the block, if unstable, to fail by sliding on plane B. The introduction of a second type B plane to the three-dimensional block would further constrain the failure mode to double plane sliding, in a direction given by their notional line of intersection, whether the planes actually intersected or not. Introduction of further type B fixed faces could further constrain movement directions to render the block kinematically infeasible. The algorithm proceeds by introducing each of the fixed faces in turn until all of the faces of the polyhedron have been considered. This process may render the block kinematically infeasible or may permit one of three types of block movement: translation through free air, single plane sliding or double plane sliding. It is easy to imagine that most complex polyhedra, particularly those with re-entrant corners, will end up being kinematically infeasible.

The three types of block movement identified by Warburton (1981), plus the kinematically infeasible case, correspond to the four categories of block behaviour identified by Priest (1985). The factors of safety of the sliding mechanisms identified by Warburton's vectorial methods are determined in the usual way: by decomposing r along the sliding direction and the normal(s) to the sliding plane(s), and then applying equation 8.15 or equation 8.16 as appropriate. A FORTRAN computer program BLOCKS, implementing the vectorial algorithms outlined above and incorporating new algorithms to compute the geometrical properties of three-dimensional blocky systems, has been published by Warburton (1983 and 1985).

Warburton (1990) presents essentially qualitative results of an interesting laboratory model test of the predictions of his vectorial methods. He constructed a 0.4 by 0.2 m L-shaped blocky model, containing 13 discontinuities and 25 blocks, from a medium-density fibre board faced with a range of graphic art and abrasive papers to provide control over inter-block friction. With a few exceptions the blocks were either stable, or slid out of the block assemblage, according to the predictions of the program BLOCKS. Warburton noted, however, that some blocks that were predicted to be unstable became self-supporting by rotation while others that were predicted to be stable failed by a combination of toppling and rotation. This latter discrepancy is related to the fact that the blocks were statically indeterminate, making it impossible to calculate normal reactions from the equations of static equilibrium. Certain blocks that were predicted to be stable were pushed out by neighbouring blocks. This final observation is important since it highlights the need to consider block interactions when designing rock support; the analysis of just a few exposed key blocks could provide an over-optimistic view of rock mass stability.

8.6.2 Goodman and Shi's method

Goodman and Shi (1985) present a new method for the geometrical analysis of rigid blocks; a method that can be implemented either graphically on a stereographic projection or analytically by means of vector methods. Their substantial book takes the reader through the elements of their new **block theory** to its application in the analysis of block stability and the design of surface and underground rock excavations.

The basis of block theory is the idea that a single plane divides three-dimensional space into an upper and lower semi-infinite half-space. Goodman and Shi adopt an efficient nomenclature to describe the topology of a block, based on an ordered string of digits that specify which planes, and which half spaces, form a particular block. For example, taking 0 to indicate the upper

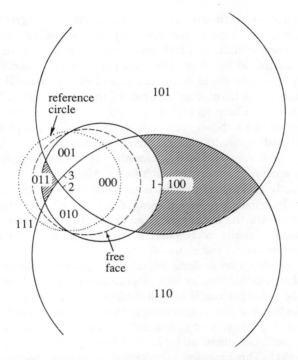

Figure 8.13 Application of the finiteness theorem by spherical projection (after Goodman and Shi, 1985).

half space and 1 the lower half space, the string 0101 corresponds to a block formed on the upper side of plane 1 (the left-hand digit is 0), the lower side of plane 2, the upper side of plane 3 and the lower side of plane 4. This nomenclature is similar to that introduced in section 4.3 for the analysis of discontinuity frequency extrema. Since much of the analysis is essentially topological, it is convenient to translate each of the discontinuities and free faces so that they each pass through a common origin to form a series of pyramids. The **block pyramid,** which is the assemblage of planes forming a particular set of blocks, comprises a group of discontinuity planes (rock-to-rock interfaces) called the **joint pyramid,** plus a group of excavation surfaces (rock-to-air interfaces) called the **excavation pyramid.**

Goodman and Shi adopt the full sphere stereographic projection, shown in Figure 8.13, in which the horizontal reference plane plots as a circle in the usual way. All other discontinuities and free faces also plot as circles, which may be truncated by the edge of the sheet of paper or screen. On this lower-focal-point projection the region **inside** a particular great circle represents orientations pointing **above** a particular plane. In Figure 8.13 the joint pyramid

100 is the only spherical triangle that lies entirely outside the great circle of the free face. If this free face is the overhanging roof of an excavation, the important theorems of finiteness and removability tell us that the block 100 is kinematically feasible at this face. The joint pyramid 011 is the only spherical triangle that lies entirely inside the great circle of the free face. If this free face is the non-overhanging floor of an excavation, then block 011 is kinematically feasible at this face. These ideas, which form the basis of the stereographic implementation of block theory, can be extended to more complex non-convex polyhedra exposed at multi-planar convex or concave rock faces. Vector methods must, however, be used to determine the surface area and volume of blocks, and to analyse the forces on each block. Many of the concepts in block theory are directly analogous to the inclined hemisphere projection methods of Priest (1985). In particular, by inclining the plane of projection so that it becomes parallel with the main rock face, Priest (1985) automatically ensures that all spherical triangles correspond to tetrahedral blocks that satisfy the requirements of finiteness and removability.

Goodman and Shi go on to demonstrate the applicability of block theory to the analysis of blocks exposed in rock slopes, underground chambers, tunnels and shafts. The principal aim is to utilise block theory in the identification of critical key blocks for a given excavation geometry. The assumption is that the maintenance of these key blocks in a stable state will guarantee the stability of the entire face. Goodman and Shi (1985) did not refer to the work of Warburton (1981). This omission is redressed in an authoritative commentary by Warburton (1987), who concluded that the support of all key blocks in an assemblage could not in practice be relied on to stabilise a given excavation. He also suggested that Goodman and Shi's method is better suited to excavation design because it provides a quick summary of a range of potential block geometries formed by combinations of a few representative discontinuities. The method of Warburton (1981) is, however, easier to understand, is more direct and is more amenable to computer implementation. Features such as its ability to reconstruct the hidden block structure adjacent to a complex excavation geometry, make the Warburton vectorial method better suited to analysing blocks whose actual geometry has been surveyed during the construction phase.

Mauldon and Goodman (1990) extended the principles of block theory to consider the rotational kinematics and equilibrium of tetrahedral blocks. Admitting that the more stringent kinematic constraints make rotational failure modes far less common than translation, they suggested that certain combinations of block geometry and high friction angles could cause toppling modes to dominate. They concluded (i) that a block could rotate if its joint pyramid subtended an angle greater than 90° in at least one plane through the origin, and (ii) that rotation about a block edge could develop if its joint pyramid contains at least one of the block-side discontinuity normals. Mauldon (1990) went on to apply block theory in an analysis of the probability that

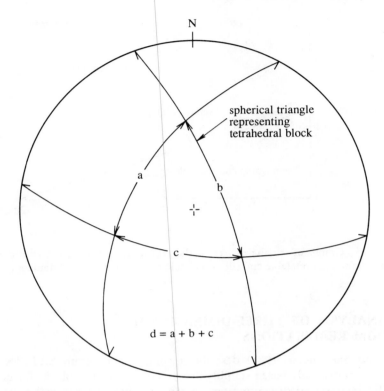

Figure 8.14 Angular measurements on a spherical triangle representing a tetrahedral block.

tetrahedral blocks are kinematically removable and 'rotatable'. His analysis is based on the sum d of the three angles a, b and c measured on the spherical triangle representing the tetrahedral block, as shown in Figure 8.14. Small values of d correspond to sharply-pointed tetrahedral blocks, such as block 1,3,4 in Figure 8.10, which cannot rotate. Large values of d indicate flat or 'blunt' blocks which have a greater propensity to rotate. Figure 8.15, after Mauldon (1990) shows graphs of the angle d versus the probabilities that a given joint pyramid is (i) removable, (ii) rotatable, and (iii) removable and rotatable. Since a block can only rotate if it is also removable, graph (iii) is the most important from a practical point of view. This graph indicates a maximum probability of rotational failure of about 0.16 when $d = 1.3\pi$. The computational methods described by Priest and Samaniego (1988) for determining the kinematic feasibility of rotational failure modes provide a more direct analysis that is amenable to computer modelling. These methods are summarised in the next section.

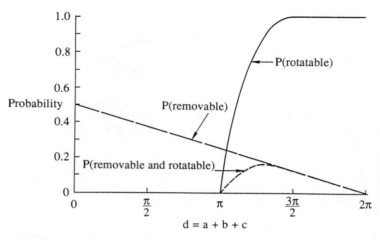

Figure 8.15 Graphs of the angle d versus the probabilities that a given joint pyramid is (i) removable, (ii) rotatable and (iii) removable and rotatable (after Mauldon, 1990).

8.7 ANALYSIS OF THREE-DIMENSIONAL RANDOM REALISATIONS

Priest and Samaniego (1988) describe a computer program SATIRN that conducts a statistically based stability analysis of tetrahedral blocks formed by mutually intersecting discontinuities in random three-dimensional networks. The program adopts similar procedures to those described in section 6.8.1 for the generation of three-dimensional random networks on the basis of diagnostic data for the orientation, frequency and size of discontinuity sets in the fracture network. All kinematically feasible tetrahedral blocks are then identified and each is analysed to determine whether it is kinematically stable, free to move in the direction of the resultant force or whether, if unstable, it will be subject to single plane or double plane sliding. Kinematically stable blocks are assigned a factor of safety of 10.0, freely moving blocks a factor of safety of zero and sliding blocks a factor of safety determined from equation 8.15 or equation 8.16 as appropriate.

A total of 12 rotational modes and 6 toppling modes of displacement are analysed for any tetrahedral block that has a translational factor of safety greater than 1.0. Each of the rotational modes is a rigid body rotation about an axis constructed normal to one of the faces of the block and located so that it passes through one of the three vertices on that face; four faces with three vertices in each face give the 12 independent rotational modes. Each of the toppling modes is a rigid body rotation about an axis formed by the block edge joining a pair of vertices; there are six block edges and therefore six independent toppling modes. Each of these rotation and toppling modes is

Table 8.3 Discontinuity data for stability analysis of quartzite rock face at Koolan Island Iron Ore Mine (after Priest and Samaniego, 1988)

Set	Orientation Dip direction/ dip angle	Fisher's constant	Mean trace length m	Mean normal frequency m^{-1}	Cohesion kPa	Angle of friction Degrees
1	113/79	262	3.7	1.72	15	30
2	100/59	99	3.7	3.03	15	30
3	027/27	84	2.4	1.67	20	35
4	036/55	106	1.9	1.35	20	35
5	006/65	69	2.4	1.96	20	35
6	345/68	100	2.2	0.27	20	35
7	309/70	41	4.1	4.55	15	30
8	215/49	91	100	1.89	10	28

analysed for a positive and a negative sense of rotation, giving a total of 36 independent mechanisms. Any of these mechanisms is deemed to be active (i) if it is kinematically feasible, and (ii) if it leads to a nett loss in the potential energy of the block. These two conditions are tested for each rotation and toppling axis by allowing the axis to generate a small angle (typically 1°) of virtual rotation in the block. The new locations of the centroids of each face of the block are then inspected; if none of these centroids has moved into the adjacent rock the mechanism is deduced to be kinematically feasible. The second condition is tested by observing the centroid of the block; if this centroid moves with a positive component in the direction of the resultant force there is a nett loss in potential energy.

The geometrical properties, factors of safety and other details of all kinematically feasible tetrahedral blocks, which can number several thousand in a typical analysis, are presented in tabular and graphical form by the program SATIRN. Because a given element of rock may lie within more than one block there is a tendency to overestimate the volume of potentially unstable rock by a factor of between 2 and 5. To address this problem Priest and Samaniego created a 50 by 50 by 50 element, three-dimensional grid that is superimposed over the problem domain. Each element is initially assigned a factor of safety $F_e = 20.0$ and a number of active modes of rotational instability $N_e = 0$. When the factor of safety F_b and the number of active modes of rotational instability N_b of a given block have been computed, the block is placed in the grid at its correct location and orientation. If for any grid element within the block $F_e > F_b$ then F_e is assigned the value F_b. Similarly, if for any element $N_e < N_b$ then N_e is assigned the value N_b. As each block is analysed, the values of F_e and N_e for the contained elements are updated in this way to generate a three-dimensional map of rock stability.

Table 8.3 summarises the discontinuity data for a case study presented by

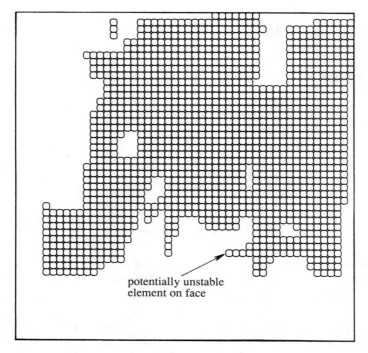

potentially unstable
element on face

Figure 8.16   Grid map showing potentially unstable rock elements for a 65° rock face, Koolan Island (after Priest and Samaniego, 1988).

Priest and Samaniego, involving stability studies for an open pit iron ore mine on Koolan Island off the coast of Western Australia. A typical fractured quartzite rock face in this mine is illustrated in Figure 9.1. Figure 6.15c shows the pattern produced where one of the random realisations intersected the 65° rock face excavated in quartzitic rock. This realisation contained 1592 discontinuity traces, 29 184 intersections, 15 149 triangles at the face and 2664 kinematically feasible tetrahedral blocks. About half of the face triangles were associated with blocks that were infeasible because they diverged into the rock mass; a further 5000 were infeasible because one or more of the involved discontinuities was too small to form a complete face of the notional block. Priest and Samaniego considered water pressure gradients of 3, 5, 10 and 20 kPa per metre normal to the rock face. Figure 8.16 is a map of a 20 m square area of the 65° rock face showing those elements that have a factor of safety of less than 1.0 under a water pressure gradient of 20kPa m^{-1}. Figure 8.17 shows cumulative distributions of the volume of rock per unit area of face that has a factor of safety less than F in the range 0 to 6.0 for the 65° slope angle. This figure shows that, at water pressure gradients of 10 and 20 kPa, a

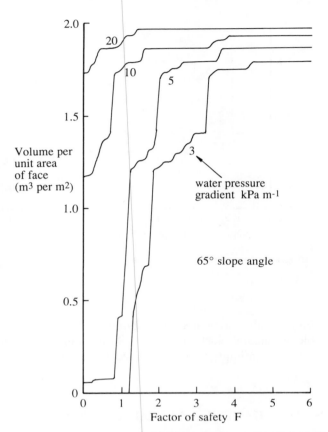

Figure 8.17 Rock volumes at a range of factors of safety for a 65° face, Koolan Island (after Priest and Samaniego, 1988).

significant volume of rock has a factor of safety of zero, indicating that blocks have 'burst' from the rock face under the high water pressures. Lower water pressures give a significantly more stable volume–factor of safety profile.

The use of random realisations for the analysis of rigid block stability introduces an element of random variability into the results. To investigate this effect Priest and Samaniego (1988) conducted 30 repeat analyses at a slope angle of 65° and a water pressure gradient of $5\,kPa\,m^{-1}$, taking the same discontinuity data but adopting a different seed for the random number generator each time. The volume, $V_{1.0}$, of rock per unit area of face with a factor of safety of less than 1.0 for each of the 30 analyses has been plotted on the histogram in Figure 8.18. The wide distribution of values illustrates the influence that random variability in discontinuity geometry can have on rock face stability. The high values of $V_{1.0}$ are due to the chance occurrence of one

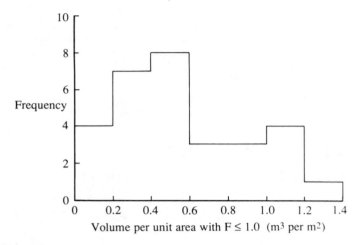

Figure 8.18   Histogram of unstable rock volumes (after Priest and Samaniego, 1988).

or two large, unfavourably orientated discontinuities, leading to the formation of large unstable tetrahedral blocks and high failure volumes. This dominating influence of large discontinuities was confirmed by observations in the open pit.

EXERCISES FOR CHAPTER 8 AND APPENDIX D

8.1

The figure below shows a vertical cross-section normal to the crest of a bench which has a horizontal top. The rigid block ABCD is defined by the rock face AB and by an inclined tension crack CD which are parallel to each other, dipping at an angle of 60°. The tension crack daylights 6 m from the crest and contains water to a vertical depth of 2 m above D as shown. AD is a silt-filled discontinuity, dipping at an angle of 30° and daylighting at a vertical distance of 10 m below the crest. The cohesion and angle of friction for the discontinuity surface AD are respectively 10 kPa and 32°. The unit weights for the rock and for water are 27 and 9.81 kN m^{-3}, respectively. Taking a 1 m slice of rock normal to the plane of the cross-section, and assuming a linear water pressure distribution on the plane AD calculate:

(i)   the weight of the block ABCD,
(ii) the shear strength capacity of the sliding surface AD in kN, and
(iii) the factor of safety against single plane sliding on AD.

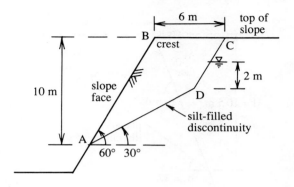

8.2

The figure below shows a cross-section through a bench in an open pit mine that is intersected by a planar discontinuity and a tension crack. The following angles of dip have been measured:

Face of the bench	$\beta_f = 68°$
Top of the bench	horizontal
Planar discontinuity	$\beta_s = 37°$
Tension crack	$\beta_c = 75°$

All of the above features were found to have a strike within 15° of the crest of the slope. The dimensions H and W were found to be 10.5 m and 5.5 m, respectively. The planar discontinuity was observed to have a Joint Roughness Coefficient JRC of 7. Tests on the rock material immediately adjacent to the discontinuity gave a uniaxial compressive strength σ_d of 35 MPa and a basic friction angle ϕ_b of 33°. Assuming that the surface of the water in the tension crack lies 1.5 m below the top of the bench, that water pressure decays linearly along the sliding plane and that the planar discontinuity obeys Barton's shear strength law (section 9.2.3), calculate:

(i)   the weight of a 1 m slice of the block,
(ii) the effective normal stress on the discontinuity, and
(iii) the factor of safety against bench failure by single-plane block sliding.

Unit weights: rock $26\,\mathrm{kN\,m^{-3}}$, water $9.81\,\mathrm{kN\,m^{-3}}$

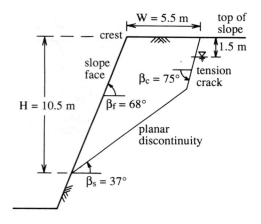

8.3

The figure below shows a vertical cross-section through a strip foundation 4 m wide carrying a uniformly distributed load at the crest of a 60° slope excavated in a rock mass of unit weight 28 kN m^{-3}. The slope is cut by three discontinuities as shown, each of which strikes parallel to the crest of the slope and exhibits a yield behaviour governed by the Coulomb criterion with a cohesion of 20 kPa and an angle of friction of 35°. Assuming dry conditions, use the double block mechanism to determine the collapse load per unit area of foundation.

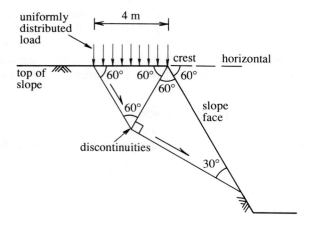

8.4

The hanging-wall of an underground mine is formed by an overhanging planar face of dip direction/dip angle 236/40. This face is intersected by **five** sets of planar discontinuities with the following orientations:

Set	Dip direction Degrees	Dip angle Degrees
1	024	46
2	163	64
3	245	75
4	289	33
5	325	52

Construct an inclined hemisphere projection for this face and analyse the modes of failure that could be induced by simple gravitational loading of all significant tetrahedral blocks formed by the discontinuities. In the case of sliding mechanisms give the plane(s) of sliding and the trend/plunge of the sliding direction.

8.5

A non-overhanging rock face of dip direction/dip angle 268/56 and its top of dip direction/dip angle 281/07 are intersected by two extensive planar discontinuities of dip directions/dip angles (1) 205/63 and (2) 323/49 which form the base of a kinematically feasible tetrahedral block 56.47 m³ in volume. Geometrical calculations reveal that the surface of the block formed by discontinuity (1) has an area of 31.28 m² and that the surface formed by discontinuity (2) has an area of 41.17 m². A preliminary site investigation gave the following data:

Discontinuity	Cohesion kPa	Angle of friction Degrees	Mean water pressure kPa
1	10	37	8
2	20	32	12

Unit weight of rock material = 27 kN m^{-3}.

The foundations of a pylon to be sited on the block will exert a force of 420 kN downwards along a line of trend/plunge 275/70. Determine (i) the orientation, magnitude and sense of the resultant force acting on the block, (ii) the plane(s) on which the block will slide if unstable, and (iii) the factor of safety against sliding by this mechanism.

Answers to these exercises are given on page 463.

9

Discontinuities and
rock strength

9.1 INTRODUCTION

Discontinuities usually have negligible tensile strength and a shear strength that is, under most circumstances, significantly smaller than that of the surrounding rock material. It is reasonable to assume, therefore, that discontinuities will have a marked weakening effect on rock masses, and that this weakening will depend, amongst other things, on the orientation, frequency, size and shear strength of the various discontinuities. The influence of low discontinuity tensile strength is clearly evident at overhanging and at steep non-overhanging faces in fractured rock masses, such as the one shown in Figure 9.1. Free faces such as this release the compressive stresses that may have existed in the rock, and allow the development of tensile stresses beneath overhangs. It is clear that blocks of rock have slid and fallen from this face both during and after the excavation process. Rigid block mechanisms such as this have been discussed in Chapter 8.

Deeper within rock masses we can expect that the stress state will be generally compressive, but not necessarily hydrostatic. Non-hydrostatic stresses lead to the development of shear stresses within the mass. These shear stresses can induce shear failure of the intact rock material and/or shear displacement along one or more suitably orientated discontinuities. Although the kinematics of discontinuity failure mechanisms in extensive rock masses generally require the stressing, and also perhaps the yielding, of intact rock, it seems reasonable to assume that the rock mass will be weakened by the presence of discontinuities. It is the aim of this chapter to investigate this weakening influence of

Figure 9.1 Typical fractured quartzite rock face, Koolan Island iron ore mine.

discontinuities in rock masses where the state of stress is generally compressive. We will start by considering shear strength models that take account of surface geometry and normal stress on single discontinuities. In the next section these models are combined with yield criteria for intact rock, to produce the so-called single-plane and multiple-plane of weakness models. Rock mass classification schemes and their link with empirical rock mass strength criteria are discussed in section 9.4 and Appendix C. This chapter concludes with an analysis of laboratory and field loading tests on naturally and artificially fractured materials. Discrete element and other numerical modelling techniques for blocky rock masses are discussed in Chapter 10.

9.2   THE SHEAR STRENGTH OF DISCONTINUITIES

This major section is concerned with experimental and theoretical studies of the shear strength of discontinuities. Since the extensive body of literature on this subject has already been reviewed competently in books by a number of authors, notably Goodman (1976), Hoek and Bray (1981) and Brady and Brown (1985), the work in this section will seek only to set out the basic principles and to comment briefly upon recent developments.

9.2.1   The fundamentals of discontinuity shear behaviour

A simple way to estimate the shear strength of a single discontinuity is to take a sample of rock containing the discontinuity and then to incline the discontinuity from the horizontal until the upper half slides (Barton et al., 1985). A photograph of a simple test set up is presented in Figure 9.2. If the weight of the upper block is W and the gross area of contact is A, at an angle of inclination β the effective normal stress σ'_n and the shear stress τ down the line of maximum dip are respectively given by

$$\sigma'_n = \frac{W \cos \beta}{A} - u \quad \text{and} \quad \tau = \frac{W \sin \beta}{A} \tag{9.1}$$

where u is the water pressure within the discontinuity, generally zero in this particular test.

If the angle of inclination at the point of sliding is β_f, and the associated effective normal and shear stresses are σ'_n and τ_f, the ratio of shear stress to effective normal stress at the point of slip is, applying equations 9.1, given by

$$\frac{\tau_f}{\sigma'_n} = \frac{\sin \beta_f}{\cos \beta_f} = \tan \beta_f$$

This simple result forms the basis of the Coulomb yield criterion

$$\tau_f = \sigma'_n \tan \phi \tag{9.2}$$

Figure 9.2 Simple tilt test apparatus for determining friction angles for natural and artificial discontinuities.

The parameter ϕ in the above expression is referred to as the angle of friction, and is theoretically equal to the angle of inclination β_f at the point of sliding. Although ϕ is the angle of friction under conditions of effective stress the 'prime' has been omitted for brevity and to conform with the symbolism

Table 9.1 Basic friction angles for a range of rock materials (Barton and Choubey, 1977)

Rock type	ϕ_b dry Degrees	ϕ_b wet Degrees
Sandstone	26–35	25–34
Siltstone	31–33	27–31
Limestone	31–37	27–35
Basalt	35–38	31–36
Fine granite	31–35	29–31
Coarse granite	31–35	31–33
Gneiss	26–29	23–26
Slate	25–30	21

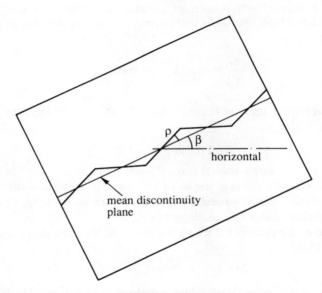

Figure 9.3 Idealised saw-tooth model for discontinuity roughness.

adopted in the primary reference texts. The difficulty with the approach in equation 9.2 is that a rough discontinuity surface will exhibit a higher apparent angle of friction than a smooth surface in the same rock material. This problem can be addressed by regarding ϕ as being composed of two angular components: (i) ϕ_b the basic friction angle for an apparently smooth surface of the rock material, and (ii) a component i, called the effective roughness angle, due to visible roughness and other surface irregularities, such that

$$\phi = \phi_b + i \qquad (9.3)$$

Barton and Choubey (1977) have listed values of ϕ_b determined experimentally by a number of authors. Some representative values are listed in Table 9.1.

The lower friction angles for the wet samples suggest that transient pore water pressures may have reduced the effective normal contact stresses during shearing, thereby reducing the observed angle of friction. There are, however, other explanations for this phenomenon, linked to the fact that rock materials can be weakened significantly as their moisture content increases from close to zero to about 1% (Colback and Wiid, 1965).

The significance of the roughness component i can be appreciated by considering the idealised saw-tooth model of Figure 9.3 in which there is a uniform roughness inclined at an angle ρ to the mean discontinuity plane. If this model were tilted at an angle β to the horizontal, the saw-tooth surfaces would be inclined at angles $\beta - \rho$ and $\beta + \rho$. Only those surfaces inclined at $\beta - \rho$, however, will remain in contact and control sliding. Applying equations 9.1 to obtain the shear and normal stresses on the contact surfaces at the point of slip gives

$$\frac{\tau_f}{\sigma'_n} = \tan(\beta_f - \rho) = \tan \phi_b$$

Hence the apparent angle of friction, given by the overall angle of inclination at the point of slip, is

$$\phi = \beta_f = \phi_b + \rho \qquad (9.4)$$

The above result shows that the roughness component i for the saw-tooth model is theoretically equal to the saw-tooth angle ρ. Any shear displacement s of this saw-tooth geometry must be associated with an opening, or dilation, n of the discontinuity at a rate $dn/ds = \tan \rho$.

Replacing ϕ in equation 9.2 by $\phi_b + i$ gives the well-known result presented by Patton (1966).

$$\tau_f = \sigma'_n \tan(\phi_b + i) \qquad (9.5)$$

In a review of shear test results on rough discontinuities, Hoek and Bray (1981) concluded that effective roughness angles of between 40 and 50° could be applicable at effective normal stresses below about 0.7 MPa. Taking a basic friction angle of 35° in equation 9.5 implies that roughness features inclined at more than 55° would impart infinite shear strength to the discontinuity; this would indeed be the case if the rock adjacent to the discontinuity were infinitely strong. In practice, however, the shear stress rises until it is high enough to induce shearing through the rock material forming the roughness feature.

The shear behaviour discussed above is complicated by a number of additional geometrical and mechanical factors. In reality, roughness features

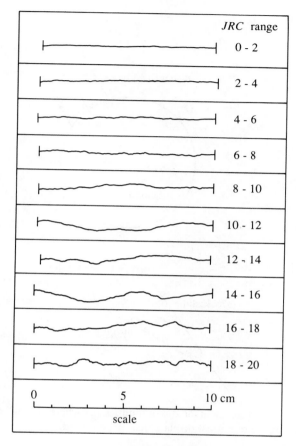

Figure 9.4 Typical discontinuity roughness profiles and associated *JRC* values (after Barton and Choubey, 1977).

do not conform to the saw-tooth model of Figure 9.3; in most cases discontinuity surfaces exhibit asperities that are variable in their angle, amplitude and wavelength, as shown in Figure 9.4. Steeper asperities induce a more rapid rate of dilation and generally have a narrower base, so these features will tend to break off earlier than asperities exhibiting a lower roughness angle. The process of dilation itself can lead to an increase in normal stress if the adjacent rock material is confined within the rock mass, as shown in Figure 9.5a. Discontinuities adjacent to a free face, however, can dilate without inducing significant changes in normal stress, as shown in Figure 9.5b. A further complication arises where weathering effects cause a weakening and softening of the rock material adjacent to the discontinuity, or where an infill

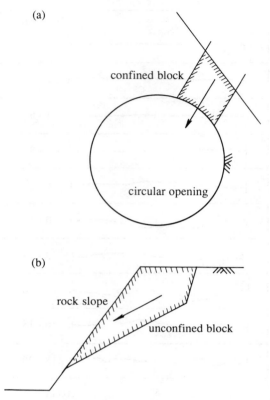

Figure 9.5 Shear displacement of discontinuities (a) where normal displacement is restrained, and (b) where normal displacement is permitted.

material has been deposited in a previously open discontinuity. The simple roughness angle model of equation 9.5 is, therefore, inadequate to describe the shear behaviour of real discontinuities. In order to address this problem it is necessary to conduct shear tests on real discontinuities under conditions that reflect those encountered *in situ*.

9.2.2 Shear testing of discontinuities

Large scale *in situ* tests can be conducted on isolated discontinuities by adopting a test set-up such as that described by Romero (1968) and illustrated in Figure 9.6. Such tests are, however, expensive and can only be justified for major excavation projects or for research purposes. A simpler and cheaper testing system is the portable shear box described by Ross-Brown and Walton (1975) and shown in Figure 9.7 after Hoek and Bray (1977).

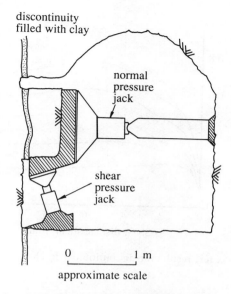

discontinuity
filled with clay

normal
pressure
jack

shear
pressure
jack

0   1 m

approximate scale

Figure 9.6 *In situ* shear test on a clay-filled discontinuity (after Romero, 1968).

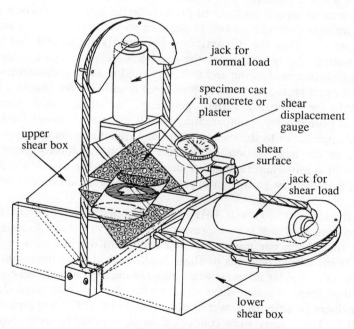

jack for
normal load

specimen cast
in concrete or
plaster

shear
displacement
gauge

upper
shear box

shear
surface

jack for
shear load

lower
shear box

Figure 9.7 Portable field shear box (after Hoek and Bray, 1977).

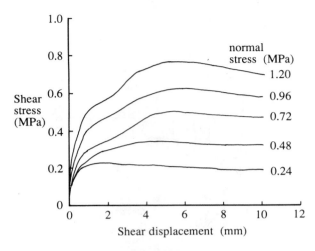

Figure 9.8 Shear box test results for discontinuities in chalk (after Priest, 1975).

The portable shear box can accept specimens up to a size of about a 140 mm cube. The idea is to select a specimen from a rock face or borehole core containing a single discontinuity suitable for testing, trim the specimen to size and then wire or tape it together to protect the discontinuity surface texture. The specimen is then cast in two stages into special moulds using mortar or plaster, ensuring that the discontinuity is correctly positioned and aligned. Prior to testing, the two halves of the specimen are annotated to indicate the proposed direction of shearing and then separated to allow measurement of the contact area and surface geometry. Ross-Brown and Walton discuss a number of methods for recording surface geometry, including visual description, mechanical profilometry, photogrammetry and the use of rubber impressions. Statistical approaches to the measurement and quantification of roughness are discussed in the next section. Whichever method is adopted for recording roughness, it is important to annotate the resulting profile to indicate the shear direction and thereby ensure an appropriate interpretation of any roughness features.

Normal stresses up to about 3 MPa can be applied through the normal load jack. The shear load jack is then pressurised to achieve a shear displacement of no more than 2 mm per minute up to a maximum displacement of between 5 and 10 mm, taking readings of shear load, shear displacement and normal displacement at regular intervals while maintaining the normal load constant at the specified value. Typical shear stress versus shear displacement curves for irregular discontinuities in Lower Chalk, from Priest (1975) are reproduced in Figure 9.8. These tests were conducted using a portable shear box at five different effective normal stresses in the range 0.24 to 1.2 MPa. The charac-

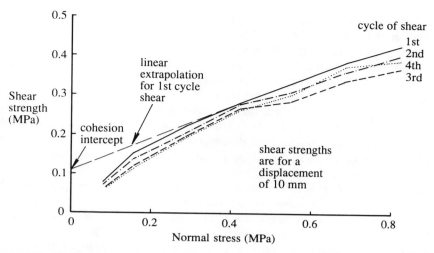

Figure 9.9   Multiple cycle shear box test on discontinuities in basalt (after Ross-Brown and Walton, 1975).

teristic shape of the curves in Figure 9.8, which exhibit a gradual decline in shear stress from a peak value at displacements of between 1 and 5 mm, is probably linked to the wearing of asperities and the accumulation of debris in the discontinuity. This wearing effect is clearly demonstrated in multiple reversal shear box tests conducted on basalt from Scotland, and reported by Ross-Brown and Walton (1975). The results of these tests, plotted in Figure 9.9, give the shear stress at a shear displacement of 10 mm for six constant effective normal stresses in the range 0.15 to 0.8 MPa during the first, second, third and fourth cycles of shearing. Although there is a small, but significant reduction in shear stress between the first and second cycles, this reduction is not maintained consistently in later cycles.

Although the portable shear box is widely used for routine testing it does have a number of disadvantages when precise control over testing conditions is required. The use of manually-operated jacks can make it difficult to control shear displacement and to maintain a constant normal stress throughout the test. There is a tendency for the upper half of the shear box to tilt over at large shear displacements on rough specimens, making it difficult to interpret measurements of shear and normal displacement. Many workers now prefer to use a shear testing apparatus based on the conventional soils shear box. This apparatus is, however, limited to laboratory use, can only apply normal stresses up to about 2 MPa and can cope with only a limited degree of discontinuity surface roughness.

Skinas *et al.* (1990) describe an alternative approach to the shear testing of discontinuities, involving the application of normal stress through a system of springs and tendons designed to simulate constant rock mass stiffnesses of between 0.13 and 13.33 MPa mm^{-1}. Their results show how shear stress, normal stress and normal displacement all vary as a shear displacement is applied to sand, barytes and cement models of natural rough discontinuities. They found that larger values of constant normal stiffness induced higher values of shear stress and normal stress, but lower values of normal displacement, at a given value of shear displacement in these tests. Fortin et al. (1988, 1990) and Archambault et al. (1990) have applied a graphical algorithm to predicting the behaviour of discontinuities sheared under conditions of constant normal stiffness based on results obtained from tests conducted at constant normal stress.

Papaliangas et al. (1990) present a comprehensive investigation of the influence of infill thickness on the shear strength, dilation angle and shear stiffness of model rock joints filled with pulverised fuel ash (pfa), marble dust and kaolin. They found that as the ratio of infill thickness/roughness amplitude increased from zero to 0.5, shear strengths reduced from about 50 kPa to 35 kPa for pfa and marble dust infill and from about 35 kPa to 15 kPa for kaolin infill at normal stresses of 50 kPa. Similar effects have been reported in recent papers by Pereira (1990) and by Phien-wej et al. (1990).

9.2.3 Models for the shear strength of discontinuities

It is important to note that the graphs of shear stress versus effective normal stress in Figure 9.9 are not linear, as could be expected from equation 9.5, but are curved such that there is a lower slope, and therefore a lower instantaneous angle of friction, at higher normal stresses. This characteristic curvature in the shear stress versus effective normal stress graph has been observed in tests on natural and artificial discontinuities over a range of normal stresses, reported by Barton (1976), Brown et al. (1977), Krahn and Morgernstern (1979) and Bandis et al. (1981). The generally accepted explanation for this phenomenon is linked to the role of roughness features during the shearing process, and in particular to the degree to which a discontinuity rides over, or shears through, these asperities. A valuable insight into this effect is presented by Goodman (1976) and discussed further by Goodman (1980) and Brady and Brown (1985). In order to understand this process it is helpful to consider the transfer of energy as a rough discontinuity, such as one of those shown in Figure 9.4, is sheared under normal stress. As the shearing force generates a shear displacement it provides an energy input for the system. This energy can (i) dilate the discontinuity as slip along roughness features causes displacement of the adjacent blocks and/or causes compression of the adjacent rock material, and/or (ii) induce shearing through the rock material forming some of the asperities. When the effective normal stress is small compared with the discontinuity wall material strength there is a tendency for dilation effects to dominate because the energy required for dilation is less than that needed to

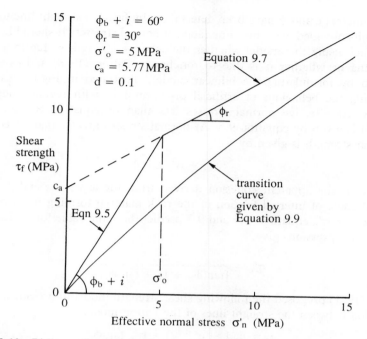

Figure 9.10 Bi-linear shear strength models (equations 9.5 and 9.7) with empirical transition curve (equation 9.9).

cause yielding of the rock material. When the effective normal stress is high, the energy required to dilate the discontinuity exceeds that required to shear through the steeper asperities, so asperity failure dominates over dilation. At low effective normal stresses, therefore, shearing tends to be associated with riding over asperities, allowing their roughness angle to enhance the basic friction angle. At progressively higher normal stresses there is a greater tendency for asperities to shear off, so the roughness angle component is smaller and the shear stress-normal stress curve has a lower slope.

An important consequence of the non-linear shear stress-normal stress relation is observed when the linear models in equations 9.2 and 9.5 are applied to results obtained at even moderate normal stresses. Figure 9.9 indicates that extrapolation of the linear model would give a positive shear strength at zero normal stress. This component of shear strength is traditionally termed cohesion, c, in the following general form of the Coulomb shear strength criterion.

$$\tau_f = c + \sigma'_n \tan \phi \qquad (9.6)$$

Equation 9.6 can provide an adequate prediction of the shear strength of a discontinuity over a specified limited range of effective normal stresses when the parameters c and ϕ have been determined by fitting a straight line to shear test results obtained over this same range of normal stresses. It should be made clear when using this model whether the cohesive strength is due to genuine cementing or whether it is due to roughness. Patton (1966) addressed this problem by formulating the bilinear model, illustrated in Figure 9.10, for explaining the behaviour of artificial discontinuities with regular roughness features. At effective normal stresses less than or equal to σ'_o the shear strength is given by equation 9.5. At normal stresses greater than or equal to σ'_o shear strength is given by

$$\tau_f = c_a + \sigma'_n \tan \phi_r \tag{9.7}$$

where c_a is the apparent cohesion derived from the asperities and ϕ_r is the residual angle of internal friction of the rock material forming the asperities. When $\sigma'_n = \sigma'_o$ equations 9.5 and 9.7 predict the same value for τ_f. Equating these two expressions gives

$$\sigma'_o = \frac{c_a}{[\tan(\phi_b + i) - \tan \phi_r]} \tag{9.8}$$

Jaeger (1971) proposed the following shear strength model to provide a curved transition between the straight lines of the Patton model

$$\tau_f = c_a(1 - e^{-d\sigma'_n}) + \sigma'_n \tan \phi_r \tag{9.9}$$

The parameters c_a and ϕ_r are, respectively, the intercept and slope of a straight line fitted to experimental shear strength data at high normal stresses, and d is an experimentally determined empirical parameter which controls the shape of the transition curve, as shown in Figure 9.10.

Ladanyi and Archambault (1970) proposed a curved shear strength model involving the dilation rate at peak shear stress, the shear strength of the rock material forming the asperities and the proportion of the discontinuity surface that has sheared through asperities. Recognising that this latter parameter is difficult to measure, Hoek and Bray (1981) formulated an empirical extension of the Ladanyi and Archambault equation involving only the parameters i and ϕ_b and the parameter σ_d, the uniaxial compressive strength of the rock material immediately adjacent to the discontinuity.

A direct, practical approach to predicting the shear strength of discontinuities on the basis of relatively simple measurements has been developed by Barton and his co-workers, and published in a sequence of papers throughout the 1970s and the early 1980s. Reviews of this empirical model, and also the shear strength of discontinuities in general, are presented by Barton (1976) and more recently by Barton and Bandis (1990). According to the Barton model, the shear strength τ_f of a discontinuity subjected to an effective normal stress σ'_n in a rock material with a basic friction angle ϕ_b is given by

$$\tau_f = \sigma'_n \tan\left(\phi_b + JRC \log_{10}\left(\frac{\sigma_d}{\sigma'_n}\right)\right) \tag{9.10}$$

As before, σ_d is the uniaxial compressive strength of the rock material immediately adjacent to the discontinuity; this parameter is referred to by Barton as JCS, the joint wall compressive strength. The parameter JRC, the joint roughness coefficient, provides an angular measure of the geometrical roughness of the discontinuity surface in the approximate range 0 (smooth) to 20 (very rough). It is important to appreciate, however, that JRC is not equal to the effective angle of roughness i . If the discontinuity is unweathered, σ_d is equal to the uniaxial compressive strength of the rock material σ_c, determined by point load index tests or compression tests on cylindrical specimens. If there has been softening or other forms of weathering along the discontinuity, then σ_d will be less than σ_c and must be estimated in some way. Barton and Choubey (1977) explain how the Schmidt hammer index test can be used to estimate σ_d from the following empirical expression

$$\log_{10} \sigma_d \approx 0.88 \, \gamma R + 1.01 \qquad (9.11)$$

where γ is the unit weight of the rock material ($\mathrm{MN\,m^{-3}}$), R is the rebound number for the L-hammer and σ_d has the units MPa in the range 20 to approximately 300 MPa. Although the Schmidt hammer is notoriously unreliable, particularly for heterogeneous materials, it is one of the few methods available for estimating the strength of a surface coating of material.

The JRC, which is the key parameter in the Barton model, can be estimated in a number of ways. Barton and Choubey (1977) present a selection of scaled typical roughness profiles, reproduced in Figure 9.4, which facilitate the estimation of JRC for real discontinuities by visual matching, as discussed in Chapter 2. Alternatively a simple tilt shear test can be conducted on a discontinuity specimen and the JRC can be back-figured from equation 9.10, using equations 9.1 to calculate σ'_n and τ_f. Chryssanthakis and Barton (1990) present a case study of this approach applied to a one metre long natural joint in syenite and model replicas of the joint cast in cement and fine sand. It is worth noting two important limitations on the use of equation 9.10 for estimating the shear strength of discontinuities. Barton and Choubey (1977) suggest that the curves should be truncated such that the maximum allowable shear strength for design purposes is given by arctan $(\tau_f/\sigma'_n) = 70°$. Barton (1976) cautioned that when the effective normal stress exceeds the unconfined compressive strength of the rock material, the measured shear strength is always appreciably higher than that predicted by equation 9.10. Noting that this discrepancy was probably due to the effect of confining stresses increasing the strength of asperities, Barton proposed that a high stress version of equation 9.10 could be obtained by replacing σ_d by $(\sigma'_{1f} - \sigma'_3)$, where σ'_{1f} is the effective axial stress required to yield the rock material under an effective confining stress σ'_3. The failure stress σ'_{1f} can either be determined experimentally or can be estimated from an appropriate yield criterion such as the one proposed by Hoek and Brown (1980b).

Tse and Cruden (1979) present an interesting method for estimating JRC based upon a digitisation of the discontinuity surface into a total of M data points spaced at a constant small distance Δx along the profile. If y_i is the amplitude of the ith data point measured above (y_i +ve) and below (y_i −ve) the centre line, then the root mean square Z_2 of the first derivative of the roughness profile is given by

$$Z_2 = \sqrt{\frac{\sum\limits_{i=1}^{M} (y_{i+1} - y_i)^2}{M(\Delta x)^2}} \qquad (9.12)$$

By digitising the ten typical roughness profiles presented by Barton and Choubey (1977) and then conducting a series of regression analyses, Tse and Cruden found that there was a strong correlation between JRC and Z_2, and proposed the following expression for estimating JRC

$$JRC \approx 32.2 + 32.47 \log_{10} Z_2 \qquad (9.13)$$

Tse and Cruden also observed correlations between JRC and other statistical properties of the discontinuity profiles. The increasing availability of image analysis hardware and low-cost digitising pads could make the methods of Tse and Cruden a valuable objective alternative for the assessment of JRC. This approach should be used with caution, however, since Bandis et al. (1981) have shown that both JRC and σ_d (JCS) reduce with increasing scale. The idea of applying statistical and probabilistic analysis of surface profiles to the calculation of JRC has recently been examined and extended by several authors, notably McWilliams et al. (1990), Roberds et al. (1990), Yu and Vayssade (1990), and Zongqi and Xu (1990). These last authors, noting that the value of JRC is dependent upon the sampling interval along the profile, proposed the following extension to equation 9.13

$$JRC \approx AZ_2 - B \qquad (9.14)$$

where the constants A and B depend on the sampling interval, taking values of 60.32 and 4.51, respectively, for an interval of 0.25 mm, 61.79 and 3.47 for an interval of 0.5 mm and 64.22 and 2.31 for an interval of 1.0 mm. Lee et al. (1990), applying the concept of fractals to discontinuity surface profiles, obtained an empirical relation linking the fractal dimension to the JRC value. Unfortunately Lee et al. did not explain adequately how the fractal dimension should be determined in practice. McWilliams et al. (1990), in an authoritative investigation of the application of the fractal dimension, the fractal intercept and Z_2 for characterising surface geometry, also developed a group of empirical relations for predicting shear strength. They found, however, that parallel profiles taken along natural fractures were independent of each other, even when spaced only 5 mm apart. They went on to recommend that fracture surface geometry should be analysed on a three-dimensional basis, rather than along profiles. Huang and Doong (1990) pointed out that the single value of JRC obtained by equations such as 9.13 and 9.14 does not take account of the two alternative directions of shearing, which can yield different shear strengths. Through a series of model tests they showed that natural discontinuity surface profiles can give rise to significant anisotropy in shear strength.

Example 9.1 (Figure 9.11)

A simple tilt test on a dry sample of siltstone, containing a specimen of a particular joint set, produced slip on the discontinuity at an inclination of 53°. The gross contact area during shearing was 89.3 cm², the volume of the upper block was 738 cm³ and the mass of the upper block was 2.06 kg. A tilt test on a dry, smooth, sawn specimen of the siltstone produced slip at an inclination of 32°. A series of Schmidt hammer tests with the L-hammer gave an average rebound value of 19.5 for the natural discontinuity surface. Another discontinuity from the same joint set forms the sliding plane for a major rigid block failure mechanism in which the effective normal stress across the discontinuity is computed to be 85 kPa.

(i)   Estimate the joint roughness coefficient JRC and,
(ii) assuming that the sliding plane has the same JRC, estimate its shear strength at the computed effective normal stress.
(iii) Use graphical or other methods to estimate the equivalent cohesion and angle of friction for this discontinuity over the effective normal stress range 80 to 90 kPa.

Solution
(i) The tilt test on the sawn specimen indicates that the rock material has a basic friction angle ϕ_b of 32°. In the tilt test on the natural discontinuity, the upper block has a mass of 2.06 kg or a weight of 20.2 N. Hence, by equation 9.1, noting that there is no water pressure, at an inclination of 53° the effective normal stress σ'_n on the discontinuity is 1.36 kPa and the shear stress τ_f is 1.81 kPa. The upper block has a volume of 738 cm³, indicating a unit weight of 0.0274 MN m⁻³. Inputting this result, together with the average rebound value of 19.5, into equation 9.11 gives an estimated joint wall compressive strength σ_d of 30.2 MPa. Putting this result into equation 9.10 with $\sigma'_n = 1.36$ kPa, $\tau_f = 1.81$ kPa and $\phi_b = 32°$, then solving for JRC gives an estimated joint roughness coefficient of 4.83.

(ii) Applying equation 9.10, to estimate the shear strength τ_f of the sliding plane at an effective normal stress of 85 kPa gives $\tau_f = 83.0$ kPa.

(iii) Applying equation 9.10 again, to estimate the shear strength τ_f of the sliding plane at effective normal stresses of 80 and 90 kPa gives $\tau_f = 78.5$ and 87.5 kPa, respectively. A straight line through these points, plotted in Figure 9.11, has a slope and intercept indicating an angle of friction and cohesion of approximately 42° and 6.5 kPa, respectively. This figure also contains the

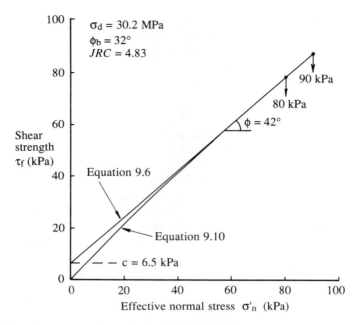

Figure 9.11   Shear strength envelopes for Example 9.1.

complete shear strength envelope given by equation 9.10 for effective normal stresses in the range 0 to 100 kPa.

The shear strength model of Barton and co-workers has been discussed and extended by means of theoretical studies of the link between discontinuity surface geometry and shear strength, and also by shear tests on natural and artificial discontinuities. Those who want to pursue this subject further may wish to consult the papers by Leichnitz (1985), Reeves (1985), Swan and Zongqi (1985), Gerrard (1986) and Hutson and Dowding (1990).

9.3 THE SINGLE PLANE OF WEAKNESS MODEL

Intact specimens of rock tested under uniaxial conditions, or tested under triaxial conditions at confining pressures below the brittle–ductile transition, often fail by shearing along a nearly planar surface inclined at about 20 to 30° to the major principal stress axis (Paterson, 1978), as shown in Figure 9.12. In tests such as this, the stress environment leads to the creation of a discontinuity and to a mechanism of shear failure that is similar to the one discussed in the previous section for natural discontinuities. The single plane of weakness model, described by Jaeger (1960) and by Jaeger and Cook (1979), combines these two modes of failure into a single strength model for rocks that contain one or more planar discontinuities of any orientation.

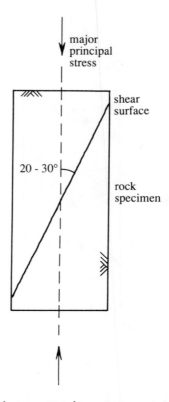

Figure 9.12 Shear fracture in a compression test.

Figure 9.13 shows a cylindrical specimen of rock subjected to an axial total major principal stress σ_1, a lateral total minor principal stress σ_3 and an internal pore water pressure u. Applying two-dimensional stress transformation, the effective normal stress σ'_n and the shear stress τ on a plane whose **normal** makes an angle θ with the σ_1 axis are, respectively, given by

$$\sigma'_n = \tfrac{1}{2}(\sigma_1 + \sigma_3) + \tfrac{1}{2}\cos 2\theta(\sigma_1 - \sigma_3) - u \qquad (9.15)$$

$$\tau = \tfrac{1}{2}\sin 2\theta(\sigma_1 - \sigma_3) \qquad (9.16)$$

It is important to appreciate that equations 9.15 and 9.16 are based on the principles of two-dimensional stress transformation and relate to **any plane**, whether an actual discontinuity or a notional plane through intact rock. We have seen in the previous section, and in particular in equations 9.6 and 9.9, that the shear strength τ_f of a discontinuity can be modelled as a function of the effective normal stress σ'_n, a friction term ϕ and a cohesion term c. The friction term can be predicted from non-linear empirical models such as the

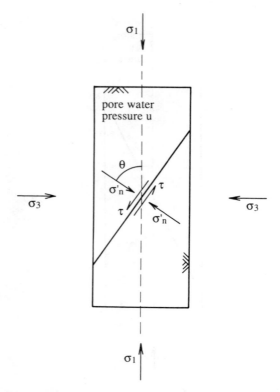

Figure 9.13 Normal and shear stresses on an inclined plane in a cylindrical specimen.

one proposed by Barton (1976) or can be estimated by fitting a straight line to shear box test results over a specified range of effective normal stresses. The cohesion term is zero for the non-linear models but is non-zero for the linear model of equation 9.6. Introducing the subscript 'd', to indicate that the parameters relate to the shear strength of an existing discontinuity, gives the following

$$\tau_{fd} = c_d + \sigma'_{nd} \tan \phi_d \qquad (9.17)$$

It must remembered that c_d and ϕ_d may vary with the effective normal stress, so constant values of c_d and ϕ_d in the above expression may limit its applicability to a narrow range of σ'_{nd}. This limitation will be set aside for the time being, but will be cited later as a possible explanation for discrepancies between theory and experimental behaviour. An important feature of single plane of weakness theory is that for discontinuity shear, the angle θ in equations 9.15 and 9.16 is given by the angle θ_d between the discontinuity normal and the σ_1 axis. Replacing θ in equations 9.15 and 9.16 by θ_d, adopting the result to substitute for σ'_{nd} and τ_{fd} in equation 9.17 and then rearranging, gives the following explicit expression for σ_{1d} the total major principal stress required to cause shear failure along the discontinuity

$$\sigma_{1d} = \sigma_3 + \frac{2(c_d + (\sigma_3 - u) \tan \phi_d)}{\sin 2\theta_d(1 - \tan \phi_d \cot \theta_d)} \tag{9.18}$$

The Coulomb criterion of equation 9.6 also provides the basis for a widely accepted linear model for the shear strength of intact rock material (Paterson, 1978). Introducing the subscript 'm' to indicate rock material parameters gives the following version of equation 9.6 for shear failure through intact rock

$$\tau_{fm} = c_m + \sigma'_{nm} \tan \phi_m \tag{9.19}$$

The angle θ in equations 9.15 and 9.16 is given by the angle θ_m between the normal to the plane of potential shear failure and the σ_1 axis. Replacing θ in equations 9.15 and 9.16 by θ_m, adopting the result to substitute for σ'_{nm} and τ_{fm} in equation 9.19 and then rearranging as before, gives the following explicit expression for σ_{1m} the major principal stress required to cause shear failure of the intact rock

$$\sigma_{1m} = \sigma_3 + \frac{2(c_m + (\sigma_3 - u) \tan \phi_m)}{\sin 2\theta_m(1 - \tan \phi_m \cot \theta_m)} \tag{9.20}$$

Although there are an infinite number of possible values of θ_m, in theory the rock material will fail along the shear plane that is orientated to give the smallest value of σ_{1m}. The minimum value for σ_{1m} as a function of θ_m in equation 9.20 can be found by maximising the denominator. Differentiating this denominator then equating it to zero shows that the minimum σ_{1m} occurs when $\theta_m = (\pi/4) + (\phi_m/2)$. Making this substitution for θ_m in equation 9.20 and then rearranging gives the well-known result

$$\sigma_{1m} = 2c_m \tan\left(\frac{\pi}{4} + \frac{\phi_m}{2}\right) + (\sigma_3 - u) \tan^2\left(\frac{\pi}{4} + \frac{\phi_m}{2}\right) \tag{9.21}$$

The term

$$\tan^2\left(\frac{\pi}{4} + \frac{\phi_m}{2}\right) = \frac{1 + \sin \phi_m}{1 - \sin \phi_m}$$

occurs frequently in geomechanical studies that involve the application of the Coulomb yield criterion. In soil mechanics studies this term is usually referred to as the passive earth pressure coefficient.

Brady and Brown (1985) present the result in equation 9.21 in the following form

$$\sigma_{1m} = \sigma_3 + \frac{2(c_m + (\sigma_3 - u) \tan \phi_m)}{\tan \phi_m + \sqrt{1 + \tan^2 \phi_m}} \tag{9.22}$$

Single plane of weakness theory assumes that failure during compressive loading of a specimen subject to a lateral stress σ_3, such as that in Figure 9.13, will occur when σ_1 exceeds the smaller of σ_{1d} and σ_{1m} given by equations 9.18 and 9.21, respectively. Application of these expressions to a given rock necessitates the computation of σ_{1m} for the material and then σ_{1d} for each of the through-going discontinuities. The theoretical strength of the discontinuous mass is given by the smallest value of the major principal stress at yield, as illustrated in the following example.

Example 9.2

A dry cylindrical specimen of weak fractured sandstone contains three through-going planar discontinuities that have the following Coulomb shear strength parameters and are orientated such that their normals make the following angles θ_d with the cylinder axis:

Table for Example 9.2

Discontinuity	Cohesion c_d MPa	Friction angle ϕ_d Degrees	Orientation θ_d Degrees
1	0.35	32	37
2	0.10	40	49
3	0.20	35	57

The strength of the rock material can be modelled by the Coulomb criterion with shear strength parameters $c_m = 0.95$ MPa and $\phi_m = 42°$. The specimen is subjected to a confining pressure of $\sigma_3 = 2.5$ MPa in a triaxial test cell. Calculate the theoretical axial major principal stress σ_1 at which the specimen will fail either by slip along one of the discontinuities or by shear failure of intact rock.

Solution
Applying equation 9.18 to each of the discontinuities in turn gives axial major principal stresses σ_{1d} at the point of shear failure of 25.8, 18.9 and 10.3 MPa, respectively. Applying equation 9.21 or 9.22 for the rock material indicates that failure will occur at a stress level σ_{1m} of 16.9 MPa. The fractured specimen will, therefore, theoretically fail by slip along discontinuity 3 at a major principal stress of 10.3 MPa. It is worth noting that if discontinuity 3 had not been present the specimen would be predicted to fail by shearing through intact rock material at an axial stress of 16.9 MPa. Although discontinuities 1 and 2 have lower shear strength parameters than the rock

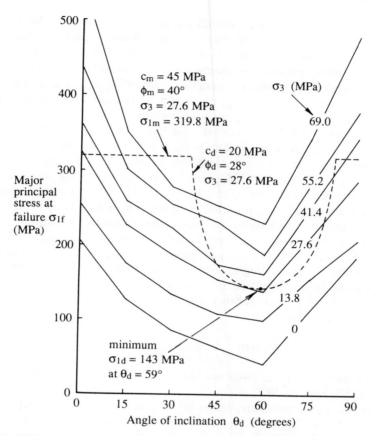

Figure 9.14 Experimental and theoretical strength anisotropy for Penrhyn slate, data from Attewell and Sandford (1974).

material they are not predicted to fail because their angles θ_d are too small to generate the necessary shear stress.

The influence of planes of weakness on the strength of a range of rock types has been investigated by a number of authors, including McLamore and Gray (1967), Donath (1972), Attewell and Sandford (1974) and Brown et al. (1977). Attewell and Sandford conducted a series of triaxial tests on specimens of Penrhyn slate cored to achieve seven different θ_d angles for the slaty cleavage in the range 0 to 90° and tested at six different confining pressures (σ_3) in the range 0 to 69.0 MPa . Their results are summarised in Figure 9.14 as graphs showing the variation of the major principal stress at failure σ_{1f} as a function of θ_d. Although these graphs show the expected result that strength increases with confining pressure, at a given confining pressure the strength also varies significantly with θ_d, passing through a minimum at $\theta_d \approx 60°$. Most authors agree that strength anisotropy such as this reflects a transition from shear failure through intact rock when θ_d is below ϕ_d or when θ_d is close to 90°, to shear failure along planes of weakness when θ_d is close to about 60°.

The theoretical anisotropy in strength predicted by single plane of weakness theory, for given values of c_d, ϕ_d, c_m, ϕ_m, σ_3 and u, can be obtained by taking the smaller value of the major principal stresses σ_{1d} and σ_{1m} given by equations 9.18 and 9.21, respectively, for θ_d in the range 0 to 90°. One such theoretical curve has been plotted in Figure 9.14 by adopting the following values determined by Attewell and Sandford: $c_d = 20\,\text{MPa}$, $\phi_d = 28°$, $c_m = 45\,\text{MPa}$, $\phi_m = 40°$, $\sigma_3 = 27.6\,\text{MPa}$ and u = 0. The maximum strength on this plot is controlled by the constant value $\sigma_{1m} = 319.8\,\text{MPa}$ for the intact rock, given by equation 9.21. Application of equation 9.18 reveals that shear failure along the discontinuities occurs at stress levels below this maximum when θ_d lies between about 35.4° and 82.6°. The minimum value for σ_{1d} as a function of θ_d in equation 9.18 can, as before, be found by maximising the denominator. Differentiating this denominator then equating it to zero shows that, as found earlier for intact rock, the minimum σ_{1d} occurs when $\theta_d = (\pi/4) + (\phi_d/2)$. Making this substitution for θ_d in equation 9.18 and then rearranging gives the result

$$\sigma_{1d\min} = 2c_d \tan\left(\frac{\pi}{4} + \frac{\phi_d}{2}\right) + (\sigma_3 - u)\tan^2\left(\frac{\pi}{4} + \frac{\phi_d}{2}\right) \qquad (9.23)$$

Applying this result to Attewell and Sandford's data gives a minimum strength of 143.0 MPa at $\theta_d = 59°$.

There are significant discrepancies between the theoretical and experimental curves plotted in Figure 9.14 for this particular rock type at the confining pressure $\sigma_3 = 27.6\,\text{MPa}$. In particular, the planes of weakness seem to have a weakening effect well outside the theoretical range of orientations, producing a more gradual variation of strength with θ_d. This discrepancy is probably partly caused by variations in c_d and ϕ_d occurring as a function of changes in normal stress at the different values of θ_d. Another factor may be the development of non-shearing failure mechanisms, such as axial splitting and block rotation, at certain values of θ_d. Noting that discrepancies such as this have been observed by a number of authors for a range of rock types, Hoek and Brown (1980) have proposed an empirical expression for modelling the strength of anisotropic rocks. Determination of as many as 10 parameters for their expression requires a regression analysis on the results of an extensive series of tests conducted over a range of angles θ_d. The resulting empirical curves do, however, provide a good representation of strength anisotropy for a number of slates and other brittle rocks containing well-defined planes of weakness.

A logical extension of the single plane of weakness model is to consider the theoretical strength anisotropy of a rock that contains several planes of weakness at various orientations, such as the rock described in Example 9.2. In order to implement this extension of the essentially two-dimensional strength model, it is necessary to stipulate that each of the discontinuity normals lies in the plane containing σ_1 and σ_3 so that shear failure always occurs in this plane during rotation about a single axis. The following example illustrates this extension of the single plane of weakness model.

Example 9.3 (Figure 9.15)

A dry cylindrical specimen of very weak mudstone contains three through-going planar discontinuities that have the following Coulomb shear strength parameters:

Table for Example 9.3

Discontinuity	Cohesion c_d MPa	Friction angle ϕ_d Degrees
1	0.15	37
2	0.05	31
3	0.10	41

The orientations of the discontinuities are such that when the angle θ_{d1} between the normal to discontinuity plane 1 and the major principal stress is 0, the corresponding angles θ_{d2} and θ_{d3} for discontinuity planes 2 and 3 are 25° and 55°, respectively. The strength of the rock material can be modelled by the Coulomb criterion with shear strength parameters $c_m = 0.6$ MPa and $\phi_m = 43°$. The specimen is subjected to a confining pressure of $\sigma_3 = 2.8$ MPa in a triaxial test cell. Assuming that the three discontinuity planes have the same strike direction within the specimen, plot a graph of the theoretical axial major principal stress σ_1 at which the specimen will fail either by slip along one of the discontinuities or by shear failure of intact rock, for values of θ_{d1} in the range 0 to 90°.

Solution

Equation 9.18 is applied to each of the three discontinuity planes to determine the major principal stress at failure for values of θ_{d1}, θ_{d2} and θ_{d3} in the range 0 to 90°. These calculations are best achieved by means of a spread-sheet, or similar tool, taking angular increments of 5°. The crucial aspect of this problem is understanding how variations in θ_{d2} and θ_{d3} are linked to variations in θ_{d1}. If we make the decision to adopt θ_{d1} as the controlling parameter, then the failure stress on plane 2 for $\theta_{d2} = 25°$ and the failure stress on plane 3 for $\theta_{d3} = 55°$ will plot at $\theta_{d1} = 0$, the failure stresses for $\theta_{d2} = 30°$ and for $\theta_{d3} = 60°$ will plot at $\theta_{d1} = 5°$ and so on. This relation does not, however, give the complete picture because of the symmetrical geometry of the specimen. For

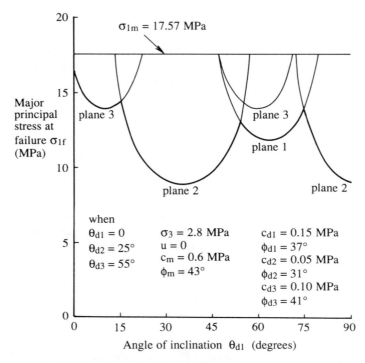

Figure 9.15 Theoretical strength anisotropy for a specimen containing three through-going planar discontinuities, Example 9.3.

example, the failure stress on plane 2 for $\theta_{d2} = 65°$ and the failure stress on plane 3 for $\theta_{d3} = 35°$ will plot at $\theta_{d1} = 90°$, the failure stresses for $\theta_{d2} = 70°$ and for $\theta_{d3} = 40°$ will plot at $\theta_{d1} = 85°$ and so on. The resulting graphs of major principal stress at failure versus θ_{d1} for discontinuity planes 1, 2 and 3 are plotted in Figure 9.15. Although the rock material is very weak, its failure stress of 17.57 MPa, given by equation 9.21, is not exceeded for any value of θ_{d1} in the range 0 to 90°.

The above example demonstrates that, according to single plane of weakness theory, several groups of discontinuity planes can combine to produce a rock mass that is weaker in all directions than the rock material. Hoek and Brown (1980b) investigated this phenomenon and concluded that it is justifiable to treat rock masses containing four or more discontinuity sets as isotropic. The above example indicates that this conclusion is only valid if all of the discontinuity sets have similar shear strength parameters.

Attewell and Woodman (1971) and Amadei (1988) extended the concept of single plane of weakness theory to consider the possibility of shear failure along weakness planes of arbitrary orientation within a rock subjected to a general state of stress $\sigma_1 \geqslant \sigma_2 \geqslant \sigma_3$. The analysis essentially involves three-dimensional stress transformation to determine the normal stress and extreme shear stress for a plane of specified orientation in a given stress field. Attewell and Woodman, and also Amadei adopted the methods discussed in Chapter 7, expressed in analytical form together with the Coulomb criterion, to obtain explicit expressions that delineate those ranges of discontinuity orientations that are subject to slip and those that are stable. Attewell and Woodman coupled their single plane of weakness analysis with a statistical analysis of discontinuity orientation, presenting the results on a digital hemispherical projection. Amadei extended his analysis by applying the isotropic form of the Hoek–Brown empirical strength criterion to the rock material. It is important to appreciate that these extensions of single plane of weakness theory to multiple planes do not recognise the possibility of simultaneous slip on more than one plane nor do they take account of other failure mechanisms involving multiple block displacements and axial splitting. Methods for analysing simple two-dimensional multiple block mechanisms, involving simultaneous slip on several planes, have been discussed in section 8.3.

9.4 ROCK MASS STRENGTH CRITERIA

The aim in developing a rock mass strength criterion is to predict the critical states of stress at which a given rock mass exhibits a significant change in behaviour, from being essentially stable to developing the large deformations associated with yield and failure. Studies of the failure of intact rock material give some guidance as to the likely form of a rock mass strength criterion.

If the rock mass is subjected to effective principal stresses $\sigma'_1 \geqslant \sigma'_2 \geqslant \sigma'_3$, in which σ'_1 is gradually increased while σ'_2 and σ'_3 are held constant, then the major effective principal stress at failure σ'_{1f} will depend upon the values of σ'_2 and σ'_3. This much is clear by considering the Coulomb criterion and by examining test results such as those in Figure 9.16; most materials become stronger when subjected to higher confining pressures. Most yield criteria either make the assumption that $\sigma'_2 = \sigma'_3$ or assume that the intermediate effective principal stress σ'_2 has a negligible influence on the yield stress level. The wide use of 'triaxial' test cells for material testing, in which $\sigma'_2 = \sigma'_3$, has tended to perpetuate this approach and to limit the amount of experimental data available for rock materials subjected to true triaxial stress states.

Rock material tests also demonstrate that rock materials possess an intrinsic strength that is dependent upon mineralogy, grain size and other factors related to the geological history of the rock. These factors are, for example, represented in the Coulomb criterion by the shear strength parameters cohesion and friction. The number of intrinsic strength parameters must be increased if the rock material exhibits significant anisotropy or if the intrinsic strength itself varies with stress level.

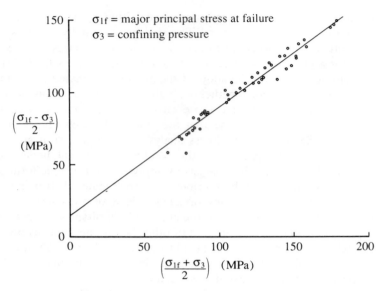

Figure 9.16 Triaxial test results for specimens of slate tested under dry conditions at cleavage angles that ensured failure through the rock material.

In order to develop a strength criterion for a rock mass it is necessary to incorporate some measure of the mechanical and geometrical properties of the discontinuities. This aspect of the problem has presented, over the last 20 years, one of the greatest challenges to engineers and scientists working in this area. A brief review of Chapters 3–6 reveals that the major geometrical properties of discontinuities: orientation, frequency, spacing and size, are not simple deterministic scalar properties. These discontinuity characteristics must be analysed on a probabilistic basis, are of a vectorial nature and generally require several parameters for their adequate representation in three-dimensions. The work on stress analysis, rigid blocks, discontinuity shear strength and deformation in Chapters 7–10 must be added to these geometrical data to provide a complete description of discontinuity properties. The classic diagram in Figure 9.17, after Hoek (1983), provides a convincing argument that any yield criterion for a discontinuous rock mass must also be sensitive to the scale of the problem, ranging from rock material strength at small scale, through single plane of weakness, multiple plane of weakness and multiple block interactions at intermediate scale, to fully-interlocked blocky/granular behaviour at the large scale.

The boldest step towards developing a practical rock mass strength criterion was taken by Hoek and Brown (1980b) in their development of an empirical rock mass strength criterion. In its application to rock mass strength, this criterion relies on the rock mass classification scheme developed by Bieniawski

(1973 and 1976), summarised in Appendix C and discussed in Chapter 2. The Hoek–Brown criterion has been described adequately elsewhere, in particular by Hoek and Brown (1980a), Brady and Brown (1985) and by Hoek and Brown (1988), so it will only be discussed briefly here. Hoek and Brown (1980b) found that the major effective principal stress at failure, σ'_{1f}, for a range of isotropic rock materials subjected to an effective confining pressure σ'_3 could be described by the following empirical expression

$$\sigma'_{1f} = \sigma'_3 + \sqrt{R_m \, m_i \, \sigma_c \, \sigma'_3 + s(\sigma_c)^2} \qquad (9.24)$$

where σ_c is the uniaxial compressive strength of the intact rock material and the parameters R_m, m_i and s are empirical constants that depend on the rock type and the degree of fracturing. The parameter m_i was found to depend only upon the rock type and its crystal structure, ranging from about 7 for carbonate rocks to 25 for coarse grained polyminerallic rocks, as tabulated in Table 9.2.

Table 9.2 Values of the Hoek–Brown parameter m_i for a range of rock types (after Hoek and Brown, 1980b)

m_i	General rock type	Examples
7	Carbonate rocks with well-developed crystal cleavage	Dolomite, limestone, marble
10	Lithified argillaceous rocks	Mudstone, siltstone, shale, slate
15	Arenaceous rocks with strong crystals and poorly-developed crystal cleavage	Sandstone, quartzite
17	Fine grained polyminerallic igneous crystalline rocks	Andesite, dolerite, diabase, rhyolite
25	Coarse grained polyminerallic igneous and metamorphic crystalline rocks	Amphibolite, gabbro, gneiss, granite, norite, quartz–diorite

The parameters R_m and s were found by Hoek and Brown to depend on the degree and nature of fracturing in the rock mass. Both parameters take the value 1.0 for intact unfractured rock, with R_m reducing to about 10^{-3} and s reducing to about 10^{-7} for a rock mass that has closely spaced, heavily weathered joints. Hoek and Brown (1980a) proposed, and then Hoek and Brown (1988) refined, a set of equations with empirical parameters for estimating R_m and s from the CSIR Rock Mass Rating, RMR as follows

$$R_m = \exp\left(\frac{RMR - 100}{RSF_m}\right) \qquad (9.25)$$

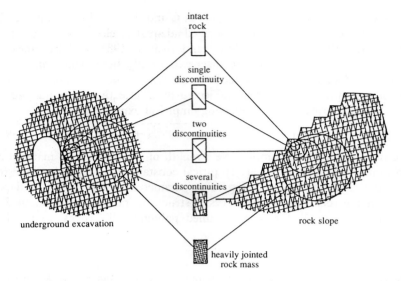

Figure 9.17 The influence of scale on the selection of an appropriate failure mechanism and yield criterion for a discontinuous mass (after Hoek, 1983).

$$s = \exp\left(\frac{RMR - 100}{RSF_s}\right) \tag{9.26}$$

The parameters RSF_m and RSF_s are rock structure factors that depend on the degree of loosening in the rock mass. Hoek and Brown (1988) suggested that RSF_m and RSF_s take values of 28 and 9, respectively, for an undisturbed or interlocked rock mass such as that adjacent to machine bored tunnels, but that values of 14 and 6, respectively, are applicable for a disturbed rock mass such as that adjacent to rock slopes exposed to blast vibrations. It is clear from equation 9.26 that s becomes very small when RMR is less than about 85. For many practical purposes, therefore, it is adequate simply to take $s = 1$ for intact rock, $s = 0.1$ for a tightly interlocked very good quality fractured rock mass for which RMR exceeds 85, and to take $s = 0$ for all other rock masses for which RMR is less than about 85. In discussing the limitations in the use of their failure criterion, Hoek and Brown (1988) emphasised that it is not applicable to anisotropic rocks nor to elements of rock masses that behave anisotropically by virtue of containing only a few discontinuities. They suggested that an anisotropic criterion, such as that proposed by Amadei (1988), should be adopted when the element of rock mass being considered contains only a few discontinuities.

Equation 9.24 can be expressed in the following form

$$\left(\frac{\sigma'_{1f} - \sigma'_3}{\sigma_c}\right)^2 = \frac{R_m m_i \sigma'_3}{\sigma_c} + s \qquad (9.27)$$

This result indicates that a graph of $\dfrac{\sigma'_3}{\sigma_c}$ on the x-axis versus $\left(\dfrac{\sigma'_{1f} - \sigma'_3}{\sigma_c}\right)^2$ on the y-axis will, in theory, have a slope $(R_m\, m_i)$ and an intercept s. If the results of a series of triaxial tests are plotted in this way, a simple linear regression can be applied to estimate R_m and s, assuming that the parameter m_i can be determined from a geological examination of the rock material. The following example, based on hypothetical test data, illustrates this process.

Example 9.4 (Figure 9.18)

The site investigation for a proposed room and pillar mine yielded 150 mm diameter test specimens that were described by the mine geologist as '. . . a moderately fractured, moderately weathered dolomitic limestone . . .'. Five of these fractured specimens were dried at room temperature and then tested under triaxial compression in a Hoek cell. The following results were obtained.

1st table for Example 9.4

Confining pressure σ'_3 MPa	Total axial load at failure MN
5	0.188
10	0.317
15	0.437
20	0.552
25	0.664

Tests on 37 mm diameter, unfractured, unweathered specimens of the dolomitic limestone gave a mean uniaxial compressive strength of 45 MPa. Apply graphical techniques to estimate the empirical constants R_m and s in the Hoek–Brown failure criterion for this rock.

A plane strain boundary element analysis predicts that effective principal stresses of 4.0 and 1.2 MPa will develop within the limestone pillars. Estimate whether the pillars will be stable under this stress state.

Solution

The tests on the small, unfractured specimens indicate that the uniaxial compressive strength of the rock material, σ_c, is 45 MPa. The 150 mm diameter specimens have a cross-sectional area of $17.67 \times 10^{-3}\,\text{m}^2$. Dividing the axial load at failure by this area, and assuming that pore water pressures are zero, gives the following values for the major effective principal stress at failure, σ'_{1f}, and for the pair of dimensionless parameters in equation 9.27.

2nd table for Example 9.4

σ'_{1f} MPa	$\dfrac{\sigma'_3}{\sigma_c}$	$\left(\dfrac{\sigma'_{1f} - \sigma'_3}{\sigma_c}\right)^2$
10.64	0.111	0.016
17.94	0.222	0.031
24.73	0.333	0.047
31.24	0.444	0.062
37.57	0.555	0.078

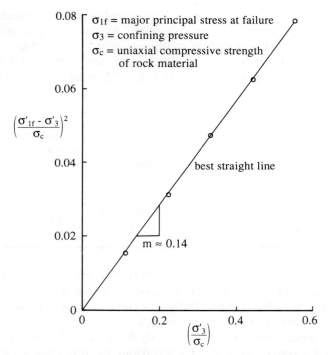

Figure 9.18 Graphical estimation of the parameters for the empirical Hoek–Brown rock strength criterion, Example 9.4.

The best straight line through the above data plotted in Figure 9.18 has a slope of approximately 0.14 and an intercept close to zero. (It is worth noting that these are hypothetical data; real test data rarely conform to theory as well as this). Taking m_i to be 7 for this carbonate rock indicates that $R_m = 0.02$. This result agrees reasonably well with the values tabulated by Hoek and

Brown (1988) for a disturbed, moderately fractured, moderately weathered carbonate rock mass with a CSIR Rock Mass Rating of about 45.

The predicted value for the minor effective principal stress, σ'_3, within the pillars is 1.2 MPa. Putting this value into equation 9.24, with $\sigma_c = 45$ MPa, $R_m = 0.02$, $m_i = 7$ and $s = 0$, gives a major effective principal stress at yield, σ'_{1f}, of 3.95 MPa. The computed major principal effective stress of 4.0 MPa is above this yield level, indicating that the pillars are likely to be unstable at this location.

Priest and Brown (1983) proposed an iterative method for determining the equivalent values of instantaneous cohesion c_e and instantaneous angle of friction ϕ_e for a plane under an effective normal stress σ'_n in a rock material or rock mass that conforms to the Hoek–Brown criterion. In a personal communication Bray (1984) has developed a more direct method for determining these parameters. This method has been reported by Hoek and Brown (1988). If we consider an element of rock subjected to an axial total major principal stresses σ_1, a lateral total minor principal stress σ_3 and an internal pore water pressure u, then the effective normal stress σ'_n and the shear stress τ on a plane whose **normal** makes an angle θ with the σ_1 axis are given by equations 9.15 and 9.16, respectively. Bray (1984) developed a group of expressions, which utilise three temporary intermediate parameters h, ω and ρ as follows

$$h = 1 + \frac{16(R_m \, m_i \, \sigma'_n + s \, \sigma_c)}{3(R_m \, m_i)^2 \sigma_c} \tag{9.28}$$

where σ'_n is given by equation 9.15.

$$\omega = \frac{1}{3}\left\{\frac{\pi}{2} + \arctan\left(\frac{1}{\sqrt{h^3 - 1}}\right)\right\} \tag{9.29}$$

$$\rho = 2\sqrt{h} \cos \omega \tag{9.30}$$

(note: the parameter ρ has no connection with the term ρ in equation 9.4.)
The instantaneous effective coefficient of friction is given by

$$\tan \phi_e = \frac{1}{\sqrt{\rho^2 - 1}} \tag{9.31}$$

The shear strength τ_f of the plane whose normal is inclined at an angle θ to the σ_1 axis is given by

$$\tau_f = \frac{(\rho - 1)R_m \, m_i \, \sigma_c}{8\rho \tan \phi_e} \tag{9.32}$$

Finally, the instantaneous effective cohesion is given by

$$c_e = \tau_f - \sigma'_n \tan \phi_e \tag{9.33}$$

If the shear stress τ, given by equation 9.16, for the particular plane exceeds the shear strength τ_f given by equation 9.32, then the material is predicted to fail by shearing on this plane. There will, however, be planes at other orientations which may be more critical or less critical than the arbitrarily selected plane. Although the orientation of the critical plane will depend upon the instantaneous angle of friction, unlike the Coulomb criterion the critical plane will not in general be orientated such that its normal makes an angle of $(\pi/4) + (\phi_e/2)$ with the σ_1 axis. Moreover, with the Hoek–Brown failure criterion the instantaneous angle of friction ϕ_e varies with the effective normal stress σ'_n, which in turn varies with the orientation of the selected plane as measured by the angle θ. There is not, therefore, a simple direct way of determining the orientation of the critical plane, as there is with the Coulomb criterion. This complication does not, however, present any difficulties since it is a relatively simple matter to calculate the major effective principal stress at failure σ'_{1f}, by applying equation 9.24 directly, noting that $\sigma'_3 = \sigma_3 - u$. The total major principal stress at failure is given by $\sigma_{1f} = \sigma'_{1f} + u$. The following example illustrates the application of the Hoek–Brown criterion and the related analysis summarised above.

Example 9.5

Site investigation studies reveal that a disturbed, fractured mudstone behind a major open pit mine slope has a material uniaxial compressive strength of 180 MPa and a CSIR Rock Mass Rating of 44. It is expected that the slope could fail by slip along a curved shear surface through the rock mass. Stress analysis and hydrological studies reveal that at a particular point A on the potential shear surface the total vertical and horizontal stresses are principal stresses with values of 5.4 and 0.8 MPa, respectively, and that the fracture water pressure is 0.1 MPa. The shear surface is inclined at 55° to the horizontal at this point. Apply the empirical Hoek–Brown criterion to determine whether slip is likely to occur at point A.

Solution
At location A the slip surface is inclined at 55° to the horizontal, so its normal must also be inclined at 55° to the vertical major principal stress axis. Putting $\theta = 55°$ into equations 9.15 and 9.16, together with the given values for the total principal stresses and water pressure gives a shear stress τ of 2.161 MPa and an effective normal stress σ'_n of 2.213 MPa at this point. The m_i value in Table 9.2 for the slate, a lithified argillaceous rock, is 10. Taking the RMR value of 44 and applying equations 9.25 and 9.26, with the parameters RSF_m and RSF_s set at 14 and 6, respectively, for this disturbed rock, gives $R_m = 1.832 \times 10^{-2}$ and $s = 8.843 \times 10^{-5}$. Putting these figures, together with the quoted uniaxial compressive strength of 180 MPa, into equations 9.28 to 9.33 gives the results $h = 1.372$, $\omega = 0.747$, $\rho = 1.718$, $\phi_e = 35.6°$, $\tau_f = 2.407$ MPa

and $c_e = 0.823\,\text{MPa}$. The shear strength τ_f of the potential slip surface is, therefore, greater than the induced shear stress τ, indicating that the specified slip surface will be stable at this point. It is, however, necessary to check whether the rock mass is likely to yield under the computed stress levels. At location A the effective principal stresses σ'_1 and σ'_3 are found by subtracting the water pressure from the computed total stresses, giving 5.3 and 0.7 MPa, respectively. Putting the value for σ'_3 into equation 9.24, together with the other parameters computed above, gives a major effective principal stress at yield, σ'_{1f}, of 5.793 MPa. The computed major principal effective stress of 5.3 MPa is below this yield level, indicating that the rock mass will be stable at this location.

It is interesting to consider what would have happened in the above example if the Rock Mass Rating had been lower. If the rock had been more heavily fractured, with an RMR of only 12, equations 9.31 to 9.33 would give the results $\phi_e = 16.1°$, $\tau_f = 1.051\,\text{MPa}$ and $c_e = 0.413\,\text{MPa}$, indicating that the shear surface would be unstable at this particular location. The friction angle of 16.1° is well below what one would expect for a heavily broken rock mass. It must be appreciated, however, that the shear strength parameters are only **equivalent values** that give the appropriate shear strength through the application of the Coulomb criterion. The relatively high value of cohesion compensates for the apparently 'low' angle of friction in this case.

9.5 MODEL TESTS

A number of authors have sought to understand the influence of discontinuities on the strength of rocks by conducting tests on artificially fractured model materials. This approach has the advantage of permitting full control of the crucial parameters — rock material strength and discontinuity geometry. Brown and Trollope (1970) and Brown (1970) conducted triaxial compression tests on prismatic 'hydrocal' gypsum plaster models containing a range of through-going and intermittent fractures. They found that at confining pressures below the brittle–ductile transition the strength of the fractured specimens was significantly lower than that of the unfractured specimens. Brown and Trollope (1970) also found that those fractured specimens that failed through the model material exhibited a curved shear strength envelope with a zero cohesion intercept, even though the individual fractures obeyed a linear shear strength law over a wide range of normal stresses. Brown and Hudson (1972) investigated the progressive collapse of regularly fractured block assemblages constructed from a high strength gypsum plaster. The prismatic assemblages, containing up to 40 blocks, were tested under uniaxial compression in a closed-loop servo-controlled testing machine. Brown and Hudson observed a progressive collapse phenomenon involving extensile fracture of individual blocks, block rotation, buckling and rotation of columns,

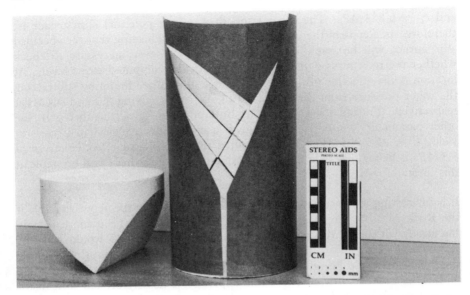

Figure 9.19 Blocky specimen being assembled in a 150 mm diameter paper cylinder prior to testing.

slip on fractures and shear deformation of blocks. They concluded that the inhomogeneous stress distribution induced in blocky media leads to a considerable reduction in strength compared with unfractured specimens, even when the dominant collapse mechanism is by the fracture of individual blocks. They also found that the peak load bearing capacity of the block models depended on the fracture pattern and the shape of the individual blocks. Reik and Zacas (1978) conducted laboratory compression tests to investigate the strength and deformation characteristics of jointed model materials under true triaxial loading $\sigma_1 > \sigma_2 > \sigma_3$. They observed a wide range of failure modes including shear fracture through intact material, sliding on pre-existing joints, rotation and composite mechanisms. They found that although the intermediate principal stress had a relatively small influence when the main joint set was parallel to the σ_2 axis, other joint configurations allowed σ_2 to exercise a dominant influence, in some cases increasing the strength of the jointed model by more than 200%.

Meyers (1992) and Meyers and Priest (1992a and b) conducted a series of laboratory triaxial tests on fractured specimens of a range of plaster-based model materials in order to establish an objective method for determining the input parameters for the Hoek–Brown rock mass strength criterion. They commissioned and instrumented a Hoek cell capable of testing 300 mm by 150 mm diameter cylindrical specimens under triaxial loading with electronic

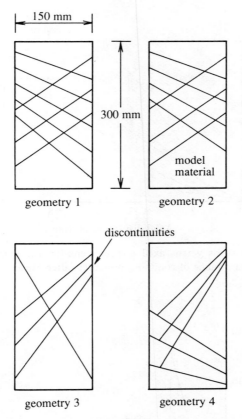

Figure 9.20 Four discontinuity geometries for 150 mm diameter specimens (after Meyers, 1992).

data logging of cell pressure, piston load and piston displacement. A linear displacement pump with feedback control was also designed and built to permit the control of cell pressure to within ±3 kPa and the measurement of changes in sample volume to within 0.05 ml (Meyers and Priest, 1992a). Meyers and Priest (1992b) developed a technique for making reproducible cylindrical specimens containing partially- or fully-cutting inclined discontinuities. This technique involved the cutting of 150 mm diameter cylindrical specimens of high density foam with a hot wire to produce the desired fracture geometries. The foam elements were then cast into silicone rubber to create a matched group of re-usable moulds. The selected model material was then poured into the moulds to create a set of model elements which were then assembled within a cylindrical paper former, as shown in Figure 9.19, prior to

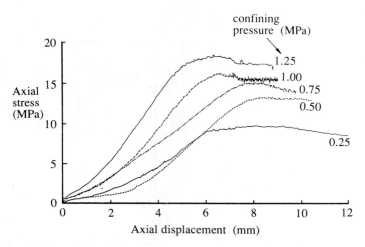

Figure 9.21 Axial stress versus axial displacement for a specimen of discontinuity geometry 2, tested at a range of confining pressures (after Meyers, 1992).

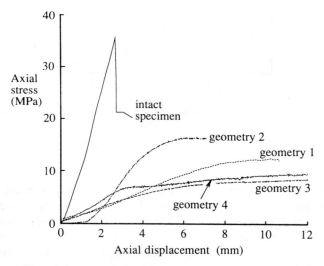

Figure 9.22 Axial stress versus axial displacement for a range of discontinuity geometries tested at a confining pressure of 1 MPa (after Meyers, 1992).

being lowered into the triaxial cell for testing. This approach allowed identical fracture geometries to be reproduced many times in a range of material types.

Series of 73 uniaxial compression tests, 68 triaxial tests and 63 shear box tests were conducted by Meyers (1991) on specimens made from various combinations of a proprietary gypsum based material, Patternstone-F, sand and celite to determine the mechanical properties of both the material and of planar discontinuities cutting through the material. A total of 157 blocky specimens, with four different discontinuity geometries shown in Figure 9.20, containing 8, 7, 4 and 6 discontinuities and 20, 17, 8 and 10 block elements, respectively, were assembled and then tested in the triaxial cell at confining pressures ranging from 0.25 to 1.25 MPa. Figure 9.21 shows graphs of axial stress versus axial displacement for geometry 2 tested over this range of confining pressures. Typical graphs of axial stress versus axial displacement for the intact model material and the four discontinuity geometries tested at a confining pressure of 1 MPa are presented in Figure 9.22. These graphs illustrate the dominant influence that discontinuity geometry can have on strength and deformability. At the time of writing, these tests results were being evaluated in the context of the analytical models for rock strength presented in this chapter and by reference to the predictions of discrete element modelling described in section 10.6.2.

EXERCISES FOR CHAPTER 9

9.1

A simple tilt test on a dry sample of limestone, containing a specimen of an unweathered bedding plane, produced slip on the discontinuity at an inclination of 64°. The gross contact area during shearing was 132.4 cm², the volume of the upper block was 1.373 litres and the mass of the upper block was 3.640 kg. A tilt test on a dry, smooth, sawn specimen of the limestone produced slip at an inclination of 33°. Compression tests on the limestone rock material gave a mean uniaxial compressive strength of 42 MPa. A bedding plane in the limestone rock mass forms the sliding plane for a major rigid block failure mechanism in which the effective normal stress across the discontinuity is computed to be 260 kPa.

(i) Estimate the joint roughness coefficient JRC for the bedding plane and,
(ii) assuming that the sliding plane has the same JRC, estimate its shear strength at the computed effective normal stress.

9.2

A dry cylindrical specimen of weak fractured mudstone contains four through-going planar discontinuities that have the following Coulomb shear strength parameters and are orientated such that their normals make the following angles θ_d with the cylinder axis:

Discontinuity	Cohesion c_d MPa	Friction angle ϕ_d Degrees	Orientation θ_d Degrees
1	0.3	30	35
2	0.1	38	43
3	0.1	36	56
4	0.2	40	75

The strength of the rock material can be modelled by the Coulomb criterion with shear strength parameters $c_m = 1.5\,\text{MPa}$, $\phi_m = 40°$. The specimen is subjected to a confining pressure of $\sigma_3 = 5.0\,\text{MPa}$ in a triaxial test cell. Calculate the theoretical axial major principal stress σ_1 at which the specimen will fail either by slip along one of the discontinuities or by shear failure of intact rock.

9.3

Five 150 mm diameter, 300 mm long cylindrical specimens of dry, weak mudstone were tested in the following way: (a) each specimen was placed in a Hoek cell under zero confining pressure and then loaded through yield to an axial compression of 2 mm, (b) a confining pressure was then applied and the (now fractured) specimen was loaded through yield by compressing it a further 10 mm. The following data were obtained:

Specimen	Peak axial load under uniaxial compression MN	Confining pressure MPa	Peak axial load under triaxial compression MN
1	1.103	4	0.441
2	1.136	8	0.669
3	1.087	12	0.842
4	1.115	16	1.018
5	1.064	20	1.156

Apply graphical techniques to estimate the empirical constants R_m and s in the Hoek–Brown failure criterion for the fractured rock created by uniaxial compression.

9.4

An 85 mm long, 41 mm diameter cylindrical specimen of unfractured quartzitic sandstone failed at a uniaxial load of 87.5 kN. Calculate its uniaxial compressive strength (in MPa).

Geologists advise that the same quartzitic sandstone exposed in the walls of an open stope is in a relatively undisturbed state with an estimated Rock Mass Rating of 75. Numerical modelling of the fully-developed stope indicates that in a particular region the hanging-wall rock will be subjected to a uniaxial compressive stress of 19 MPa. Apply the Hoek–Brown empirical rock mass strength criterion to determine whether there is likely to be local failure of the rock in this region of the stope. If you find that local failure is likely to occur, calculate the minimum support pressure that would be required to stabilise the hanging wall of the stope in this region.

Answers to these exercises are given on pages 463–4.

10

Discontinuities and rock deformability

10.1 INTRODUCTION

Discontinuities can have an influence on rock mass deformability by a combination of one or more of the following processes:

(i) Displacement of the adjacent blocks can create an air space, or open aperture, that has negligible stiffness compared with the surrounding rock material.

(ii) Shear displacement along a discontinuity with an irregular surface can create a mismatch between the adjacent surfaces. Normal compression across such a discontinuity will lead to local crushing at the contact points and a relatively complex normal force-normal displacement characteristic that depends on such factors as the initial surface geometry, the elastic properties of the rock material and the post-peak characteristics of the rock.

(iii) The rock material adjacent to the discontinuity can weather, can become fractured by shear displacement, or the discontinuity can become filled with imported material, to create a zone that has different mechanical properties from the surrounding rock material.

In most cases the above processes produce a zone of material that is more deformable than the surrounding rock, with an areal extent that reflects the geometry of the original discontinuity and a thickness ranging from a fraction of a millimetre to several metres. In this chapter we are concerned with the influence that such discontinuities can have on the deformability of the rock mass. Rock mass deformability can be a crucial parameter in the design of foundations for large structures such as dams, bridges and high-rise buildings, and in the design of pressure tunnels. Sections 10.2 to 10.4 present some of the basic principles of rock material deformability, discontinuity stiffness and strain energy. Section 10.5 draws on experimental results and analytical models in a discussion of the factors that influence the normal and shear stiffness of discontinuities. This section is followed by a brief survey of the analytical and numerical methods that have been adopted to predict the influence of discontinuities on rock mass deformability.

10.2 PRINCIPLES OF DEFORMABILITY, STIFFNESS, STRAIN ENERGY AND CONSTITUTIVE RELATIONS FOR A CONTINUUM

The concept of deformability of a continuous material can be understood by considering the uniaxial loading of a cylindrical specimen of length L and diameter D subjected to a uniform uniaxial force F, as shown in Figure 10.1a. Changes in L and D relative to their values at zero load are l and d, respectively. Taking compressive forces and contractile values of l and d to be positive, we would expect a response such as that shown diagrammatically in Figure 10.1b. If the axial force is kept well within the load capacity band for the specimen, it is reasonable to assume that compressive axial force will produce a gradual reduction in length and an increase in diameter of the specimen, and that a tensile axial force will increase the length and reduce the diameter.

Materials such as unfractured rocks generally exhibit non-linear load-displacement characteristics, particularly at small loads and at loads that exceed about 80% of the load capacity. Characterisation of the deformability properties of materials such as rocks must take account of their non-linear properties by specifying the loads at which properties are measured. The secant force stiffness K_{sec} is defined as follows

$$K_{sec} = \frac{F_{sec}}{l_{sec}} \tag{10.1}$$

where l_{sec} is the total axial displacement produced by changing the axial force from zero to F_{sec}. The tangent force stiffness K_{tan} is defined as

$$K_{tan} = \frac{\Delta F_{tan}}{\Delta l_{tan}} \tag{10.2}$$

where $\Delta F_{tan}/\Delta l_{tan}$ is the slope of a straight line that is tangential to the axial force-axial displacement curve at some specified axial force F_{tan}. Stiffnesses that link lateral displacement to axial force are rarely used.

The conventional method of plotting force-displacement curves, with force on the ordinate axis, carries the implicit understanding that force is the dependent variable, varying according to some function $F = f(l)$ of the

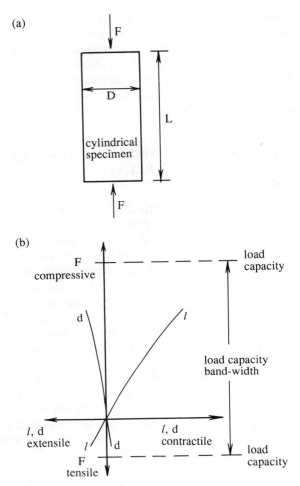

Figure 10.1 Response of a cylindrical specimen to uniaxial loading: (a) specimen geometry; (b) diagrammatic idealised force-displacement relation.

independent variable l, the change in specimen length from its value at zero load. The work done, and therefore the total strain energy stored in the specimen during a small axial displacement δl associated with a small change in the axial load from F to F + δF is approximately F δl. In the limit as δl approaches zero the total strain energy stored during a displacement from l_1 to l_2 is given by

$$W = \int_{l_1}^{l_2} f(l)\,dl \tag{10.3}$$

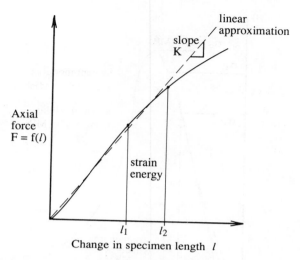

Figure 10.2   Strain energy stored during axial loading.

which is the area beneath the load-displacement curve between l_1 and l_2, as shown in Figure 10.2. For materials that exhibit approximately linear load-displacement characteristics the secant and tangent force stiffnesses can be represented by the linear force stiffness K. Hence $f(l) = Kl$ and the total strain energy stored during a displacement from l_1 to l_2 is given by

$$W = K\left(\frac{l_2^2 - l_1^2}{2}\right)$$ (10.4)

The parameters in equations 10.1 to 10.4 depend upon the size of the specimen as well as the properties of the material from which it is made. For extensive materials such as rocks it is desirable to divide force by area to give traction (pressure or stress) and to divide displacement by length to give strain, in order to provide quantities that are independent of specimen size. Axial stress σ_a, axial strain ε_a and lateral strain ε_d for a cylindrical specimen of initial length L, initial diameter D and cross-sectional area $A = \pi D^2/4$ are given by

$$\sigma_a = \frac{F}{A} \qquad \varepsilon_a = \frac{l}{L} \qquad \text{and} \qquad \varepsilon_d = \frac{d}{D}$$ (10.5)

Graphs of axial stress, axial strain and diametral strain, which are simply scaled versions of the force-displacement curves in Figure 10.1, can be plotted for a given specimen as shown in Figure 10.3. The typically non-linear response of most materials imposes the usual constraints on the definition and measurement of stiffness. In this case the ratio σ_a/ε_a is referred to as the axial

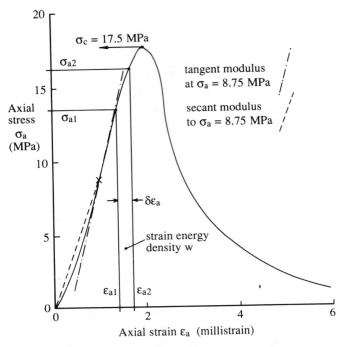

Figure 10.3 Axial stress versus axial strain for a 125 mm long, 50 mm diameter specimen of Bath limestone tested under uniaxial compression at a moisture content of 0.42%.

deformation modulus M. As with stiffness it is appropriate to define a secant modulus M_{sec} and a tangent modulus M_{tan} which can either be scaled directly from the stress-strain curve or calculated from the equivalent secant and tangent stiffnesses as follows

$$M_{sec} = K_{sec}\frac{L}{A} \qquad M_{tan} = K_{tan}\frac{L}{A} \qquad (10.6)$$

For an ideal linear elastic material $M_{sec} = M_{tan} = \sigma_a/\varepsilon_a = E$, the Young's modulus, and $-\varepsilon_d/\varepsilon_a = \nu$ the Poisson's ratio. It is necessary to introduce the negative sign in this latter expression since ε_d and ε_a will have opposite signs under uniaxial loading.

As with force-displacement curves, the conventional way of plotting stress-strain curves, with stress on the ordinate axis, carries the implication that axial stress is the dependent variable, varying according to some function $\sigma_a = g(\varepsilon_a)$ of the independent variable ε_a, which is the axial strain relative to the zero load condition. Axial force is $A \sigma_a$ and the axial displacement increment $\delta l = L \delta\varepsilon_a$, where $\delta\varepsilon_a$ is a small increment in axial strain. The work done, and therefore the total strain energy stored in the specimen during a small increment in axial strain $\delta\varepsilon_a$ associated with a small change in the axial stress from σ_a to $\sigma_a + \delta\sigma_a$ is approximately $A \sigma_a L \delta\varepsilon_a$. In the limit as $\delta\varepsilon_a$ approaches zero the total energy stored between axial strains ε_{a1} and ε_{a2} is given by

$$W = AL \int_{\varepsilon_{a1}}^{\varepsilon_{a2}} g(\varepsilon_a)\, d\varepsilon_a \qquad (10.7)$$

The term under the integral sign is the area beneath the axial stress-axial strain curve between strains ε_{a1} and ε_{a2} as shown in Figure 10.3. The product AL is, of course, the volume of the cylindrical specimen, so the area beneath the axial stress-axial strain curve is the strain energy per unit volume of specimen, or strain energy density w. For an ideal linear elastic material of Young's modulus E, the strain energy stored per unit volume under an increment in uniaxial stress σ_{a1} to σ_{a2} associated with an increment in axial strain ε_{a1} to ε_{a2} is given by the area of the triangular region beneath the stress-strain curve as follows

$$w = \left(\frac{\sigma_{a2}\varepsilon_{a2} - \sigma_{a1}\varepsilon_{a1}}{2}\right) = E\left(\frac{\varepsilon_{a2}^2 - \varepsilon_{a1}^2}{2}\right) \qquad (10.8)$$

10.3 CONSTITUTIVE RELATIONS

Equations that enable us to calculate stresses from strains, or vice versa, for a material are called the constitutive relations. Adopting the Cartesian system of Appendix E, the components of the stress tensor $[\sigma]$ and the strain tensor $[\varepsilon]$ can be presented as column arrays as follows

$$[\sigma] = \begin{bmatrix} \sigma_{xx} \\ \sigma_{yy} \\ \sigma_{zz} \\ \sigma_{xy} \\ \sigma_{yz} \\ \sigma_{zx} \end{bmatrix} \qquad [\varepsilon] = \begin{bmatrix} \varepsilon_{xx} \\ \varepsilon_{yy} \\ \varepsilon_{zz} \\ \varepsilon_{xy} \\ \varepsilon_{yz} \\ \varepsilon_{zx} \end{bmatrix}$$

In some texts the strain terms ε_{xy}, ε_{yz} and ε_{zx} are replaced by $\gamma_{xy}/2$, $\gamma_{yz}/2$ and $\gamma_{zx}/2$ where γ_{xy}, γ_{yz} and γ_{zx} are shear strain components defined as the change in angle (radians) between a pair of lines that were originally at right angles to each other and in alignment with the pair of coordinate axes given by the subscripts. The general form of the constitutive relations for a linear elastic material is as follows

$$[\varepsilon] = [S][\sigma] \qquad (10.9)$$

where $[S]$ is a 6 by 6 matrix of coefficients referred to as the **stiffness matrix**. Reciprocity and the conservation of energy dictate that the matrix $[S]$ is symmetrical, so there are a maximum of 21 independent elastic constants. This number of elastic constants would only be required if the material were completely anisotropic; reduced levels of anisotropy necessitate fewer independent or non-zero terms in the stiffness matrix. For example, orthotropic materials require 9 independent terms, transversely isotropic materials require 5, while isotropic materials require only two independent elastic constants as follows

$$[S] = \begin{bmatrix} \dfrac{1}{E} & \dfrac{-v}{E} & \dfrac{-v}{E} & 0 & 0 & 0 \\[2mm] \dfrac{-v}{E} & \dfrac{1}{E} & \dfrac{-v}{E} & 0 & 0 & 0 \\[2mm] \dfrac{-v}{E} & \dfrac{-v}{E} & \dfrac{1}{E} & 0 & 0 & 0 \\[2mm] 0 & 0 & 0 & \dfrac{(1+v)}{E} & 0 & 0 \\[2mm] 0 & 0 & 0 & 0 & \dfrac{(1+v)}{E} & 0 \\[2mm] 0 & 0 & 0 & 0 & 0 & \dfrac{(1+v)}{E} \end{bmatrix}$$

where E and v are Young's modulus and Poisson's ratio for the isotropic elastic continuum. The terms in the stiffness matrix will be referred to by their row and column numbers as $S_{row, column}$. So for isotropic materials $S_{11} = S_{22} = S_{33} = 1/E$, $S_{12} = S_{13} = S_{21} = S_{23} = S_{31} = S_{32} = -v/E$, $S_{44} = S_{55} = S_{66} = (1 + v)/E$ and all other terms are zero. The shear modulus for the isotropic elastic continuum is given by $G = E/(2(1 + v))$ so the terms S_{44}, S_{55} and S_{66}, which link shear stresses and shear strains, may be replaced by $1/(2G)$. The inverse form of equation 10.9 is as follows

$$[\sigma] = [C][\varepsilon] \tag{10.10}$$

where [C] is a symmetrical 6 by 6 matrix which is generally referred to as the **compliance matrix**. The terms in this compliance matrix can be found by direct inversion of the stiffness matrix. Adopting the same row and column numbering system as before, $C_{11} = C_{22} = C_{33} = E(1 - v)/[(1 + v)(1 - 2v)]$, $C_{12} = C_{13} = C_{21} = C_{23} = C_{31} = C_{32} = Ev/[(1 + v)(1 - 2v)]$, $C_{44} = C_{55} = C_{66} = E/(1 + v) = 2G$ and all other terms are zero for a linear elastic isotropic material.

10.4 PRINCIPLES OF DEFORMABILITY, STIFFNESS AND STRAIN ENERGY FOR A DISCONTINUITY

It is desirable to define the deformability of a single discontinuity as the ratio of stress (rather than force) to displacement in order to yield values that can be applied to discontinuities of unknown areal extent within rock masses. The discontinuity normal stress stiffness k_n is defined as

$$k_n = \frac{\Delta \sigma_n}{\Delta v} \tag{10.11}$$

where Δv is an increment in normal displacement across the discontinuity produced by an increment $\Delta \sigma_n$ in normal stress. The discontinuity shear stress stiffness is

$$k_s = \frac{\Delta \tau}{\Delta u} \tag{10.12}$$

where Δu is an increment in shear displacement along the discontinuity produced by a shear stress increment $\Delta \tau$ in the direction of Δu. Discontinuities always exhibit markedly non-linear stress-displacement characteristics so it is crucial to indicate whether the normal and shear stress stiffnesses are secant ($k_{n,sec}$, $k_{s,sec}$) or tangent ($k_{n,tan}$, $k_{s,tan}$) and to specify the stress levels at which the stiffnesses are measured or defined. There can be difficulties in assigning material properties to discontinuities that contain no material. In particular, a discontinuity that is tightly closed may exhibit infinite normal and shear stress stiffnesses. Discontinuities are assumed to have zero tensile strength so normal stiffness is zero under tensile stress. It is not helpful to consider strain energy density for discontinuities, which may have a negligible volume; indeed the strain energy is stored in the surrounding rock material. The total strain energy apparently stored by displacement across, or along, a discontinuity can be found by taking the products $A_d \Delta \sigma_n \Delta v$ or $A_d \Delta \tau \Delta u$, respectively, where A_d is the area of the discontinuity. As before, the area beneath graphs of force ($A_d \Delta \sigma_n$ or $A_d \Delta \tau$) versus displacement (Δv or Δu) give the total strain energy. Discontinuities, particularly those with infilling, are often highly inelastic so only a small proportion of this strain energy may be recovered during unloading; the lost energy is dissipated in local crushing and shearing of the asperities.

The reciprocal of stress stiffness is generally referred to as compliance c, given by relative displacement divided by stress. In general there are three stress components that can produce displacements on a discontinuity: one normal stress and two shear stresses. These stresses can produce three components of displacement on the discontinuity: one normal and two shear. If we represent the three stresses and three displacements as a pair of 3 by 1 column matrices $[\sigma]$ and $[\delta]$, they can be linked by a 3 by 3 compliance matrix $[c]$ through vector multiplication as follows (Sun et al., 1985)

$$[\delta] = [c][\sigma]$$

The above compliance matrix is analogous to, but not the same as, the compliance matrix for a continuum discussed in section 10.3. The 3 by 3 stiffness matrix $[k]$ can be defined such that

$$[\sigma] = [k][\delta]$$

It follows, therefore, that $[k]$ is the inverse of $[c]$. Sun *et al.* (1985) noted that if the compliance matrix has non-zero components only on its leading diagonal, then the stiffness matrix will also have non-zero components only on its leading diagonal, with values given by the reciprocal of the corresponding components of the compliance matrix.

Non-zero off-diagonal components of the compliance matrix indicate, for example, that an increment of a particular shear stress can produce an increment of normal displacement or that an increment of normal stress produces some shear displacement. This characteristic, which is commonly observed in rough discontinuities, carries the requirement that, in general, stiffness terms should be evaluated by inversion of the complete compliance matrix and not by taking the reciprocal of individual components. Elements of the compliance matrix can be found experimentally by holding two of the stresses constant (for example at zero) and then monitoring the three relative displacement components associated with changes in the third stress component. Elements of the stiffness matrix can be found experimentally by monitoring changes in the three stress components required to maintain two of the displacement components at zero while producing specified changes in the third displacement component. It is clear that conventional discontinuity testing methods discussed in Chapter 9 are directed towards the measurement of compliance terms; the direct measurement of stiffness terms requires sophisticated closed-loop servo-controlled systems that are beyond the budgets of most rock mechanics testing laboratories. Most authors (including this one) continue to refer to discontinuity stiffness, even though the values have been obtained from compliance tests. Strictly speaking, unless the compliance matrix has off-diagonal components that are zero, such 'stiffness' values should be interpreted as 'reciprocal-compliance' terms and not as components of the stiffness matrix. Some may regard these points as excessively pedantic, particularly in view of the great difficulties that are encountered in the characterisation, sampling and testing of natural discontinuities. It is, none the less, desirable at least to be aware of the theoretical background. Those who wish to learn more about discontinuity compliance and its experimental determination are advised to read the authoritative papers by Sun *et al.* (1985) and Amadei and Saeb (1990).

10.5 DEFORMABILITY OF A SINGLE DISCONTINUITY

10.5.1 Normal stiffness

A discontinuity subjected to increments in normal stress and shear stress will exhibit local normal displacements and shear displacements, which may be expected to depend on the following factors (Bandis *et al.*, 1983; Bandis 1990):

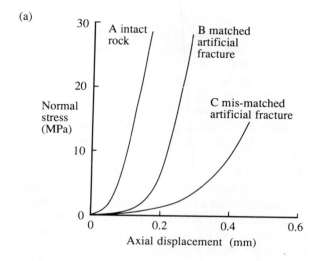

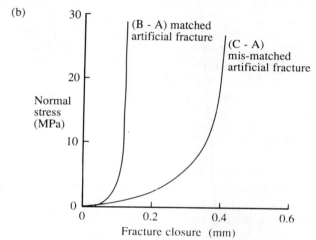

Figure 10.4   Normal compression of an artificial fracture in a specimen of granodiorite: (a) total displacement; (b) fracture closure (after Goodman, 1976).

1. the initial surface geometry of the discontinuity,
2. the geometrical match between the two surfaces; in particular the variation in aperture and the initial contact area,
3. the strength and deformability of the rock material adjacent to the discontinuity,
4. the thickness and mechanical properties of any infill material, and
5. the current values of shear and normal stress on the discontinuity.

It is assumed that the discontinuity cannot sustain a tensile normal stress and that there will be a limiting compressive stress beyond which the discontinuity is mechanically indistinguishable from the surrounding rock material. Figure 10.4 after Goodman (1976) contains the results of some simple tests that illustrate the above points. Curves A, B and C in Figure 10.4a show axial stress versus total axial displacement for a cylindrical specimen 91 mm long and 44 mm in diameter. Curve A is for intact rock material, curve B is the same specimen containing a perfectly matched artificial fracture running normal to the loading axis, and curve C is the same specimen with the upper block rotated to create mismatched surfaces. The displacement due to compression of the rock material has been subtracted from curves B and C in Figure 10.4b to isolate discontinuity closure. These curves show that both in its matched and mismatched attitudes the fracture has a dramatic influence on specimen deformability at normal stresses up to about 5 MPa. When taken to a stress level of 5 MPa, curves A, B and C give secant deformation moduli for the cylindrical specimen of approximately 5.7, 2.4 and 1.4 GPa, respectively. In its matched attitude the fracture becomes mechanically indistinguishable at a normal stress of about 15 MPa after a normal closure of 0.11 mm; the corresponding values for the mismatched fracture are approximately 25 MPa and 0.38 mm. When taken to a stress level of 5 MPa, the matched fracture has a secant normal stress stiffness of 47.6 MPa mm^{-1} while the unmatched fracture has a stiffness of only 18.2 MPa mm^{-1}.

Goodman (1976) proposed the following hyperbolic relation between normal stress σ_n and normal displacement Δv

$$\sigma_n = \sigma_{ni} + R\sigma_{ni} \left(\frac{\Delta v}{\Delta v_{max} - \Delta v}\right)^t \qquad \Delta v < \Delta v_{max} \qquad (10.13)$$

where σ_{ni} is the initial seating pressure such that $\Delta \sigma_n = \sigma_n - \sigma_{ni}$, Δv_{max} is the maximum normal displacement produced by increasing σ_n from the specified seating pressure, and the parameters R and t are determined experimentally. Taking an arbitrary seating pressure of 0.5 MPa, Goodman found that the relation for the matched fracture in Figure 10.4a could be represented by taking R = 3.0 and t = 0.605 and that the unmatched fracture could be modelled by R = 5.95 and t = 0.609.

Figures 10.5 and 10.6, from Bandis *et al.* (1983), summarise the results of compression tests on various weathered and unweathered discontinuities, including joints, bedding and cleavage, in a range of rock types. These figures contain graphs of normal stress versus normal displacement taken relative to the discontinuity aperture at the start of each loading cycle, for three cycles of loading. The measured parameters σ_d, JRC and e_i listed on each graph are the compressive strength of the rock material immediately adjacent to the discontinuity, the Joint Roughness Coefficient and the average initial aperture measured by feeler gauges. The parameter JRC, devised by Barton (1976), provides a measure of the roughness of the discontinuity surface in the ap-

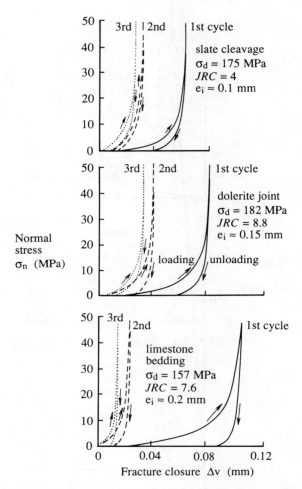

Figure 10.5 Normal stress σ_n versus discontinuity closure Δv for **unweathered** discontinuities in a range of rock types for three loading cycles; experimental data points omitted (after Bandis *et al.*, 1983).

proximate range 0 (smooth) to 20 (very rough). The measurement and estimation of JRC and σ_d are discussed in section 9.2.3; discontinuity aperture is
discussed further in Chapter 11 in the context of fluid flow. Figures 10.5 and
10.6 confirm that the normal stress-displacement relation is highly non-linear
and that there is an identifiable first-cycle maximum closure of between about
0.06 and 0.1 mm for unweathered discontinuities and between about 0.3 and
0.4 mm for weathered discontinuities. This maximum closure reduces significantly in all cases under repeated loading.

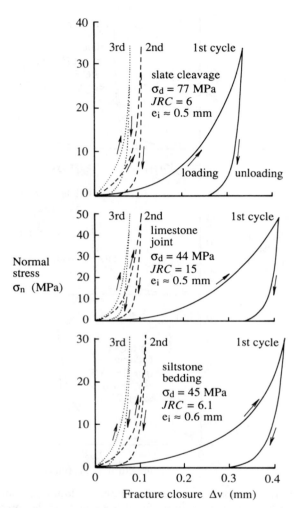

Figure 10.6 Normal stress σ_n versus discontinuity closure Δv for **weathered** discontinuities in a range of rock types for three loading cycles; experimental data points omitted (after Bandis *et al.*, 1983).

Bandis *et al.* (1983) investigating the suitability of equation 10.13 for modelling compression tests on the unweathered discontinuities, identified certain limitations in the hyperbolic relation. They proposed an alternative expression that gives the normal stress σ_n for a specific small initial seating stress σ_{ni} as follows

$$\sigma_n - \sigma_{ni} = \frac{\Delta v}{a - b\Delta v} \tag{10.14}$$

where a and b are empirical constants. When σ_n becomes very large, Δv approaches its limiting value Δv_{max}. A zero value on the denominator of equation 10.14, which gives an infinite value for σ_n, can be obtained by setting $\Delta v = a/b = \Delta v_{max}$. Bandis *et al.* obtained an expression for the normal stress stiffness $k_{n,tan}$ by taking the first derivative of σ_n with respect to Δv as follows

$$k_{n,tan} = \frac{\partial(\sigma_n - \sigma_{ni})}{\partial \Delta v} = \frac{1}{a\left(1 - \dfrac{b\Delta v}{a}\right)^2} \tag{10.15}$$

When $\Delta v = 0$ the initial normal tangent stiffness $k_{ni,tan} = 1/a$. It is now possible to replace the parameters a and b in equations 10.14 and 10.15 by $1/k_{ni,tan}$ and $1/(\Delta v_{max} k_{ni,tan})$, respectively, to give the following results

$$\sigma_n - \sigma_{ni} = \frac{k_{ni,tan} \Delta v \, \Delta v_{max}}{\Delta v_{max} - \Delta v} \tag{10.16}$$

or

$$\Delta v = \left(\frac{k_{ni,tan}}{(\sigma_n - \sigma_{ni})} + \frac{1}{\Delta v_{max}}\right)^{-1} \tag{10.17}$$

and

$$k_{n,tan} = k_{ni,tan}\left(1 - \frac{(\sigma_n - \sigma_{ni})}{(\sigma_n - \sigma_{ni}) + (k_{ni,tan} \Delta v_{max})}\right)^{-2} \tag{10.18}$$

Bandis *et al.* (1983) omitted the initial seating stress σ_{ni} from their expressions for normal stress and normal stiffness. This omission creates minor difficulties when dealing with non-zero values of seating stress. Although the initial seating stress does appear explicitly in equations 10.14 to 10.18, the values Δv_{max} and $k_{ni,tan}$ obtained in a particular test are themselves critically dependent on the selected value of σ_{ni}. In practice $k_{ni,tan}$ can be estimated from the secant slope of the stress displacement curve at a small value of Δv. Bandis *et al.* found that equation 10.16 provided a good representation of the normal stress-normal displacement characteristics for natural discontinuities in slate, dolerite and limestone.

In a multiple regression analysis of their experimental data, Bandis *et al.* (1983) found that the maximum closure Δv_{max} could be estimated from the compressive strength of the rock material immediately adjacent to the discontinuity σ_d, and the average initial aperture e_i measured by feeler gauges, as follows

$$\Delta v_{max} \approx R\left(\frac{\sigma_d}{e_i}\right)^S \tag{10.19}$$

where the units for Δv_{max} and e_i are mm, those for σ_d are MPa, and the empirical parameters R and S are as tabulated below.

Table 10.1 Empirical parameters in equation 10.19

Parameter	Cycle 1	Cycle 2	Cycle 3
R	8.57	4.46	6.41
S	−0.68	−0.65	−0.72

Analyses by Bandis *et al.* of experimental data for discontinuities with different values of the Joint Roughness Coefficient *JRC* indicated that the following relation was appropriate

$$\Delta v_{max} \approx A + B(\textit{JRC}) + C\left(\frac{\sigma_d}{e_i}\right)^D \qquad (10.20)$$

where again the units for Δv_{max} and e_i are mm, those for σ_d are MPa, and the empirical parameters A,B,C and D are as tabulated below.

Table 10.2 Empirical parameters in equation 10.20

Parameter	Cycle 1	Cycle 2	Cycle 3
A	−0.2960	−0.1005	−0.1032
B	−0.0056	−0.0073	−0.0074
C	2.2410	1.0082	1.1350
D	−0.2450	−0.2301	−0.2510

The negative values for C given by Bandis *et al.* (1983) for the first and second cycles are presumably typographical errors and have been corrected in Table 10.2. Bandis *et al.* quoted 68% confidence band-widths that were typically between ±30% and ±55% of the values in Table 10.2, indicating that there was a significant spread in the experimental data. They emphasised that equation 10.20 is only applicable to unfilled, interlocked discontinuities for which *JRC* lies between 5 and 15, σ_d is between 22 and 182 MPa, e_i is between 0.1 and 0.6 mm and σ_{ni} is less than 1 kPa. Bandis *et al.* went on to suggest that the initial discontinuity aperture e_i in mm under a normal stress of approximately 1 kPa could be estimated with fair approximation from

$$e_i \approx \textit{JRC}\left(\frac{0.04\sigma_c}{\sigma_d} - 0.02\right) \qquad (10.21)$$

where e_i is in mm and σ_c is the uniaxial compressive strength of the rock material.

The initial normal stiffness $k_{ni,tan}$ can be estimated from

$$k_{ni,tan} \approx -7.15 + 1.75 \mathcal{J}RC + 0.02 \left(\frac{\sigma_d}{e_i} \right) \qquad (10.22)$$

where the units for $k_{ni,tan}$, σ_d and e_i are MPa mm^{-1}, MPa and mm, respectively. Bandis *et al.* also found that the normal stiffness for mismatched discontinuities $k_{n,tan,mis}$ was significantly lower than that for matched specimens $k_{n,tan,mat}$ given by equations 10.18 to 10.21, and that $k_{n,tan,mis}$ could be estimated as follows

$$k_{n,tan,mis} \approx \frac{k_{n,tan,mat}}{2.0 + 0.0004(\mathcal{J}RC \, \sigma_d \sigma_n)} \qquad (10.23)$$

Equations 10.16 to 10.23 provide a valuable, practical method for obtaining a first estimate of the normal stress-normal displacement relation for rough discontinuities. The primary input data are the rock strength values σ_c and σ_d, and the Joint Roughness Coefficient $\mathcal{J}RC$ which can be estimated by following the methods explained in Chapter 10. The initial aperture e_i can be estimated from equation 10.21 and then input either to equation 10.19 or 10.20 to estimate the maximum normal displacement Δv_{max} for the particular loading cycle. The initial normal stiffness $k_{ni,tan}$ found from equation 10.22 can then be input to equation 10.16, to obtain the normal stress for a specified value of normal displacement $\Delta v < \Delta v_{max}$, and can be input to equation 10.18 to obtain the associated normal stiffness for an interlocked or matched discontinuity. The normal stiffness for a mismatched discontinuity is given by equation 10.23.

There is a slight incompatibility between equations 10.20 and 10.21. Experimental data, which form the basis for equation 10.20, clearly show that Δv_{max} decreases almost linearly with increasing values of the roughness coefficient $\mathcal{J}RC$. Bandis *et al.* explained this somewhat unexpected behaviour by suggesting that the more effective interlocking of the rougher discontinuity surfaces not only reduces the amount of initial closure but also provides an effective lateral confinement 'thus stiffening the deformational response of the asperities'. Equation 10.21, however, predicts that the initial aperture e_i will increase linearly with $\mathcal{J}RC$. The adoption of equation 10.21 to substitute for e_i in equation 10.20 produces an expression that predicts an increase in Δv_{max} with $\mathcal{J}RC$, which runs counter to experimental observations. This conflict highlights one of the pitfalls of combining empirical expressions that have been obtained from separate groups of experimental data.

Example 10.1 (Figure 10.7)

A discontinuity in a sandstone rock material with a uniaxial compressive strength of 130 MPa is observed to have a Joint Roughness Coefficient of 10. The compressive strength of the rock material immediately adjacent to the discontinuity is estimated from Schmidt hammer rebound tests to be 105 MPa.

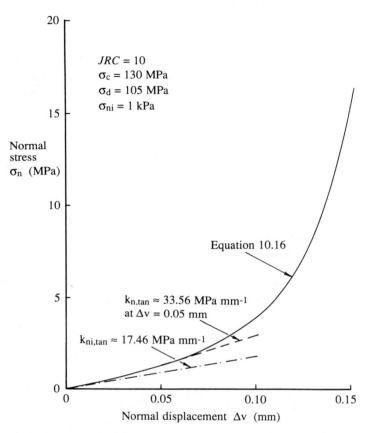

Figure 10.7 Normal stress–normal displacement relation for the discontinuity in Example 10.1.

Taking a nominal initial normal stress of 1 kPa, estimate the normal stress that would be required to close the aperture by 0.05 mm for matched surfaces. Estimate the tangent and secant normal stress stiffness at this closure. Estimate also the tangent stiffness that would apply for mismatched surfaces. Plot the theoretical variation of normal stress with normal displacement in the range 0 to 0.15 mm for this discontinuity.

Solution
Equations 10.16 to 10.22 give the following results: initial aperture $e_i \approx$ 0.295 mm (eqn 10.21), initial tangent stress stiffness $k_{ni,tan} \approx$ 17.46 MPa mm^{-1} (eqn 10.22), maximum normal displacement $\Delta v_{max} \approx$ 0.158 mm (eqn 10.19) or $\Delta v_{max} \approx$ 0.179 mm (eqn 10.20). At a normal displacement Δv

of 0.05 mm, normal stress $\sigma_n \approx 1.21$ MPa (eqn 10.16) and tangent stiffness $k_{n,tan} \approx 33.56$ MPa mm^{-1} (eqn 10.18). The secant stiffness is given by $\sigma_n/\Delta v \approx 24.23$ MPa mm^{-1}. The tangent stiffness for mismatched discontinuity surfaces is, by equation 10.23, 9.24 MPa mm^{-1}. Figure 10.7 shows the theoretical variation of normal stress with normal displacement predicted by equation 10.16, for Δv in the range 0 to 0.15 mm. This figure also contains straight lines that indicate the slope of the initial tangent stiffness, $k_{ni,tan}$ and the slope of the tangent stiffness $k_{n,tan}$ at $\Delta v = 0.05$ mm.

10.5.2 Shear stiffness

A widely accepted model for the shear strength of discontinuities, proposed by Barton (1976) and discussed in Chapter 9, predicts that the shear strength τ_f of a discontinuity subject to a normal stress σ_n in a rock material with a basic friction angle ϕ_b is given by

$$\tau_f = \sigma_n \tan\left(\phi_b + JRC \log_{10}\left(\frac{\sigma_d}{\sigma'_n}\right)\right) \tag{10.24}$$

where, as before, σ_d is the uniaxial compressive strength of the rock material immediately adjacent to the discontinuity and JRC is the Joint Roughness Coefficient. Analysing the results of shear tests on 136 discontinuities in eight different rock types, Barton and Choubey (1977) found that the shear displacement at peak shear stress, Δu_{peak} was consistently approximately 1% of the discontinuity length L measured in the direction of shear. This relation leads directly to the following expression for the secant shear stress stiffness at peak shear stress, $k_{s,sec,peak}$

$$k_{s,sec,peak} = \frac{\tau_f}{\Delta u_{peak}} = \frac{\sigma_n}{0.01L} \tan\left(\phi_b + JRC \log_{10}\left(\frac{\sigma_d}{\sigma'_n}\right)\right) \tag{10.25}$$

Bandis et al. (1981) in a survey of the peak shear stiffness $k_{s,sec,peak}$ measured on some 450 discontinuities ranging in length from 200 mm to faults extending for more than 100 km, found that for a given normal stress, shear stiffness was inversely proportional to discontinuity length, i.e. $k_{s,sec,peak} \propto 1/L$. For example, a discontinuity with a peak shear stiffness of 5 MPa mm^{-1} when tested over a length of 100 mm would be expected to have a peak shear stiffness of only 0.5 MPa mm^{-1} when tested over a length of 1 m. Although these results support the peak shear stiffness relation in equation 10.25, care should be exercised when extrapolating stiffness values from small to very large discontinuities because of the grossly inhomogeneous distribution of shear stress that can develop over large discontinuities.

Graphs of shear stress versus shear displacement, such as those in Figure 10.8 for unweathered and weathered limestone joints, and Figure 10.9 for unweathered and weathered dolerite joints, are usually non-linear, displaying a

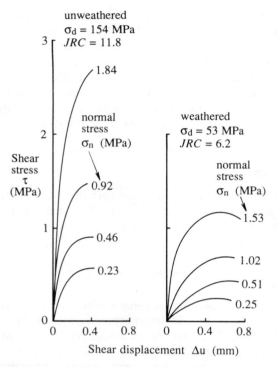

Figure 10.8 Shear stress τ versus shear displacement Δu for unweathered and weathered limestone joints; experimental data points omitted (after Bandis *et al.*, 1983).

reducing slope (i.e. a reducing tangent stiffness) at high levels of shear displacement. Duncan and Chang (1970), Kulhaway (1975) and Bandis *et al.* (1983) have utilised hyperbolic functions to model this non-linear relation between shear stress τ and relative shear displacement Δu, adopting the following general form

$$\tau = \left(\frac{1}{\Delta u \; k_{si,tan}} + \frac{1}{\tau_{ult}} \right)^{-1}$$
(10.26)

where $k_{si,tan}$ is the initial tangent shear stiffness and τ_{ult} is the ultimate shear stress at large shear displacement. Acknowledging that ultimate shear stress can be difficult to estimate or to measure, Bandis *et al.* found it convenient to replace $1/\tau_{ult}$ by the term R_f/τ_f where R_f is the **failure ratio** given by τ_f/τ_{ult}. The advantages of this substitution are that τ_f can be estimated from equation 10.24 while the failure ratio R_f has been found to vary little over a wide range of discontinuity types and surface geometries.

Figure 10.10 after Bandis *et al.* (1983) shows the variation in secant shear

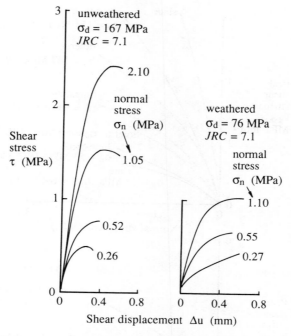

Figure 10.9 Shear stress τ versus shear displacement Δu for unweathered and weathered dolerite joints; experimental data points omitted (after Bandis *et al.*, 1983).

stress stiffness at peak shear stress, $k_{s,sec,peak}$ with normal stress in the range 0 to 2.0 MPa for discontinuities exhibiting a range of σ_d and *JRC* values in (a) dolerite, limestone and slate, and (b) sandstone materials. It is clear that shear stiffness increases with normal stress, until, at high normal stresses, the stiffness approaches a value that reflects the properties of the adjacent rock material. Bandis *et al.* (1983) also found that the initial tangent stiffness $k_{si,tan}$ increased with normal stress, and that its value could be estimated from the following power function

$$k_{si,tan} \approx k_j(\sigma_n)^{n_j} \qquad (10.27)$$

where k_j and n_j are empirical constants termed the **stiffness number** and the **stiffness exponent** respectively. From an analysis of 17 shear tests on discontinuities in dolerite, limestone, sandstone and slate for normal stresses in the range 0.23 to 2.36 MPa, Bandis *et al.* found that n_j was consistently in the range 0.615 to 1.118 $MPa^2 mm^{-1}$ with a mean of approximately 0.761, and that R_f ranged between 0.652 and 0.887 with a mean of approximately 0.783. An R_f value of less than 1.0, which indicates that $\tau_f < \tau_{ult}$, implies that dilation effects have caused strain hardening at large shear displacements. The stiff-

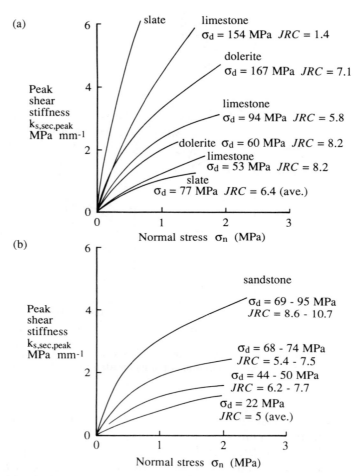

Figure 10.10 Variation of peak shear stiffness $k_{s,sec,peak}$ with normal stress σ_n for (a) discontinuities in dolerite, limestone and slate, and (b) discontinuities in sandstone; experimental data points omitted (after Bandis *et al.*, 1983).

ness number k_j ($MPa\,mm^{-1}$) was found to vary with JRC according to the following empirical relation obtained from the best fit line for 13 tests

$$k_j \approx -17.19 + 3.86JRC \qquad \text{(for } JRC > 4.5) \qquad (10.28)$$

Equation 10.26 can be re-arranged, replacing $1/\tau_{ult}$ by R_f/τ_f to give relative displacement Δu in terms of $k_{si,tan}$, τ and τ_f as follows

$$\Delta u = \left[k_{si,tan} \left(\frac{1}{\tau} - \frac{R_f}{\tau_f} \right) \right]^{-1} \qquad (10.29)$$

where τ_f and $k_{si,tan}$ are found from equations 10.24 and 10.27 respectively.

The reciprocal of the tangent shear stiffness $1/k_{s,tan}$ at a shear stress τ can be found by taking the first derivative of equation 10.29 with respect to shear stress τ, to give the following result

$$\frac{1}{k_{s,tan}} = \frac{d\Delta u}{d\tau} = \left[k_{si,tan} \left(1 - \frac{\tau R_f}{\tau_f} \right)^2 \right]^{-1}$$

so that

$$k_{s,tan} = k_{si,tan} \left(1 - \frac{\tau R_f}{\tau_f} \right)^2 \qquad (10.30)$$

The following simple example serves to illustrate the application of equations 10.24 to 10.30.

Example 10.2 (Figure 10.11)

A fresh discontinuity in a dolerite rock material with a uniaxial compressive strength of 167 MPa was found to have a Joint Roughness Coefficient of 7.1. Taking a basic friction angle of 35°, a stiffness exponent of 0.761 MPa^2 mm^{-1} and a failure ratio of 0.783 plot the shear stress versus relative shear displacement curve that you would expect for a 50 mm square sample of this discontinuity, tested under dry conditions at a normal stress of 2.1 MPa.

Solution

Inputting $\sigma_d = 167$ MPa for this fresh discontinuity into equation 10.24 gives a shear strength τ_f of 2.373 MPa. For a 50 mm specimen equation 10.25 indicates a peak secant shear stiffness $k_{s,sec,peak}$ of 4.746 MPa mm^{-1}. Taking a *JRC* of 7.1 equation 10.28 gives a stiffness number k_j of 10.216 MPa mm^{-1}. Inputting this result, together with the specified values for normal stress and the stiffness exponent, to equation 10.27 gives an initial tangent shear stiffness $k_{si,tan}$ of 17.968 MPa mm^{-1}. Putting shear stress values of 0.4, 0.8, 1.2, 1.6, 2.0 and 2.4 MPa into equation 10.29 with $R_f = 0.783$ gives relative shear displacements Δu of 0.026, 0.060, 0.111, 0.189, 0.327 and 0.642 mm, respectively. Putting these same six shear stresses into equation 10.30 gives associated tangent shear stiffnesses $k_{s,tan}$ of 13.54, 9.73, 6.56, 4.00, 2.08 and 0.78 MPa mm^{-1}, respectively. Tangent shear stiffness approaches zero when the shear stress τ approaches the ultimate value $\tau_{ult} = \tau_f/R_f = 3.031$ MPa. The dashed line in Figure 10.11 is the graph of shear stress versus shear displacement for this specimen as predicted by equation 10.29. The solid line in this figure represents experimental values reported by Bandis *et al.* (1983) for a fresh discontinuity in dolerite with *JRC* = 7.1, $\sigma_d = 167$ MPa and $\sigma_n = 2.1$ MPa; the same values adopted in this example.

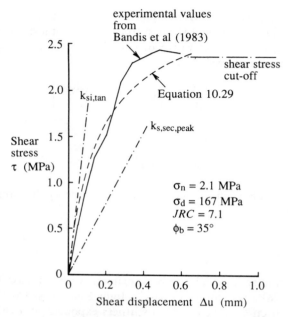

Figure 10.11 Experimental and theoretical shear stress versus shear displacement curves for a fresh discontinuity in dolerite, Example 10.2.

It is clear from the above example that the empirical methods presented in this section, for modelling shear displacement and shear stiffness, have the capacity to provide a good representation of the behaviour of natural discontinuities. The main deficiency with the model is that tangent shear stiffness is non-zero on the point of shear failure. This problem can be overcome simply by imposing a shear stress cut-off at $\tau = \tau_f$, linked to a horizontal shear stress-shear displacement relation, as shown in Figure 10.11.

10.6 THE DEFORMABILITY OF ROCK CONTAINING DISCONTINUITIES

Research discussed in the previous section has successfully addressed the problem of predicting and modelling the normal and shear deformation behaviour of single discontinuities. Our task in this section is to incorporate this information into a model that describes the behaviour of a rock mass containing several discontinuities. Two different approaches can be adopted:

1. The mechanical properties of discontinuities in a specified rock structure can be combined with the mechanical properties of the rock material to produce a constitutive relation for a continuum that is mechanically equiv-

alent to the discontinuous mass. This latter approach has the advantage of enabling relatively simple analytical and numerical models to be used for the prediction of stresses and displacements in the equivalent continuum. A number of authors, including Kulhawy and Goodman (1980), Amadei and Goodman (1981a and b), Gerrard (1982), Amadei (1983), Fossum (1985), Yoshinaka and Yamabe (1986), Chen (1989), Xiurun and Shuren (1991) and Gerrard (1991) have adopted this first approach.

2. The geometry and deformation properties of each discontinuity can be modelled explicitly to give the deformations produced by a specified stress increment. Analytical methods can be adopted for simple discontinuity geometries; numerical methods are required for complex geometries that contain more than about 5 discontinuities and that involve block interactions.

10.6.1 Equivalent continuum models

Figure 10.12a shows a cross-section through a cubical specimen of side length L containing a group of thin horizontal discontinuities at a mean vertical spacing $\bar{X}$. The specimen therefore contains a total of $L/\bar{X}$ horizontal discontinuities. The intact rock material is assumed to be isotropic and to have a constant Young's modulus E_r. Each discontinuity is assumed to have a constant normal stress stiffness k_n. If the vertical stress is increased from zero to σ_n the total vertical compression ΔL of the specimen due to deformation of the rock material and compression of the discontinuities will be

$$\Delta L = \left(\frac{L\sigma_n}{E_r}\right) + \left(\frac{L\sigma_n}{\bar{X}k_n}\right) \tag{10.31}$$

The equivalent 'Young's modulus' E_e for the discontinuous model is given by

$$E_e = \frac{\sigma_n L}{\Delta L} = \left(\frac{1}{E_r} + \frac{1}{\bar{X}k_n}\right)^{-1} \tag{10.32}$$

The discontinuous rock mass is not an elastic continuum so the term 'Young's modulus' is not strictly valid. This terminology will, however, be adopted for the equivalent continuum to emphasise the derivation of each of the constants.

Figure 10.12b shows a cross-section through the same cubical specimen. In this case the intact rock has a constant shear modulus G_r and each discontinuity is assumed to have a constant shear stress stiffness k_s. If the pure shear stress is increased from zero to τ the total horizontal displacement ΔH of the top of the specimen relative to its base, due to deformation of the rock material and shear along the discontinuities, will be

$$\Delta H = \left(\frac{L\tau}{G_r}\right) + \left(\frac{L\tau}{\bar{X}k_s}\right) \tag{10.33}$$

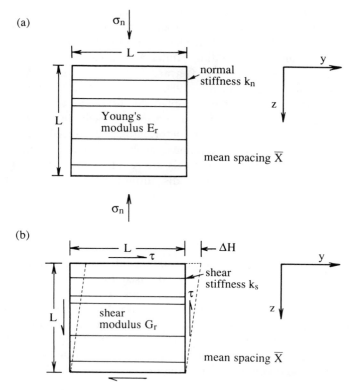

Figure 10.12 Idealised model to illustrate the deformation of a specimen containing a single set of parallel discontinuities: (a) normal compression, (b) shear displacement.

The equivalent shear modulus G_e for the material is given by

$$G_e = \frac{\tau L}{\Delta L} = \left(\frac{1}{G_r} + \frac{1}{\bar{X} k_s} \right)^{-1} \tag{10.34}$$

If the vertical direction in Figure 10.12 is the z-axis, and the x,y axes lie in the horizontal plane, then the terms of the equivalent continuum elastic stiffness matrix in equation 10.9 are $S_{11} = S_{22} = 1/E_r$, $S_{33} = 1/E_e$ (along the vertical z-axis), $S_{12} = S_{13} = S_{21} = S_{23} = S_{31} = S_{32} = -v_r/E_r$, $S_{44} = 1/(2G_r)$ (shear in the horizontal plane), $S_{55} = S_{66} = 1/(2G_e)$ and all other terms are zero. It is worth remarking that the factor 2 appears in the denominator of the last three terms because the strain matrix in equation 10.9 has been expressed in terms of the shear strain components ε_{xy}, ε_{yz} and ε_{zx} which are respectively equal to $\gamma_{xy}/2$, $\gamma_{yz}/2$ and $\gamma_{zx}/2$ where γ_{xy}, γ_{yz} and γ_{zx} are the shear strain components defined in section 10.3. The parameter v_r is the Poisson's ratio for the rock material, given by $[E_r/(2G_r)] - 1$, and does not represent an additional independent elastic constant. The stiffness matrix listed above for a rock containing a single set of parallel discontinuities has only four independent elastic constants E_r, G_r, $\bar{X}k_n$ and $\bar{X}k_s$, so the material is not strictly transversely isotropic. In a transversely isotropic material S_{12} and S_{13} are not equal; these terms are equal in the above model because it has been assumed that the elastic properties for the rock material are isotropic and that the discontinuities are too thin to contribute to any Poisson effect during deformation of the mass.

Equation 10.32 makes it possible to investigate the relation between discontinuity spacing, Young's modulus of the intact rock and the equivalent Young's modulus of the mass. The following example illustrates some typical calculations.

Example 10.3

A soft sandstone rock mass contains a set of horizontal discontinuities whose deformation properties can be characterised by a constant normal stiffness of $12.5\,\text{MPa}\,\text{mm}^{-1}$. If the intact rock material has a Young's modulus of $26.5\,\text{GPa}$, determine the ratio of the equivalent vertical Young's modulus of the rock mass to Young's modulus of the intact rock material, for mean discontinuity spacings of 0.1, 0.2, 0.5 and 1.0 m.

Solution
Inputting a Young's modulus of 26.5 GPa and a normal discontinuity stiffness of $12.5\,\text{GPa}\,\text{m}^{-1}$ ($12.5\,\text{MPa}\,\text{mm}^{-1}$) to equation 10.32 gives equivalent vertical Young's moduli of 1.194, 2.284, 5.057 and 8.494 GPa for the four mean discontinuity spacings. These results give ratios of equivalent mass modulus to intact Young's modulus of 0.045, 0.086, 0.191 and 0.321 for the four mean spacings.

If we define a modulus reduction factor M_{rf} as the ratio of the equivalent vertical Young's modulus of the rock mass to the Young's modulus of the intact rock material, rearrangement of equation 10.32 gives the following expression, which permits the direct evaluation of the modulus reduction factors calculated above

$$M_{rf} = \left(1 + \frac{E_r}{\bar{X}k_n}\right)^{-1} \tag{10.35}$$

The above simple results serve to emphasise the importance of discontinuity spacing in controlling the deformation properties of rock masses. Equation 10.22 indicates that, for typical values of initial aperture e_i between 0.1 and 1.0 mm, $k_{ni,tan}$ ($\text{MPa}\,\text{mm}^{-1}$) is likely to lie between about $0.02\,\sigma_d$ and $0.2\,\sigma_d$. Taking a modulus ratio E_r/σ_d of 200 indicates that the ratio E_r/k_n is likely to lie between about 1 and 10 m, giving a modulus reduction factor in equation

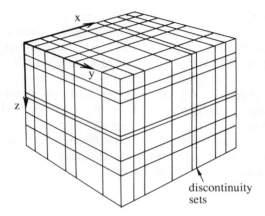

Figure 10.13 Rock mass containing three orthogonal discontinuity sets.

10.35 of between 0.01 and 0.5 for mean discontinuity spacing $\bar{X}$ in the range 0.1 to 1.0 m. These results are consistent with the modulus reduction factor of 0.07 observed for fractured chalk and discussed in section 1.4.1.

Equations 10.32 and 10.34 form the conceptual basis for the three-dimensional equivalent continuum model presented by Goodman and Duncan (1971) and Kulhawy (1978) for a rock mass containing three orthogonal discontinuity sets, as shown in Figure 10.13. If the mean spacings, normal stiffnesses and shear stiffnesses for three orthogonal discontinuity sets with normals in the x, y and z directions are, respectively, $\bar{X}_x$, k_{nx}, k_{sx}, $\bar{X}_y$, k_{ny}, k_{sy}, and $\bar{X}_z$, k_{nz}, k_{sz} then the equivalent orthotropic Young's moduli and shear moduli are

$$E_{ex} = \left(\frac{1}{E_r} + \frac{1}{\bar{X}_x k_{nx}}\right)^{-1} \tag{10.36}$$

$$G_{exy} = \left(\frac{1}{G_r} + \frac{1}{\bar{X}_x k_{sx}} + \frac{1}{\bar{X}_y k_{sy}}\right)^{-1} \tag{10.37}$$

The equivalent Poisson's ratio v_e is given by

$$v_{exy} = v_{exz} = \frac{v_r E_{ex}}{E_r} \tag{10.38}$$

where v_r is the Poisson's ratio for the isotropic intact rock material. The other six parameters that are required to describe the constitutive behaviour of this orthotropic material can be found by cyclic permutation $x \rightarrow y \rightarrow z \rightarrow x$ of the subscripts in equations 10.36 to 10.38. The terms in the equivalent continuum stiffness matrix of equation 10.9 can be found by applying the principles of anisotropic elasticity to give: $S_{11} = 1/E_{ex}$, $S_{22} = 1/E_{ey}$, $S_{33} = 1/E_{ez}$, $S_{12} =$

$S_{21} = -v_{exy}/E_{ex}$, $S_{23} = S_{32} = -v_{eyz}/E_{ey}$, $S_{31} = S_{13} = -v_{ezx}/E_{ez}$, $S_{44} = 1/(2G_{exy})$, $S_{55} = 1/(2G_{eyz})$, $S_{66} = 1/(2G_{ezx})$ with all other terms zero. The following equalities can be derived from equation 10.38 by noting that the stiffness matrix is symmetrical

$$\frac{v_{exy}}{E_{ex}} = \frac{v_{eyx}}{E_{ey}} = \frac{v_r}{E_r}, \qquad \frac{v_{eyz}}{E_{ey}} = \frac{v_{ezy}}{E_{ez}} = \frac{v_r}{E_r} \quad \text{and} \quad \frac{v_{exz}}{E_{ex}} = \frac{v_{ezx}}{E_{ez}} = \frac{v_r}{E_r}$$

The above result shows that the off-diagonal terms of the stiffness matrix $S_{12} = S_{13} = S_{21} = S_{23} = S_{31} = S_{32} = -v_r/E_r$. Although the stiffness matrix listed above for a rock containing three orthogonal sets of discontinuities has eleven independent parameters E_r, G_r, $\bar{X}_x$, k_{nx}, k_{sx}, $\bar{X}_y$, k_{ny}, k_{sy}, and $\bar{X}_z$, k_{nz}, k_{sz} the material is not strictly orthotropic. In a truly orthotropic material the off-diagonal terms listed above would not all be equal; these terms are equal in the above model because it has been assumed that the elastic properties for the rock material are isotropic.

Fossum (1985) derived a constitutive model for a rock mass that contains randomly orientated discontinuities of constant normal stiffness k_n and shear stiffness k_s. He assumed that if the discontinuities are randomly orientated, the mean discontinuity spacing would be the same in all directions taken through a representative sample of the mass. These and other aspects of the anisotropy of discontinuity frequency have been discussed in Chapter 4. Arguing that the mechanical properties of the discontinuous mass would be isotropic, Fossum derived the following expressions for the bulk modulus K_e and shear modulus G_e of the equivalent elastic continuum

$$K_e = \frac{E_r}{9} \left[\frac{3(1 + v_r)\bar{X}k_n + 2E_r}{(1 + v_r)(1 - 2v_r)\bar{X}k_n + (1 - v_r)E_r} \right] \qquad (10.39)$$

$$G_e = \frac{E_r}{30(1 + v_r)} \left[\frac{9(1 + v_r)(1 - 2v_r)\bar{X}k_n + (7 - 5v_r)E_r}{(1 + v_r)(1 - 2v_r)\bar{X}k_n + (1 - v_r)E_r} \right]$$
$$+ \frac{2}{5} \left[\frac{E_r\bar{X}k_s}{2(1 + v_r)\bar{X}k_s + E_r} \right] \qquad (10.40)$$

The equivalent Young's modulus and Poisson's ratio are obtained from

$$E_e = \frac{9K_eG_e}{3K_e + G_e} \quad \text{and} \quad v_e = \frac{3K_e - 2G_e}{2(3K_e + G_e)} \qquad (10.41)$$

At large values of mean discontinuity spacing $\bar{X}$ the equivalent moduli E_e and v_e approach the values E_r and v_r for the intact rock. At very small values of mean discontinuity spacing the equivalent moduli are given by the following expressions

$$E_e \rightarrow \frac{2E_r(7 - 5v_r)}{3(1 - v_r)(9 + 5v_r)} \quad \text{as } \bar{X} \rightarrow 0 \qquad (10.42)$$

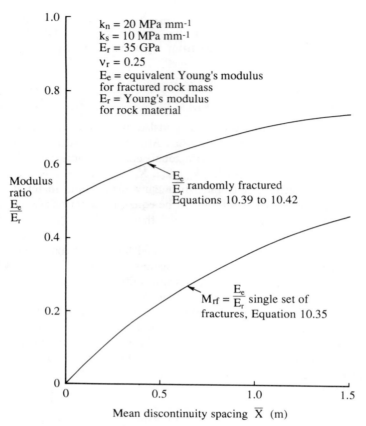

Figure 10.14 Theoretical variation of the modulus ratio M_{rf} with mean discontinuity spacing $\bar{X}$.

and

$$v_e \rightarrow \frac{(1 + 5v_r)}{(9 + 5v_r)} \quad \text{as } \bar{X} \rightarrow 0 \qquad (10.43)$$

Figure 10.14 shows the variation of the ratio E_e/E_r, given by equations 10.39 to 10.42, with mean discontinuity spacing $\bar{X}$ in the range 0 to 1.5 m for a rock mass containing discontinuities with a normal stiffness $k_n = 20\,\text{MPa mm}^{-1}$, shear stiffness $k_s = 10\,\text{MPa mm}^{-1}$ and rock material elastic moduli $E_r = 35\,\text{GPa}$, $v_r = 0.25$. The limiting value of the ratio E_e/E_r at small discontinuity spacings, given by equation 10.42, is approximately 0.5 while the limiting value of v_e by equation 10.43 is approximately 0.22 for these input parameters. Figure 10.14 also shows the theoretical relation between mean discontinuity spacing and the modulus reduction factor $M_{rf} = E_e/E_r$ given by equation 10.35 for a direction normal to a single set of parallel discontinuities, adopting the above discontinuity stiffness and rock material properties. It is interesting to note that M_{rf} for a single set of discontinuities, which ranges from 0.46 at a mean spacing of 1.5 m down to zero at very small discontinuity spacings, is significantly lower than the modulus reduction factor for the randomly fractured rock mass, which ranges from 0.74 down to 0.5 over the same range of discontinuity spacings. Bearing in mind earlier discussion in this section, it is difficult to see how a modulus reduction factor as high as 0.5 could be applicable to a very heavily fractured rock mass.

Gerrard (1991) has presented an approximate method for determining the equivalent elastic properties for a rock mass containing several sets of discontinuities. His analysis is based on the assumption that the strain energy stored in the equivalent continuum is the same as that stored in the discontinuous system. The first step is to rank the various discontinuity sets according to their mechanical significance. Taking the least significant set first, a compliance matrix for the equivalent continuum is determined by applying equations 10.32 and 10.34. This equivalent continuum is then regarded as the anisotropic 'rock material' for the next discontinuity set, and so on until all discontinuity sets have been incorporated. A rotation matrix such as equation E.2 must be applied to transform the equivalent continuum compliance matrix from local coordinate axes, associated with one discontinuity orientation, to axes associated with the next. Kaneko and Shiba (1990) applied similar principles to those adopted by Gerrard for determining the equivalent elastic properties for a rock mass. They found that the deformation behaviour predicted by their 'Equivalent Volume Defect Model' for an idealised, two-dimensional fractured mass provided a good approximation to the behaviour modelled by the displacement discontinuity method.

Although equivalent continuum models are relatively straightforward to apply, and yield results that seem to conform to expected behaviour, they do have a number of significant limitations. The most serious of these is the requirement that all discontinuities possess a constant stiffness. Experimental and theoretical work presented in section 10.5 confirm that the deformation behaviour of discontinuities is highly non-linear both in normal compression and shear. If all discontinuities are subjected to the same stress increment, constant stiffnesses based upon the secant stiffness appropriate for the particular stress range will yield acceptable results. Unfortunately, two factors ensure that stress increments will rarely be the same for discontinuities distributed through a rock mass, even if the mass is subjected to a uniform boundary stress increment. The primary factor is the orientation of discontinuities relative to an anisotropic stress field increment. Equation 9.15 shows that the normal stress increment on a discontinuity whose normal makes an angle θ with the axis of a uniaxial stress increment σ_{xx} will experience an increment in normal stress σ_n given by

$$\sigma_n = \sigma_{xx} \cos^2\theta$$

so the normal stress increment could range between zero and σ_{xx} depending on the actual angle θ. This result shows that the equivalent continuum properties for a rock mass whose discontinuities display non-linear behaviour should strictly contain information on the orientation of the stress field increment as well as the orientation of the discontinuities. The satisfaction of such a requirement would create equivalent continuum constitutive relations that are a function of the coupled rock mass-stress field system rather than providing general material properties. A secondary factor, investigated by Hyett and Hudson (1990) and by Shamir *et al.* (1990), is that the discontinuities themselves will convert a homogeneous stress field increment to a complex inhomogeneous pattern by virtue of local stress relief and stress concentrations produced by the displacement and rotation of intact blocks within the mass.

Other difficulties with equivalent continuum models include (i) stress history and stress path dependency, (ii) the strong link between shear stiffness and discontinuity size, and (iii) the separation and opening of discontinuities under local tensile stresses. These problems with equivalent continuum models have stimulated efforts to model explicitly the mechanical influence of discontinuities for a particular rock mass, excavation geometry and stress field. These explicit approaches are summarised briefly in the final section of this chapter.

10.6.2   Explicit methods

Explicit methods for evaluating the influence of discontinuities on rock deformability require the specification of discontinuity geometry, the mechanical properties of the rock material, the mechanical properties of each discontinuity and the stress changes within the zone being studied. The normal and shear displacement increments for each discontinuity are calculated and then aggregated with the displacements for other discontinuities and the rock material to provide an overall displacement for the mass. Analytical methods can only be applied for the very simplest discontinuity geometries; numerical methods are required for complex geometries that contain more than about 5 discontinuities and that involve block interactions. The following example illustrates the application of analytical methods for the prediction of displacements in a rock mass containing a small number of inclined, but non-intersecting, discontinuities.

Example 10.4 (Figure 10.15)

Figure 10.15 shows a dry cylindrical specimen of limestone, 150 mm in diameter and 300 mm long, containing three planar discontinuities P, Q and R whose normals make angles of 50°, 35° and 20°, respectively, with the speci-

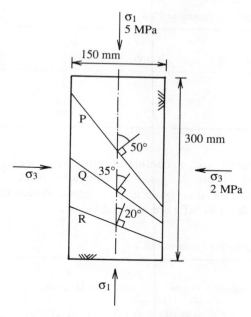

Figure 10.15 Cylindrical specimen containing three through-going discontinuities, Example 10.4.

men axis. It is assumed that the normal deformation behaviour of each discontinuity obeys equation 10.17 with the maximum displacement Δv_{max} given by equation 10.20 and the parameters A, B, C and D as listed for first cycle deformation in Table 10.2. The initial normal stiffness $k_{ni,tan}$ is assumed to be given by equation 10.22 with the initial aperture e_i given by equation 10.21. The shear deformation behaviour of each discontinuity is assumed to be given by equation 10.29, with the initial tangent shear stiffness $k_{si,tan}$ given by equation 10.27, the shear strength τ_f given by equation 10.24 and the failure ratio R_f taken to be 0.783 for all discontinuities. Discontinuities P, Q and R are unweathered with Joint Roughness Coefficients JRC of 8, 11 and 6, respectively. The rock material has a Young's modulus of 30 GPa, a Poisson's ratio of 0.25, a uniaxial compressive strength of 55 MPa and a basic friction angle of 34°. Estimate the total axial compression that the discontinuous specimen will suffer when subjected to an axial stress increment σ_1 from zero to 5 MPa and a simultaneous lateral stress increment σ_3 from zero to 2 MPa.

Solution

The normal stress σ_n and shear stress τ on discontinuities P, Q and R, calculated from equations 9.15 and 9.16 for zero water pressure are as follows:

1st table for Example 10.4

Discontinuity	θ Degrees	σ_n MPa	τ MPa
P	50	3.240	1.477
Q	35	4.013	1.410
R	20	4.649	0.964

Values of initial aperture e_i, maximum closure Δv_{max}, initial tangent stiffness $k_{ni,tan}$ and normal closure Δ_v given by equations 10.21, 10.20, 10.22 and 10.17, respectively, for the above normal stress increments and an initial normal stress σ_{ni} of 0.001 MPa are as listed below.

2nd table for Example 10.4

Discontinuity	e_i mm	Δv_{max} mm	$k_{ni,tan}$ $MPa\,mm^{-1}$	Δv mm
P	0.16	0.195	1.477	0.107
Q	0.22	0.222	1.410	0.114
R	0.12	0.170	0.964	0.117

The initial tangent shear stiffness $k_{si,tan}$, shear strength τ_f and shear displacement Δu given by equations 10.27, 10.24 and 10.29 for the tabulated normal and shear stress increments for each discontinuity are as follows:

3rd table for Example 10.4

Discontinuity	$k_{si,tan}$ $MPa\,mm^{-1}$	τ_f MPa	Δu mm
P	33.49	3.111	0.070
Q	72.75	4.230	0.026
R	19.22	3.962	0.062

It is important to note that the shear stresses on each of the discontinuities are significantly less than the respective shear strengths, so shear failure is not predicted to occur. The vertical component Δ_{vert} of the shear and normal displacements for each discontinuity can be found by direct resolution as follows

$$\Delta_{vert} = \Delta_u \sin \theta + \Delta_v \cos \theta$$

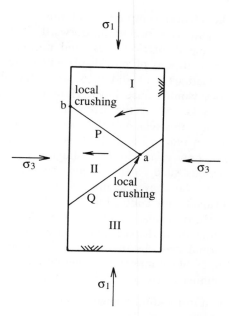

Figure 10.16 Complex block interactions produced where a specimen contains non through-going discontinuities.

giving vertical displacement components of 0.123, 0.108 and 0.131 mm for discontinuities P, Q and R, respectively, and a total vertical displacement of 0.362 mm for the three discontinuities combined.

The vertical displacement Δ_r due to compression of the rock material can be found from equation 10.9, which can be expanded to give

$$\Delta_r = \frac{L}{E_r}(\sigma_1 - 2v_r\sigma_3)$$

where E_r and v_r are the Young's modulus and Poisson's ratio for the rock material. Inputting the appropriate values to the above expression gives $\Delta_r = 0.040$ mm. The estimated total vertical compression of the cylindrical specimen due to shear and normal displacement of the inclined discontinuities and axial compression of the rock material is, therefore, 0.402 mm.

The above example can be worked through in a relatively straightforward manner because there are no block interactions; the vertical stress carried by each discontinuity is assumed to be unaffected by displacement on the discontinuity. Figure 10.16 shows a cylindrical specimen that contains two discontinuities P and Q which intersect to form a wedge-shaped block labelled

II. Estimation of the vertical compression of this specimen under constant boundary stresses σ_1 and σ_3 is not straightforward. It would be possible, of course, to determine the theoretical shear and normal stresses on the two discontinuities under conditions of zero displacement, by applying the stress transformations of equations 9.15 and 9.16, as in the above example. The induced shear stresses would cause block II to move outwards relative to blocks I and III, as indicated by the arrow in Figure 10.16. This outward movement would 'loosen' this region of the specimen and increase the stresses on the interface between blocks I and III. It is also likely that block I would rotate, creating point contacts and local crushing at points a and b in Figure 10.16. Block interactions such as this cannot be analysed by applying the direct methods used in the above example because a number of factors that influence block deformation are coupled in a complex way. For example, shear stiffness and hence shear displacement are dependent upon normal stress, while at the same time shear displacements on an inclined plane can themselves change the normal stress by the process of loosening referred to above. The analysis of complex block interactions therefore requires the simultaneous consideration of a number of factors, including the following:

1. the geometry of a three-dimensional assemblage of discontinuities and blocks,
2. the conditions of stress and displacement applied at the boundaries of the blocky model and the body forces for each block within the model,
3. constitutive relations for the rock material in the pre- and post-yield regions,
4. the normal and shear displacements induced by increments of normal and shear stress on each discontinuity, and
5. the shear strength and post-yield shear behaviour of the discontinuities.

It is necessary to keep track of the displacements and rotations of each block, the creation and loss of contacts produced by these displacements, and the deformation, yielding, fracture and plastic flow of the rock material within each block. Blocks enclosed within the model must not be allowed to overlap, while free blocks on the boundary must be allowed to move according to the laws of motion. It is desirable also to apply damping coefficients to ensure that the blocky model has the capacity to absorb energy associated with hysteretic and frictional effects. It is only possible to take account of these factors, and address the daunting task of explicitly modelling the deformation behaviour of three-dimensional assemblages of blocks by applying numerical approximations implemented on high-capacity computers. Although finite element, finite difference and boundary element formulations have gone some way towards addressing the requirements listed above, the most promising approach is the distinct element method developed by Cundall and his co-workers.

The currently accepted form of the distinct element method was introduced by Cundall (1971). A computer code UDEC, which provides a two-dimensional implementation of the method, is described by Lemos *et al.* (1985), Cundall (1987) and in a number of less widely available reports produced for the US Army. A hybrid distinct element–boundary element analysis for jointed rock is described by Lorig *et al.* (1986). A three-dimensional distinct element code 3DEC is described by Cundall (1988) and by Hart *et al.* (1988). A more recent review of the applications of the distinct element method is presented by Choi and Coulthard (1990).

The novel capability of the distinct element method, compared with other methods such as finite element analysis, is that by operating in the time domain it is able to model large block translations, rotations and separations. In order to understand how this capability is achieved it is necessary to review briefly the principal features of the distinct element method. The input data comprise mechanical properties of the rock material and discontinuities together with the geometrical properties of the discontinuity network in two- or three dimensions. The location, orientation and size of discontinuities can either be specified individually, or alternatively they can be generated to form a regular grid or they can be generated from a random realisation following the methods outlined in section 6.8 and described by Hart *et al.* (1988). A significant proportion of the computational effort, particularly in the three-dimensional formulation, is devoted to identifying blocks, locating neigh-bouring blocks, detecting contacts and implementing block translations and rotations. It is particularly important to keep track of the creation and loss of contacts between adjacent blocks.

The mechanical analysis of the interaction between blocks is achieved by applying a time step Δt in a similar way to that adopted for the analysis of transient fluid flow in section 11.7. Choice of the time step length is crucial: if it is too long the system becomes numerically unstable; if Δt is too short the system will take a large number of iteration cycles to converge to a solution. Hart *et al.* (1988) recommend an optimum time step given by

$$\Delta_t = \text{FRAC} \sqrt{\frac{m_{min}}{2k_{max}}}$$

where m_{min} is the smallest block mass in the system, k_{max} is the largest normal or shear discontinuity stiffness and FRAC is a user-defined factor, close to about 0.2, that allows for multiple block contacts.

The solution of block displacements and block forces is based upon a dynamic relaxation scheme which solves the equations of motion for each block by applying an explicit finite difference algorithm. At each time step the translational and rotational forces acting on a block are analysed to determine their out-of-balance components F_i and M_i, respectively. These components are divided by the mass and the effective moment of inertia of the block to give the translational and rotational accelerations respectively. These accel-erations are then multiplied by the time step Δt to give velocity increments, which are added to the previous translational and rotational velocities of the block to give the new velocities. A centred finite difference algorithm is adopted to determine these velocities at the mid-point of the time step $\Delta t/2$ relative to the velocities at the mid-point of the previous time step. The increments of block translation and rotation are found by multiplying the velocities at time $\Delta t/2$ by the time step Δt. The new coordinates of the block centroid and each of the block vertices are found by adding the displacements produced by translation and rotation to the previous coordinates.

The contact displacement increment vector for the interface with a neighbouring block is obtained by multiplying the computed velocity vector of the block relative to its neighbour at the contact location, by the time step Δt. The increments in normal and shear displacement for the contact plane are found by taking components of the contact displacement increment vector, following similar methods to those adopted in section 8.4. The elastic increments in normal and shear force are then found by multiplying the increments in normal and shear displacement by (i) the normal and shear stiffnesses (stress/displacement) for the discontinuity at the contact, and (ii) the contact area. The new normal and shear forces at the contact are found by adding these increments to the previous values. A shear strength law such as the Coulomb yield criterion can be applied at the interface to detect whether slip will occur under the new contact forces. If slip is predicted to occur, the shear force should be reduced to a specified limiting value. If the magnitude of the tensile force exceeds the tensile strength of the discontinuity then the normal and shear forces are reduced to zero. The new contact forces are then added to the moments and forces acting at the centroid of the block and at the centroid of its neighbour. The contact forces for each face of the block are updated in this way and added to those acting at the centroid to give a new set of translational and rotational forces for the next time step. The contact forces are also used to calculate block deformations for those blocks that have been specified as fully deformable.

An important feature of distinct element modelling is the scheme that must be applied to absorb energy within the system. A system of perfectly elastic blocks with elastic contact stiffnesses would oscillate indefinitely. It is necessary, therefore, to apply some form of damping, applied in a way that does not interfere with the 'natural' behaviour of the blocks. For example, blocks that are sliding or compressing at an interface should experience damping while those that are being carried along within a group of other blocks or that are moving freely through space should not be damped. A damping coefficient that is proportional to block velocity or displacement would not discriminate between these two categories. Cundall (1987) describes a form of adaptive damping in which the viscous damping forces are scaled so that the energy absorbed by damping is calculated to be a constant proportion of the rate of change of kinetic energy in the system. Blocks moving at a constant velocity are undamped by this system while hysteretic behaviour, involving large changes of kinetic energy in compression-dilation cycles, is effectively damped.

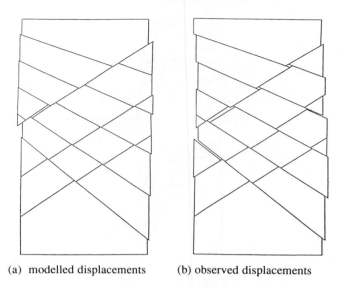

(a) modelled displacements   (b) observed displacements

Figure 10.17   Block displacement pattern for a 150 mm diameter cylindrical specimen containing eight discontinuities: (a) modelled by distinct element method, (b) observed.

After a sufficient number of time steps, the block assemblage may reach a steady state that represents static equilibrium under the specified boundary conditions. Alternatively the assemblage may develop large displacements that demonstrate a particular mechanism of rock collapse. It is in this latter area that distinct element methods find their most valuable application. Figure 10.17a shows block displacements, predicted by the two-dimensional distinct element program UDEC, for a 150 mm diameter specimen tested under triaxial compression. The observed displacements in Figure 10.17b confirm that UDEC has the capacity to represent complex block interactions. Figure 10.18, from Cundall (1987), shows distinct element modelling of three stages in the failure of a rock slope intersected by a regular pattern of discontinuities. The results in this figure highlight the capacity of the distinct element method to model large displacements. Hart *et al.* (1988) present four instructive examples of the application of the three-dimensional program 3DEC to problems containing up to 49 three-dimensional blocks. Makurat *et al.* (1990) have applied UDEC to modelling a three lane road tunnel through fractured sedimentary rocks under Oslo. They describe a comprehensive programme of geological mapping, borehole logging, pumping tests, stress measurement, material tests and joint index tests designed to provide the appropriate input data for the model.

It has been said many times that any numerical model of a geotechnical process is only as good as the input data; this is particularly true for the

(a)

(b)

(c)

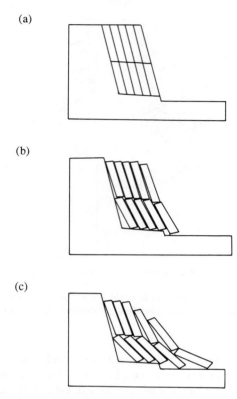

Figure 10.18   Distinct element modelling of three stages in the failure of a rock slope intersected by a regular pattern of discontinuities (after Cundall, 1987).

distinct element method. The benefits of being able to model a complex three-dimensional assemblage of rock blocks can only be realised if it is possible to determine the three-dimensional geometry of discontinuities within the rock mass that is being modelled. It is hoped that the work in this book goes some way towards addressing this problem. Early implementations of the distinct element method adopted linear normal and shear stiffnesses for the discontinuities and also assumed that shear stiffness is independent of normal stiffness. Experimental and theoretical studies presented in this chapter show that this assumption is inappropriate. Recent versions of the code have addressed this problem by incorporating the empirical models for discontinuity deformation, presented earlier in this chapter. Despite these refinements, although the distinct element method is valuable for indicating likely failure mechanisms, care must be taken when using the method to predict stresses, displacements and failure loads because results can be sensitive to the geometry and mechanical properties assumed for the discontinuity network.

EXERCISES FOR CHAPTER 10

10.1

A discontinuity in a limestone rock material with a uniaxial compressive strength of 55 MPa is observed to have a Joint Roughness Coefficient of 7. The compressive strength of the rock material immediately adjacent to the discontinuity is estimated from Schmidt hammer rebound tests to be 25 MPa. Taking a nominal initial normal stress of 1 kPa, estimate the normal stress that would be required to close the aperture by 0.2 mm for matched surfaces. Estimate the tangent and secant normal stress stiffness at this closure.

10.2

A fresh discontinuity in a siltstone rock material with a uniaxial compressive strength of 70 MPa was found to have a Joint Roughness Coefficient of 5. Taking a basic friction angle of 32°, a stiffness exponent of 0.761 MPa^2 mm^{-1} and a failure ratio of 0.783 estimate the relative shear displacements at shear stresses of 0.4, 0.8 and 1.2 MPa for a 100 mm square sample of this discontinuity, tested under dry conditions at a normal stress of 1.5 MPa.

10.3

A rock mass is composed of a rock material with a Young's modulus of 30 GPa and a Poisson's ratio of 0.25. The mass is cut by discontinuities that have a constant normal stiffness of 35 MPa mm^{-1} and a shear stiffness of 22 MPa mm^{-1}. Estimate the equivalent rock mass 'Young's modulus' for the following cases: (i) along the normal to a set of parallel discontinuities with a mean normal set spacing of 0.1 m, and (ii) where the discontinuities are randomly orientated with an effective isotropic mean spacing of 0.1 m.

10.4

The specimen geometry in Example 10.4 is modified so that the normals to the three planar discontinuities P, Q and R make angles of 40°, 25° and 10°, respectively, with the specimen axis. Keeping all other parameters the same, estimate the total axial compression that the discontinuous specimen will suffer when subjected to an axial stress increment σ_1 from zero to 20 MPa and a simultaneous lateral stress increment σ_3 from zero to 2 MPa. Estimate the equivalent Young's modulus for this discontinuous specimen.

Answers to these exercises are given on page 464.

11

Fluid flow in
discontinuities

11.1 INTRODUCTION

The water permeabilities of most rock materials lie in the range 10^{-10} to $10^{-15}\,\mathrm{m\,s^{-1}}$ (Louis, 1969), which means that from an engineering point of view an unfractured rock mass is effectively impermeable to water. All rocks, particularly those near to the ground surface, contain discontinuities which can provide major conducting pathways for migrating fluids. Natural processes such as mineralisation and aquifer recharge, together with man made processes such as water, oil and gas recovery rely upon the contribution made to mass permeability by discontinuity networks.

In relatively soft materials such as soils and some evaporitic deposits, any fractures that may develop tend to seal off over time as material flows into the fracture aperture. Mass permeability in such soils and rocks is governed by the permeability of the intact material; this is often referred to as the matrix permeability. This matrix permeability can be determined relatively easily from laboratory tests on intact samples or by carrying out packer tests in boreholes. The permeabilities determined in this way can be used with some confidence to predict fluid flow through the unfractured mass. This approach is, unfortunately, of limited applicability to fractured hard rock masses. Specimen size constraints usually limit laboratory permeability tests to specimens containing only one or two fractures. Although such tests can provide valuable information on fracture permeability and how it is influenced by stress, temperature, surface roughness and infill, the tests can provide no information on how fluid flow is influenced by the geometry of the large scale fracture network.

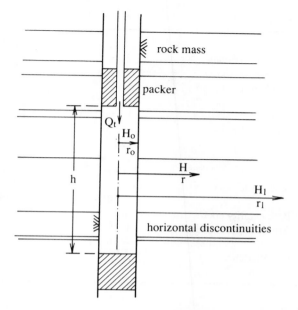

Figure 11.1   Diagrammatic representation of a packer permeability test.

Field permeability tests, particularly those carried out at a large scale, can provide valuable information about the permeability of the fracture network. The usual technique adopted is to seal off a length of borehole by some form of packer system, pump water in under pressure and monitor flow rates, as illustrated in Figure 11.1. It is a relatively straightforward matter to estimate mass permeability from the observed flow rates, following the methods summarised by Hoek and Bray (1981). There are, however, a number of difficulties in using such tests in fractured rock. The first of these is that fluid flow during the test is crucially dependant upon the geometry and condition of fractures immediately adjacent to the test zone. Such fractures can become sealed by drilling mud, opened by blast vibrations, or deformed by stress changes associated with drilling or excavation of the test zone. Secondly, the hydraulic gradients required to give measurable flows during a test are often much higher than those applicable under natural conditions. Although these large hydraulic gradients may not be a problem when testing porous media, in fractured rocks high pressure gradients can lead to the opening and extension of existing fractures. Finally, the permeability determined from a field test in a fractured rock is strongly influenced by the frequency of discontinuities immediately adjacent to the test zone, and in particular by the number of major conducting fractures that have been intersected. Consequently, computed permeabilities often show a wide scatter and exhibit extreme sensitivity

Table 11.1 Summary of symbols and units for fluid flow

Symbol	Description	Typical units	Approximate value for water
g	Acceleration due to gravity	$\mathrm{m\,s^{-2}}$	$(9.81\,\mathrm{m\,s^{-2}})$
ρ	Density	$\mathrm{Mg\,m^{-3}}$	$\rho_w = 1\,\mathrm{Mg\,m^{-3}}$
γ	Unit weight	$\mathrm{kN\,m^{-3}}$	$\gamma_w = 9.81\,\mathrm{kN\,m^{-3}}$
u	Pressure	kPa	—
μ	Viscosity	$1\,\mathrm{N\,s\,m^{-2}}$ $= 1\,\mathrm{Pl}$	$\mu_w = 10^{-3}\,\mathrm{N\,s\,m^{-2}}$ $= 10^{-3}\,\mathrm{Pl}$
v	Kinematic viscosity	$1\,\mathrm{m^2\,s^{-1}}$ $= 10^4\,\mathrm{St}$	$v_w = 10^{-6}\,\mathrm{m^2\,s^{-1}}$ $= 10^{-2}\,\mathrm{St}$
K	Permeability coefficient	$\mathrm{m\,s^{-1}}$	—
k	Absolute permeability	$1\,\mathrm{m^2}$ $= 10^{12}\,\mathrm{darcy}$	—
C	Conductance	$\mathrm{m^2\,s^{-1}}$	—

to the orientation of the conducting fractures. Although none of these points invalidates the use of permeability testing for the prediction of fluid flow in fractured rock, taken together they suggest that a better understanding of the influence of fracture geometry would not only be of benefit in its own right, but would also help in the interpretation of permeability test data.

The aim of this chapter is to examine the influence that discontinuities have on fluid flow through fractured rock masses. This will be achieved by revising some basic principles of fluid flow in section 11.2, examining flow along a single fracture in section 11.3, discussing the estimation of discontinuity aperture in section 11.4, and then finally considering flow through complex two-dimensional and three-dimensional fracture networks in sections 11.5 to 11.8. As in earlier chapters, the principles will be illustrated by examples whenever this is appropriate.

11.2 BASIC PRINCIPLES OF FLUID FLOW

Before proceeding with the analysis of fluid flow in fractures it is worthwhile defining some of the symbols and units used, and revising some of the basic principles. Table 11.1 provides a summary and also lists approximate values for water.

Unit weight γ is the force required to support a unit volume of material of density ρ in a gravitational field g, hence

$$\gamma = \rho g \qquad (11.1)$$

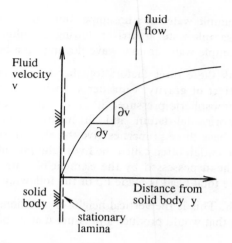

Figure 11.2 Fluid flowing past a solid body.

The fluid pressure u at a depth h below the surface of a stationary body of fluid of unit weight γ is given by

$$u = \gamma h \qquad (11.2)$$

Viscosity becomes an important fluid property when there is a velocity gradient normal to the direction of flow. For example, a fluid flowing past a solid body will leave a thin lamina of fluid that is almost stationary immediately adjacent to the surface of the body, as shown in Figure 11.2. Fluid velocity v increases with an increase in the distance y into the body of the moving fluid, away from the stationary lamina. The velocity gradient $\partial v/\partial y$ produces a shear stress τ within the fluid. Experiments show that for certain simple fluids such as water, under laminar flow conditions the shear stress is directly proportional to the velocity gradient. The constant of proportionality is the viscosity μ of the fluid, so

$$\tau = \mu \frac{\partial v}{\partial y} \qquad (11.3)$$

Many fluids flow as a direct result of their own weight. This fact is recognised in the definition of kinematic viscosity ν, which is the ratio of viscosity to fluid density. Hence, using equation 11.1

$$\nu = \frac{\mu}{\rho} = \frac{\mu g}{\gamma} \qquad (11.4)$$

Ignoring thermal, chemical and biological factors there are three things that can cause water to move by flowing:

1. **Pressure,** for example water in a hosepipe connected to mains pressure.
2. **Elevation,** for example water in a river flowing downhill.
3. **Velocity,** for example water from a wave flowing up a beach.

It is possible to link these three factors together by noting that each can be produced by the effect of gravity. Consider a small element of water (i) at a pressure u above atmospheric pressure, (ii) at a vertical elevation z relative to an arbitrary fixed horizontal datum, and (iii) moving at velocity v relative to some fixed point. These three properties give the element of water a **potential** for flowing. This potential, often called the **hydraulic potential,** is measured in terms of the **total head** possessed by the element of water, and expressed in units of length. The total head is made up of the following:

1. **Pressure head** h. This is the vertical height of a stationary column of fluid of unit weight γ that would produce a pressure u at its base. From equation 11.2, $h = u/\gamma$.
2. **Elevation head** z. This is the vertical elevation of the element of fluid above $(z = +ve)$ or below $(z = -ve)$ a fixed arbitrary horizontal datum level.
3. **Velocity head** w. This is the vertical distance through which the element of water would have to fall freely, under gravitational acceleration g, to reach the fluid velocity v. From the basic laws of motion $w = v^2/2g$.

The total head, or **hydraulic potential**, H of the element of water is given by

$$H = h + z + w \tag{11.5}$$

Fluids usually flow at velocities of less than $1\,\mathrm{m\,s^{-1}}$ through rocks and soils, so the velocity head w is usually less than about $0.05\,\mathrm{m}$. Because w is small relative to h and z it will henceforth be ignored.

A mass of water consists of many connected elements subjected to a particular set of boundary conditions. If the boundary conditions are such that the total head of one element is different from that of another element in the same connected mass, then a hydraulic gradient exists and flow will occur towards the element with a lower total head. This difference in total head can be expressed as a **hydraulic gradient** i, defined as the change in total head per unit distance. If total head increases by an amount ΔH over a distance l measured along the direction of flow, the hydraulic gradient is given by

$$i = \frac{-\Delta H}{l} \tag{11.6}$$

The negative sign in equation 11.6 arises from the fact that flow must occur in the direction of **decreasing** total head.

Figure 11.3 shows a vertical cylindrical body of porous material, such as a sandy soil or an open-textured rock, through which fluid can flow. The material has a cross-sectional area A, a length l and is held within an impermeable cylinder. The total head at the top of the cylinder is H_1 and the

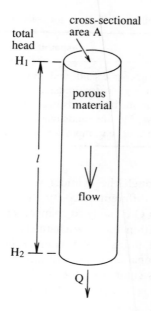

Figure 11.3 Fluid flowing through a cylindrical body of porous material.

total head at the bottom is H_2. If $H_1 > H_2$ then the hydraulic gradient $i = (H_1 - H_2)/l$ and flow will occur from H_1 to H_2. Experiments show that for certain simple fluids such as water, under laminar flow conditions, the flow volume Q per unit time is directly proportional to the product of the cross-sectional area A and the hydraulic gradient i. Introducing a constant of proportionality K gives the following result, which is usually referred to as Darcy's empirical law

$$Q = KiA \qquad (11.7)$$

The constant K in equation 11.7 is the permeability coefficient of the soil or rock for a particular fluid, sometimes referred to as the Darcy coefficient of permeability. The apparent flow velocity V is given by Q/A. This velocity is referred to as the apparent, or artificial, flow velocity because it ignores the fact that there is material other than water within the cylindrical pipe. The actual flow velocity, or seepage velocity V_s, will be higher than V because the water must in reality flow along narrow tortuous channels between the grains of soil or rock. If the porosity of the soil or rock n is defined as the volume of the void spaces divided by the total volume, then an estimate of the seepage velocity is given by V/n. Even this estimate tends to underestimate V_s because although it allows for the presence of solid material, it does not allow for the tortuous nature of the flow channels.

Table 11.2 Typical permeability coefficients for soils and rocks

$K_w \, (m \, s^{-1})$	Comments and examples
$>10^{-3}$	High, e.g. coarse sands and gravels
10^{-3} to 10^{-5}	Medium, e.g. coarse sandstones, fine sands and silts
10^{-5} to 10^{-7}	Low, e.g. medium sandstones, limestones, silty clays
10^{-7} to 10^{-9}	Very low, e.g. fine sandstones, limestones, clays
$<10^{-9}$	Impermeable, e.g. most igneous and metamorphic rock materials

If the fluid flowing through the cylinder were replaced by a fluid with a different unit weight and different viscosity then, under the same hydraulic gradient, the flow quantity Q is likely to change. This change is a result of the different viscous forces within the flow channels. Experiments show that the flow quantity Q for ideal fluids under laminar flow conditions is not only proportional to cross-sectional area and hydraulic gradient but is also directly proportional to the unit weight γ of the fluid and inversely proportional to its viscosity μ. Introducing a new constant of proportionality k gives the following

$$Q = k \frac{\gamma}{\mu} iA \qquad (11.8)$$

where k, the absolute permeability of the porous material, is dependent only upon the properties of the solid material. Flow is proportional to the unit weight of the fluid because, at a given elevation, there is more potential energy available to drive flow in heavy fluids than in light fluids. Flow is inversely proportional to viscosity because more energy is dissipated in overcoming viscous drag in the thicker fluids. Comparison between equations 11.7 and 11.8 shows that the permeability coefficient K of a porous material of absolute permeability k for a fluid of unit weight γ and viscosity μ is given by

$$K = k \frac{\gamma}{\mu} \qquad (11.9)$$

Equation 11.9 shows that for water K $(m \, s^{-1}) \approx 10^7 k \, (m^2)$. The distinction between the permeability coefficient K and absolute permeability k is important when there are different fluids flowing through the rock, such as petroleum, gas, brine and water. In such cases it is desirable to work with the absolute permeability k and to input appropriate values of unit weight and viscosity to equation 11.8. When the fluid is always water, which is generally the case in soil and rock mechanics studies, it is preferable to work with the permeability coefficient for water K_w, and to use equation 11.7 for calculating flow quantities. Typical values of K_w for soils and rocks are listed in Table 11.2. If values of 'permeability' for geomechanics applications are quoted with

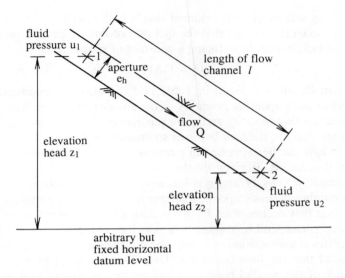

Figure 11.4 Cross-section through the idealised parallel plate model.

the dimensions of velocity it is generally safe to assume that they relate to the permeability coefficient for water.

11.3 FLOW ALONG A SINGLE FRACTURE

For most practical purposes it is acceptable to idealise flow along an open fracture in terms of the flow between a pair of smooth parallel plates. Figure 11.4 shows a cross-section through such an idealised model, in which the parallel plates lie at right angles to the plane of the diagram, at a separation e_h which represents the effective hydraulic aperture of the fracture. Consider now the flow Q per unit time occurring over a width b of the fracture measured normal to the plane of the diagram. This flow occurs at an average velocity $V = Q/(e_h b)$ over the distance l between the points 1 and 2 in Figure 11.4, as long as there is a difference in total head between these two points. Taking the fluid pressures and elevation heads of points 1 and 2 in Figure 11.4 to be u_1, u_2 and z_1, z_2, respectively, assuming that the fluid is water, and ignoring any velocity heads gives the total heads at the two points as follows

$$H_1 = \frac{u_1}{\gamma_w} + z_1 \quad \text{and} \quad H_2 = \frac{u_2}{\gamma_w} + z_2 \tag{11.10}$$

The total head loss ΔH between the two points is given by $H_1 - H_2$, hence

$$\Delta H = \left(\frac{u_1 - u_2}{\gamma_w}\right) + (z_1 - z_2) \tag{11.11}$$

For flow along a channel, it is assumed that it is the head loss that causes (or is a consequence of) flow and that the quantity of flow is directly proportional to this head loss, hence, introducing a constant of proportionality

$$Q = C \Delta H \qquad (11.12)$$

The constant C, which is listed in Table 11.1, is called the **conductance**. Its value depends both upon the geometry of the channel and the properties of the fluid. When the flow velocity and plate separation are small, and the walls of the plates are smooth, the flow becomes streamline, or laminar. The conditions for laminar flow can be expressed in terms of the Reynolds number R_e for the model. In this case R_e is given by the dimensionless ratio Ve_h/v, where V is the apparent flow velocity and v is kinematic viscosity. Although the critical Reynolds number depends upon the surface geometry of the plates, for smooth plates laminar flow occurs when R_e is less than about 500 to 600 (Louis, 1969). These values correspond to average flow velocities of 0.5 to 0.6 m s^{-1} for water between plates at a separation of 1 mm. For most applications, therefore, it can be concluded that the flow is laminar. Under conditions of laminar flow, the conductance of the parallel plate model illustrated in Figure 11.4 is given by the following expression

$$C = \frac{g\, e_h{}^3\, b}{12\, v\, l} \qquad (11.13)$$

The above expression, which is sometimes referred to as the 'cubic law' because of the $e_h{}^3$ term, is discussed in more detail by Louis (1969) and by Hoek and Bray (1981). In most cases it is convenient to consider a unit width normal to the plane of the diagram in Figure 11.4, in which case b = 1 in equation 11.13 and the analysis is essentially two-dimensional. Equation 11.12, which describes the flow along a single fracture, provides the basis for analysing the flow in a network of intersecting fractures. A number of authors, including Louis (1969, 1974), Sharp and Maini (1972) and Witherspoon *et al.* (1980) have shown how equation 11.13 should be extended and modified by the introduction of empirical constants to take account of non-planar discontinuity surfaces, non-laminar flow conditions and the presence of infill material. In view of the approximations associated with defining the geometry of a fracture network, and the difficulties in estimating the empirical constants for real fractures, it is debatable whether the improvements in flow modelling are worth the computational difficulties involved in applying these refinements to the cubic law. Interested readers are referred to the papers cited above and also to the comprehensive literature survey and discussion by Samaniego (1985).

11.4 DISCONTINUITY APERTURE AND ITS ESTIMATION

The mechanical aperture, or opening, e_m of a discontinuity is here defined as the distance between the opposing interfaces measured along the mean normal to the discontinuity surface. In the previous section it was shown that the flow quantity along a fracture is proportional to the cube of its effective hydraulic aperture e_h. This importance of aperture in controlling flow makes it appropriate for us to look in some detail at discontinuity aperture and its estimation, in particular it is necessary to examine the relation between e_m and e_h.

Mechanical aperture is usually generated as a result of geological shear displacement along an irregular discontinuity surface. Small scale irregularities on discontinuities can produce features that make angles of $i = 30°$ or more to the general discontinuity surface. Shear displacement at low normal stresses leads to a riding over, rather than a shearing through such features and the generation of as much as 0.5 mm of mechanical aperture for every 1 mm of initial shear displacement. Such a process is, however, self limiting since the normal stress increases with increasing aperture, leading to a greater tendency to shear through, rather than to ride over irregularities, as discussed in Chapter 9. There are two important geometrical consequences of this process. The first is that there must always remain certain areas of close contact over which the aperture is effectively zero. The second consequence, which follows from the first, is that there is rarely one single value of mechanical aperture for a given discontinuity, but rather a range of apertures between zero and a maximum. This latter effect has been studied by Strafford et al. (1990) and Tsang and Tsang (1990) by applying spatial correlation techniques similar to those discussed in section 2.5.

Although it is easy to envisage the creation of mechanical apertures by shear displacement, it is difficult to imagine an aperture closing by the exact reversal of this shear displacement; once created, apertures probably remain for a significant period in engineering terms. The principal mechanisms of aperture closure are elastic deformation, plastic flow of the adjacent material into the void, and the physical or chemical deposition of material held in suspension or solution. Elastic deformation and plastic flow tend to occur where the local stress is high compared with material strength; in the near surface zone this process is therefore limited to soils, and to rocks with a propensity to creep, such as evaporites. Physical or chemical deposition mechanisms can occur naturally, leading to filled fissures and veins, or can be induced artificially by grouting.

Once an aperture has been created it can be increased naturally by processes of physical and chemical erosion induced by the flow of water along the fracture. In certain circumstances, the development of local tensile stresses in a rock mass can lead to a dramatic opening of fracture apertures, to values exceeding 1 m in some cases. Although opening of fractures in this way is usually limited to the zone of de-stressed rock immediately adjacent to a free surface, it can occur at depth as a result of stresses induced during the process of hydraulic fracturing. Discontinuity apertures in rock immediately adjacent to a free surface are also particularly susceptible to opening as a result of blast-induced vibrations, erosion and the washing out of infill.

11.4.1   Direct measurement of discontinuity aperture

The above observations suggest that physical measurements of discontinuity apertures at exposed rock faces can provide, at best, only a general guide to mechanical apertures within the rock mass. One method that has been applied to the estimation of discontinuity apertures is the insertion of feeler gauges. In general, however, discontinuity apertures are too small for this method to be effective. Snow (1970) describes a method for the direct measurement of mechanical apertures based on the use of fluorescent dye. The dye is sprayed on to the surface of the rock and penetrates the discontinuity by capillarity. When the excess dye has been removed, a thin coating of developer is sprayed on, to leave a porous film of white powder. The dye penetrates the developer and stains it over the precise width of the discontinuity aperture. When the excess developer has been removed, the discontinuity is photographed and the aperture scaled directly from a negative projected on to a screen. Snow found that although this method gave a theoretical absolute error of $\pm 3.28 \times 10^{-4}$ mm the governing limitation was the sharpness of the photographic definition. A plot of the distribution of apertures obtained by this method for a granite was found to be very nearly lognormal, with a mean of 0.932 mm and a standard deviation of 1.045 mm. In the same paper Snow reported the results of measurements of effective hydraulic aperture based on the discharge from packer injection tests conducted in a variety of igneous and metamorphic rocks. (The theoretical basis for this method is described later in this section.) He concluded that the aperture distributions were again lognormal.

An alternative approach that has been used with some success for measuring mechanical fracture apertures in boreholes is the impression packer developed by Barr and Hocking (1976) at Imperial College, London. This device incorporates a thin wax-like film that is pressed, under pneumatic pressure, against the surface of the borehole. An imprint of the surface texture of the rock is transferred to the wax film and can be examined not only to estimate the aperture but also the frequency and orientation of discontinuities intersected by the borehole. Direct measurements of discontinuity aperture such as those described above, are of limited practical value. More reliable results can be obtained by adopting the indirect approach devised by Snow (1968) and summarised later in this section.

Barton et al. (1985), reporting work previously conducted by Barton for the Office of Nuclear Waste Isolation in Ohio, USA, concluded that the theoretical smooth wall effective hydraulic aperture e_h in equation 11.13 is generally less than the mechanical aperture e_m determined by the physical measurement techniques outlined above. They found that flow test results, reported for a range of rock types, indicated that the ratio e_m/e_h was close to unity for smooth-walled discontinuities of relatively large aperture, but that this ratio increased to values exceeding 7 as the roughness and the aperture increased.

Barton *et al.* found that the following equation, valid for $e_m \geqslant e_h$, provided the best model for the observed flow test data trends

$$\left(\frac{e_m}{e_h}\right)^2 = \frac{(JRC)^{2.5}}{e_h} \qquad \left(\frac{e_m}{e_h}\right) \geqslant 1 \qquad e_m \, e_h \text{ in microns} \qquad (11.14)$$

or

$$e_h = \frac{e_m{}^2}{(JRC)^{2.5}} \qquad e_m \geqslant e_h \qquad e_m \, e_h \text{ in microns} \qquad (11.15)$$

where *JRC* is the Joint Roughness Coefficient discussed in Chapter 9 and the units of e_m and e_h are **microns**. Martin *et al.* (1990) linked the approach described above, with the Barton-Bandis model of fracture closure and normal stiffness discussed in section 10.4, to provide a coupled model to assist in the interpretation of flow tests conducted in the Lac du Bonnet granite at the Underground Research Laboratory of the Canadian Centre for Mineral and Energy Technology. They found that the measured *in situ* normal stiffness of the joints compared favourably with that predicted by the Barton-Bandis model. This important hydromechanical coupling between normal stress, normal stiffness, aperture and fracture flow has also been investigated by Zimmerman *et al.* (1990).

11.4.2 Indirect estimation of discontinuity aperture

The permeability of most igneous and metamorphic rock materials, and many sedimentary rock materials, is negligibly small. This low material permeability means that the flow of fluids through, and hence the permeability of, rock masses of this type are dependent on the geometry of the fracture network. Since the flow of fluid along a single fracture is dependent on its aperture, any measure of the permeability of a mass provides, indirectly, a measure of the effective hydraulic aperture of the conducting discontinuities. Combining equations 11.12 and 11.13 gives the following expression for the flow quantity Q along a fracture of hydraulic aperture e_h, width b and length *l* under a total head loss ΔH

$$Q = \frac{g \, e_h{}^3 \, b \, \Delta H}{12 \, v \, l} \qquad (11.16)$$

where the other parameters are as defined in Table 11.1. Figure 11.5 shows an idealised element of a rock mass of rectangular cross-section with dimensions b by h by *l*, through which flow is occurring along a number of such discontinuity planes. The following assumptions are made:

(i)   The discontinuities are planar and each have a constant effective hydraulic aperture e_h.

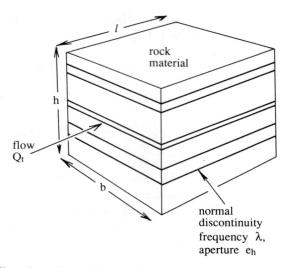

Figure 11.5   Flow through an idealised element of discontinuous rock.

(ii) The discontinuities are orientated parallel to the flow direction and normal to the dimension h.

(iii) The rock material is inert, incompressible and impermeable to the fluid in the fractures.

(iv) Flow is laminar and obeys Darcy's law.

If the normal discontinuity frequency is λ, there will be on average λh discontinuities in the element of rock mass, giving a total flow

$$Q_t = \frac{g\,e_h^{\,3}\,b\,\Delta H\,\lambda h}{12\,v\,l} \qquad (11.17)$$

If a flow test were carried out on this same element of fractured rock mass, giving an apparent mass permeability coefficient K_m then the predicted flow under the hydraulic gradient $\Delta H/l$ would be the same as that given by equation 11.17. Applying Darcy's law

$$Q_t = \frac{K_m\,b\,h\,\Delta H}{l} \qquad (11.18)$$

Combining equations 11.17 and 11.18 gives the following expression, which provides an estimate for the average effective hydraulic aperture

$$e_h = \left[\frac{12\,v\,K_m}{\lambda g} \right]^{1/3} \qquad (11.19)$$

Flow tests to determine rock mass permeability are usually carried out in boreholes, over a test length that has been isolated by either one or two packers. In order to apply the above theory to such borehole tests it is necessary to make a number of additional assumptions as follows:

(i)   The test section is vertical and is intersected by horizontal planar discontinuities.
(ii) The flow in each discontinuity is radial and laminar.
(iii) The flow in a given fracture is independent of flow in any other fracture.

Figure 11.1 shows a diagrammatic representation of a double packer constant head test, carried out at a total head H_o over a length h of a borehole of radius r_o. The generalised total head H decays with radial distance r from the borehole axis to a value H_1 at a radius r_1. The total flow Q_t can be regarded as occurring through an equivalent continuum across an expanding cylindrical surface of radius r and area $2\pi rh$. Hence, applying Darcy's law

$$Q_t = \frac{-K_m \, 2\pi \, rh \, dH}{dr} \qquad (11.20)$$

where K_m is the equivalent mass permeability and dH/dr is the gradient in total hydraulic head. The negative sign ensures positive flow in the direction of negative hydraulic gradient. Rearranging equation 11.20 gives

$$\frac{dH}{dr} = \frac{-Q_t}{K_m \, 2\pi \, rh}$$

Integrating the left hand side between the limits H_o and H_1, and integrating the right hand side between r_o and r_1 gives

$$\int_{H_o}^{H_1} dH = \frac{-Q_t}{K_m \, 2\pi h} \int_{r_o}^{r_1} \frac{1}{r} dr$$

hence

$$Q_t = \frac{K_m \, 2\pi h \, (H_o - H_1)}{\ln (r_1/r_o)} \qquad (11.21)$$

Combining equations 11.19 and 11.21, and rearranging gives the following estimate for mean effective hydraulic aperture

$$e_h = \left[\frac{Q_t \, 6v \, \ln (r_1/r_o)}{\lambda g \, \pi h \, (H_o - H_1)} \right]^{1/3} \qquad (11.22)$$

If a sufficiently large value of r_1 is selected, the associated excess head H_1 becomes close to zero, leading to a further simplification of equation 11.22. Since the computed aperture e_h is relatively insensitive to r_1, a value of approximately $(1000 \, r_o)$ can be taken to give $H_1 \approx 0$, hence

$$e_h \approx \left[\frac{42\, Q_t\, v}{\lambda\, g\, \pi h\, H_o} \right]^{1/3} \tag{11.23}$$

All of the parameters in equation 11.23 can be measured directly, except discontinuity frequency λ. Although total discontinuity frequency can be determined by examining borehole core, or alternatively by the use of devices such as the impression packer, it is only those discontinuities that are sufficiently open to conduct fluid that should be included in the computations of λ for equation 11.23. There are, unfortunately other practical difficulties involved with the use of equations 11.19, 11.22 and 11.23:

1. The analysis is based on the assumption of a single set of discontinuities oriented at right angles to the borehole axis. In reality there may be several sets at various orientations.
2. It is assumed that the aperture e_h is constant for all of the discontinuities intersected. In reality there will usually be a distribution of apertures, so that the aperture computed by equation 11.22 is only the mean effective hydraulic aperture. Although this may not be a serious problem when analysing fluid flow, it can create difficulties when trying to determine mechanical apertures for the design of grout treatments.
3. The rock material is, in practice, deformable. Under high fluid pressures, particularly when the discontinuity frequency is low and apertures are large, effective discontinuity apertures can be increased by the elastic deformation of the adjacent rock material under the influence of hydraulic pressures. At shallow depths, high hydraulic pressures during grouting operations can lead to dramatic aperture increases expressed as recoverable heave at the ground surface.

The following illustration demonstrates the amount of aperture increase that can result from elastic deformation. If the discontinuity frequency is λ then the mean spacing is $1/\lambda$. If the intact rock between a pair of discontinuities is assumed to suffer an increment of uniaxial stress given by the fluid pressure u, then the mechanical aperture increase Δe_m for each discontinuity is given by

$$\Delta e_m = \frac{u}{\lambda E}$$

where E is the Young's modulus of the rock material. If $u = 1$ MPa and $E = 30$ GPa then $\Delta e_m = 33$ microns when $\lambda = 1\,m^{-1}$ but reduces to 3.3 microns when $\lambda = 10\,m^{-1}$. These values illustrate that aperture dilation is only a significant problem in rocks with relatively low fracture frequencies.

The first of the three difficulties listed above can be tackled by applying an approach developed by Rissler (1978). He used finite element analysis to determine the flow Q_δ into a fracture whose normal makes an angle δ with the borehole axis. He expressed this flow as a ratio of the flow Q_0 for an

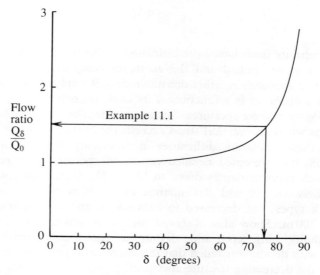

Figure 11.6 Relation between discontinuity inclination and fluid flow from a vertical borehole (after Rissler, 1978).

identical fracture inclined at an angle $\delta = 0$, and produced a series of graphs showing the relation between Q_δ/Q_0 and δ for a range of discontinuity surface geometries. A typical curve for perfectly smooth discontinuity surfaces, reproduced in Figure 11.6, shows that the correction is close to unity when δ is less than 30° but increases rapidly when δ exceeds about 60°.

When more than one set of discontinuities intersects the test section it is impossible, without further information, to determine the separate apertures for each set. One approach, adopted by Samaniego (1985), is to assume that the quantity of fluid carried by a given set is proportional to the number of discontinuities from the set that intersect the test zone. If the flow for the ith set, inclined at angle δ_i is $Q_{\delta i}$ then the measured total flow Q_t is given by

$$Q_t = \sum_{i=1}^{D} Q_{\delta i}$$

where there are D sets.

If there are n_i discontinuity intersections observed for the ith set, then the total number of intersections n_t is given by

$$n_t = \sum_{i=1}^{D} n_i$$

It is assumed that the total flow for the ith set is given by

$$Q_{\delta i} = \frac{n_i\,Q_t}{n_t}$$

When the separate flows have been estimated in this way, the appropriate flow corrections can be applied and the apertures computed for each set. The validity of this approach is rather debatable since it implicitly assumes that the aperture of a given set is a function of its angle of inclination δ, with higher values of δ giving larger apertures. Such an assumption can only be supported in situations where the vertical stress exceeds the horizontal stress.

Despite these important difficulties in measuring discontinuity aperture, Snow (1968) has presented detailed results of aperture measurements in a range of rock types at depths down to 120 m. He found that apertures were generally between 100 and 200 microns within 10 m of the ground surface for all rock types, but decreased to between 50 and 100 microns at depths exceeding 100 m. Snow also observed that there was a significant decrease in permeability with depth and, despite an associated decrease in fracture frequency with depth, concluded that this decrease in permeability was largely a result of the decreasing fracture apertures.

Kojima *et al.* (1990) describe a transient hydraulic pulse test for determining the spatial distribution of permeability in a fractured rock mass. Cycles of fluid injection and shut-in in a central test hole induce waves of hydraulic pressure through the rock mass, which are monitored at several points in observation holes. Numerical optimisation techniques are then applied to develop a hydraulic model for the test zone which best fits the observed pressure wave data.

Example 11.1

A series of packer permeability tests was conducted in a vertical 38 mm diameter borehole utilising test lengths of 1.3 m under a constant water pressure of 650 kPa. The average discharge rate for these tests was found to be $0.657\,\text{litres}\,\text{s}^{-1}$. Core logging indicates that the rock material adjacent to the test zones is an impermeable dolerite which contains a single set of parallel planar discontinuities dipping at an angle of 70° with an observed mean spacing of 0.146 m along the borehole axis . Apply the parallel plate model to estimate the mean effective discontinuity aperture for the discontinuity set.

Solution

In this example the angle δ between the discontinuity set normal and the borehole axis is 75° and the observed flow Q_δ is $0.657 \times 10^{-3}\,\text{m}^3\,\text{s}^{-1}$. Figure 11.6 shows that for smooth walled discontinuities when $\delta = 75°$ the ratio Q_δ/Q_0 is 1.5, hence the predicted flow $Q_t = Q_0$ for a horizontal discontinuity set is $0.657/1.5 = 0.438 \times 10^{-3}\,\text{m}^3\,\text{s}^{-1}$. The applied total head H_o is $650/9.81 = 66.28\,\text{m}$, and the vertical discontinuity frequency $\lambda = 1/0.146 = $

$6.84\,\text{m}^{-1}$. Inputting these values, together with a kinematic viscosity for water of $10^{-6}\,\text{m}^2\,\text{s}^{-1}$, to equation 11.23 gives an estimated mean effective hydraulic aperture of approximately 0.1 mm for the discontinuity set.

11.5 THE ANALYSIS OF FLOW THROUGH TWO-DIMENSIONAL FRACTURE NETWORKS

11.5.1 Analytical models

Much of the early work on the analysis of fluid flow through fracture systems was based on the assumption that the conducting fractures extended completely across the zone of study and that they were orientated in perfectly parallel sets (Louis, 1969; Sharp, 1970; and Maini, 1971). If it is also assumed that there are no head losses at each of the fracture intersections, this approach makes it feasible simply to sum the contribution to mass permeability provided by each fracture. Although the results of this work demonstrate the general principle that fluid flow through the mass is highly sensitive to the frequencies and apertures of the discontinuity sets, the assumption that the discontinuities are extensive across the zone of study ignores one of the most important features of rock structure: that all discontinuities are of finite length.

Sagar and Runchal (1982) sought to allow for non-extensive fractures in an analytical approach designed to link the properties of the rock structure to the macroscopic hydrological properties of the mass. They carried out a combined hydrological and geometrical analysis based on the standard parallel plate model referred to earlier, in an attempt to formulate an equivalent permeability tensor for the mass. They considered an element of rock containing non-extensive fractures of arbitrary orientation and assumed that the flow in any fracture was virtually independent of that in other fractures so that the total flow could be obtained by simple summation. It is shown later that this approach is not generally valid. Sagar and Runchal also assumed that any fracture that does not intersect the boundary of the rock element makes no contribution to the permeability of that element. Despite making these simplifications, the results are highly complex and difficult to interpret in a physical sense.

Non-extensive fractures produce a complex network in which the overall flow patterns are crucially dependent on the flow from one fracture to another. In order to determine this flow it is necessary to consider the network as a whole, to satisfy simultaneously the applied boundary heads and the requirements of mass conservation within the fractures.

11.5.2 Random realisations and their geometrical analysis

Hudson and La Pointe (1980) were among the first to incorporate a comprehensive representation of discontinuity orientation and size in their analysis

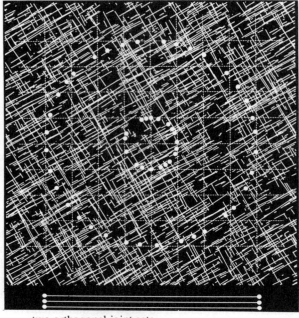

two orthogonal joint sets
negative exponential trace lengths
uniformly random locations

Figure 11.7 Printed circuit board for studying fluid flow through two-dimensional discontinuity networks (from Hudson and La Pointe, 1980).

of fluid flow through fracture networks. Their approach was to take the diagnostic parameters that characterise a given rock structure and use them to generate a two-dimensional random network, or realisation, as described in section 6.8. The resulting network was then printed on to a circuit board so that the line representing each discontinuity formed a conducting element, as shown in Figure 11.7. Since there is a direct analogy between electrical potential and hydraulic head, between current and fluid flow, and between electrical conductivity and hydraulic conductance, it is feasible to use the printed circuit board as an electrical analogue for fluid flow through fracture networks. Although Hudson and La Pointe did not present any detailed test results, they did suggest how the approach could be modified to model distributions of fracture apertures, the influence of a permeable rock matrix, and the presence of underground excavations. The work of Hudson and La Pointe stimulated a number of researchers in North America and Europe (including the Author) to develop the idea of utilising random realisations of fracture geometry in the analysis of fluid flow. A common feature of this work has been

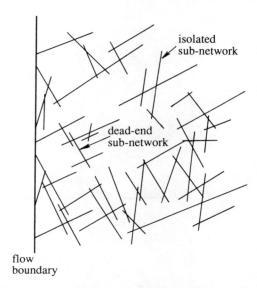

Figure 11.8 Portion of a two-dimensional random realisation showing isolated and dead-end sub-networks.

the adoption of numerical, rather than analogical, methods for the solution of flow in the network.

Section 6.8 contains an explanation of the generation of random fracture networks from diagnostic discontinuity characteristics. For the purposes of this section on fluid flow it is assumed that the realisation is in two-dimensions and that all discontinuities are normal to the plane of realisation. This requirement, which can only be relaxed by conducting a full three-dimensional analysis, ensures that there are no out-of-plane fracture connections to complicate the analysis.

A random fracture realisation is a unique and complex network of flow channels of various widths. Unlike a network of roads there will often be individual fractures, or groups of fractures, that are isolated from the main network, as illustrated in the portion of the network in Figure 11.8. There will also be other fractures, or groups of fractures, that form dead ends, as shown in Figure 11.8. These isolated, or partly isolated, fractures can make no contribution to the overall flow; at best they increase the amount of computation required to arrive at a solution, and at worst can produce a numerical instability that gives no solution at all. These groups of inactive fractures can be identified and eliminated by a geometrical analysis of the network. Although the process is essentially simple and very easy to carry out by hand on a graphical realisation, computer implementation requires the formulation of rigourous, and somewhat lengthy, search routines.

(a)

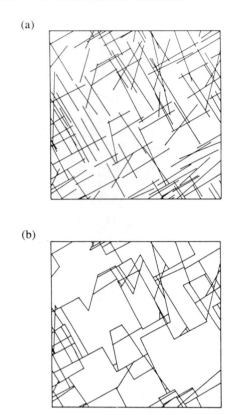

(b)

Figure 11.9 Two-dimensional random realisation illustrating (a) generated network and (b) interconnected network (after Priest and Samaniego, 1983).

Efficient routines for identifying the interconnected network have been developed by Samaniego (1985). His program DICONN has been designed to identify the subset of discontinuities that are connected either directly, or through other discontinuities, to one or more of the geometrical boundary lines. For the purposes of the search, the four lines forming a square boundary are treated as if they were discontinuities. The search starts by numbering the m discontinuities in the network and then, by examining the coordinates of their end points, finding all of the intersections of the ith discontinuity with the other discontinuities. This process, which is repeated for i = 1 to m, leads to a list of intersections which is divided into m data blocks. Each data block, which corresponds to the ith discontinuity, contains the index numbers of those discontinuities that are intersected by the ith discontinuity. Other lists record the starting positions and the number of intersections associated with the data blocks within the list of intersections. Any data blocks that contain less than two intersections must be associated with isolated or dead-end discontinuities; these are removed since they do not form part of the interconnected network. Any isolated sub-networks that remain are removed at a later stage by tracing pathways across the network. The results of this connectivity analysis are illustrated in Figure 11.9 taken from Priest and Samaniego (1983); Figure 11.9a shows the generated network and Figure 11.9b shows the interconnected network. It could be argued that the identification of the interconnected network in this way is not necessary since an efficient flow analysis routine should assign zero flow to any unconnected or dead-end fractures. An additional advantage of carrying out a connectivity analysis, however, is that it serves to identify the intersection points (or **nodes**) within the network and produces lists of the discontinuities connected to each node. Connectivity analysis therefore provides the information required to calculate the lengths of the fracture pathways between nodes. This information is vital to the analysis of flow, described below.

11.5.3 Analysis of flow

Figure 11.10 shows five interconnected nodes, representing part of a typical interconnected network. If we accept that there is a negligible probability of more than two discontinuities passing through a single point, this diagram represents the fundamental geometrical element from which all two-dimensional networks must be constructed. The following parameters are defined:

H_i = total head at node i.

Q_{ij} = flow along the channel connecting nodes i and j. Flow towards node j is taken to be positive.

C_{ij} = conductance of the channel connecting nodes i and j (equation 11.13).

The conductance of each channel can be found from its effective smooth walled aperture and length by means of equation 11.13, assuming a unit width b normal to the plane of the realisation. Gale (1990) concluded that the predicted flow for a fracture network is relatively insensitive to the fracture flow law used in the model, as long as this law is the same as that used to interpret the field permeability test data. If it is assumed that the surrounding material is impermeable, inert and incompressible, and that the fluid remains continuous and incompressible, then there will be no nett gain or loss of fluid at a given node, hence

$$Q_{15} + Q_{25} + Q_{35} + Q_{45} = 0$$

But, from equation 11.12

$$Q_{ij} = C_{ij}(H_i - H_j)$$

so

$$C_{15}H_1 - C_{15}H_5 + C_{25}H_2 - C_{25}H_5 + C_{35}H_3 - C_{35}H_5 + C_{45}H_4 - C_{45}H_5 = 0$$

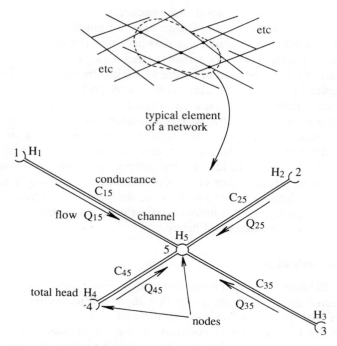

Figure 11.10   Typical element of a network formed by five interconnected nodes.

or

$$H_5 = \frac{C_{15}H_1 + C_{25}H_2 + C_{35}H_3 + C_{45}H_4}{C_{15} + C_{25} + C_{35} + C_{45}} \qquad (11.24)$$

In general, for node j

$$H_j = \frac{\sum\limits_{i=1}^{4} C_{ij} H_i}{\sum\limits_{i=1}^{4} C_{ij}} \qquad (11.25)$$

The upper limit of the summation in equation 11.25 may be 2, 3 or 4, depending on whether there are 2, 3 or 4 nodes connected to the jth node. General application of equation 11.25 does, of course, require the temporary re-numbering of the nodes in each element of the network.

In any network there will be two types of nodes:

(i) Boundary nodes at which the total head, **or** the flow, are known and constant. These nodes are connected to only one other node.

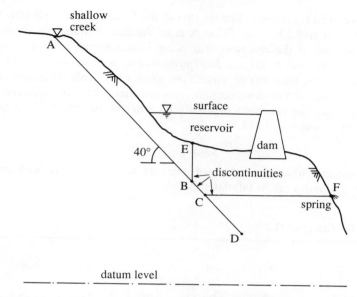

Figure 11.11   Vertical cross-section through reservoir and dam in Example 11.2.

(ii) Internal nodes at which the total head is unknown. These nodes are connected to between two and four adjacent nodes, as noted above.

For each internal node it is possible to write down an equation, based on equation 11.25, that gives the total head at that node in terms of the heads at the nodes immediately adjacent to it. There will, therefore, be the same number of equations as there are internal nodes at which the head is unknown. For very small networks (less than about 5 nodes) these heads can usually be solved directly by algebraic elimination and back substitution. Larger networks generally require the application of numerical techniques. The following example illustrates the application of direct algebraic methods for the solution of a very small network.

Example 11.2 (Figure 11.11)

Figure 11.11 shows a vertical cross-section through a reservoir and dam constructed on a rock mass that is intersected by three major discontinuities AD, BE and CF, which strike normal to the plane of the section, dip at angles of 40°, 90° and 0°, respectively, and have effective hydraulic apertures of 1.0, 0.6 and 0.8 mm respectively. The vertical elevations of the 6 nodes in Figure 11.11, expressed in metres above an arbitrary fixed horizontal datum are A 120, B 56, C 46, D 30, E 76 and F 46 m. The surface of the reservoir is

90 m above the datum level. The lengths of the 5 channels are AB 100, BC 15, CD 25, EB 20 and CF 75 m. Point A is in the bed of a shallow creek, point E is in the bed of the reservoir and point F is a spring at ground surface. Calculate (i) the total heads and fluid pressures at nodes B and C, and (ii) the directions and the amounts of water flow along each of the channels per unit distance normal to the cross-section. Assume that the rock material is impermeable, that the kinematic viscosity of water is $10^{-6} \, \text{m}^2 \, \text{s}^{-1}$ and that the unit weight of water is $9.81 \, \text{kN} \, \text{m}^{-3}$.

Solution

The known and unknown values of pressure head, elevation head and total head at the 6 nodes are as tabulated below.

1st table for Example 11.2

	A	B	C	D	E	F
			Heads at nodes m			
Pressure head	0	h_B	h_C	h_D	14	0
Elevation head	120	56	46	30	76	46
Total head	120	H_B	H_C	H_D	90	46

The lengths, apertures and conductances, determined from equation 11.13, for the five channels are as follows:

2nd table for Example 11.2

	AB	BC	CD	EB	CF
			Channel		
Length m	100	15	25	20	75
Aperture mm	1.0	1.0	1.0	0.6	0.8
Conductance $\text{m} \text{s}^{-1} \times 10^{-6}$	8.175	54.50	37.70	8.829	5.581

Putting the values tabulated above into equation 11.25 for node B gives

$$H_B = \frac{(8.175 \times 120) + (54.50 \times H_C) + (8.829 \times 90)}{8.175 + 54.50 + 8.829}$$

so

$$H_B = 24.832 + 0.762 \, H_C \qquad (11.26)$$

at node C

$$H_C = \frac{(54.50 \times H_B) + (5.581 \times 46) + (37.70 \times H_D)}{54.50 + 5.581 + 37.70}$$

so

$$H_C = 0.557\,H_B + 2.625 + 0.386\,H_D \qquad (11.27)$$

and at node D

$$H_D = \frac{37.70 \times H_C}{37.70} = H_C$$

Applying the above result, which could have been obtained by inspection, to the simultaneous solution of equations 11.26 and 11.27 gives $H_B = 91.05$ m and $H_C = 86.87$ m.

Now $H_B = (u_B/\gamma_w) + 56 = 91.05$ m, where u_B is the water pressure at B and γ_w is the unit weight of water; so $u_B = 344$ kPa. Similarly the water pressure at node C is $u_C = 401$ kPa. The flow quantity Q_{AB} in channel AB is given by $C_{AB}(H_A - H_B)$ where C_{AB} is the conductance of channel AB; hence $Q_{AB} = 0.236$ litres per second from A to B, per metre run. Similarly, the flow quantity Q_{BC} in channel BC is $C_{BC}(H_B - H_C) = 0.228$ litres per second from B to C, $Q_{BE} = 0.009$ litres per second from B to E, $Q_{CD} = 0$ and $Q_{CF} = 0.228$ litres per second from C to F, each flow quantity being per metre run normal to the plane of the cross-section. Allowing for round off errors, we have the expected result that $Q_{AB} = Q_{BC} + Q_{BE}$ and $Q_{BC} = Q_{CF}$. It is worth remarking that the water in channel BE is flowing gently **upwards** into the reservoir; the relatively high head maintained at A is preventing reservoir leakage. This theoretical result could be tested by dosing the creek at A with a non-toxic tracer and then monitoring its concentration at F.

The next example illustrates the use of numerical techniques for the solution of flow in more complex fracture networks. In order to apply numerical solution methods it is convenient to define a dimensionless parameter d_{ij} for the jth internal node, here referred to as the conductance ratio. Returning to the generalised network element shown in Figure 11.10, we define a summed conductance C_{sj} as follows

$$C_{sj} = \sum_{i=1}^{4} C_{ij} \qquad (11.28)$$

For the ith node connected to the jth internal node, d_{ij} is given by

$$d_{ij} = \frac{C_{ij}}{C_{sj}} \qquad (11.29)$$

Equation 11.25 can now be expressed in the form

$$\left(\sum_{i=1}^{4} d_{ij} H_i \right) - H_j = 0 \qquad (11.30)$$

As before, general application of equation 11.30 implies temporary local re-numbering in the network. There will be an equation such as 11.30 for each of the internal nodes. It is worth noting that, since any given node can only be connected directly to up to four other nodes, the coefficient matrix of these equations is very sparse. The degree to which the coefficient matrix is banded about the leading diagonal depends on the approach adopted when numbering the nodes. The layout of the terms in equation 11.30 is well suited to the application of recursive, or 'relaxation', numerical solution techniques. Such iterative methods are effective for relatively small networks (less than about 500 nodes) when the numbering has been designed to progress sequentially across the network. For larger networks, methods based on Gaussian elimination and other forms of factorisation tend to be more efficient and give more precise results.

Example 11.3 (Figures 11.12 and 11.13)

Figure 11.12 shows a two-dimensional network composed of two sets of impersistent discontinuities within a 10 m square area. Those discontinuities marked as dashed lines do not form part of the interconnected network and are not, therefore, included in the analysis. The apertures for the seven discontinuities in the network, labelled A–G, are listed below:

Table for Example 11.3

Discontinuity		Aperture mm
Set 1	A	0.16
	B	0.18
	C	0.13
	D	0.24
Set 2	E	0.07
	F	0.09
	G	0.06

It is assumed that the network lies in a horizontal plane, so that the elevation head is everywhere constant and the total head is given by the pressure head. It is also assumed that the left and right hand margins of the network carry constant total heads of $H_n = 3\,m$ and $H_o = 1\,m$, respectively, and that the heads on the upper and lower margins vary linearly between these values. Calculate the total head at each node, the flow in each of the discontinuities and hence determine the total flow across the network.

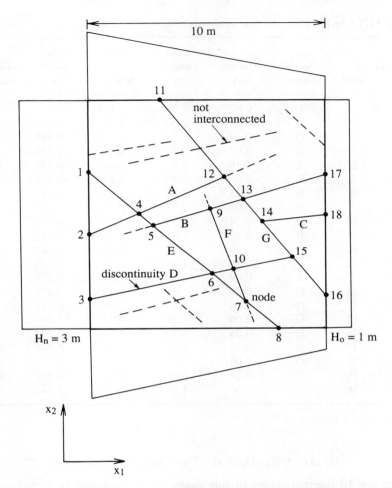

Figure 11.12 Discontinuity network and applied boundary heads for Example 11.3.

Solution
The interconnected network in Figure 11.12 comprises 18 nodes (numbered 1 to 18) and 21 active flow channels which can be identified by the numbers of the start and end nodes. The approximate length of each channel, which can be scaled directly from the network, is listed in Table 11.3 together with the effective hydraulic aperture and conductance, the latter being computed from equation 11.13.

It is now possible to write down an equation, based on the general equation 11.30, for each of the internal nodes in Figure 11.12. For example, at node 4

Table 11.3 Conductance and flow in channels in Figure 11.12

Channel Start	End	Discon- tinuity	Aperture mm	Channel length m	Conduct- ance $mm^2 s^{-1}$	Head drop* m	Flow* $mm^3 s^{-1}$
1	4	E	0.07	2.85	0.098	0.280	27.4
2	4	A	0.16	2.30	1.455	0.280	407.4
3	6	D	0.24	5.30	2.132	0.313	667.3
4	5	E	0.07	0.85	0.330	0.857	282.8
4	12	A	0.16	3.95	0.847	0.179	151.6
5	6	E	0.07	3.25	0.086	-0.825	-70.9
5	9	B	0.18	2.50	1.906	0.186	354.5
6	7	E	0.07	1.95	0.144	0.325	46.8
6	10	D	0.24	0.95	11.892	0.047	558.9
7	8	E	0.07	1.80	0.156	0.962	150.1
9	10	F	0.09	2.85	0.209	-0.963	-210.3
9	13	B	0.18	1.45	3.287	0.169	555.5
10	7	F	0.09	1.60	0.372	0.278	103.4
10	15	D	0.24	2.55	4.430	0.055	243.7
11	12	G	0.06	4.35	0.041	-0.141	-5.8
12	13	G	0.06	1.25	0.141	1.033	145.7
13	14	G	0.06	1.30	0.136	0.273	37.1
13	17	B	0.18	3.65	1.306	0.508	663.4
14	15	G	0.06	2.00	0.088	-1.350	-118.8
14	18	C	0.13	2.70	0.665	0.235	156.3
15	16	G	0.06	2.20	0.080	1.585	126.8

* Left to right is positive

$$d_{1,4} H_1 + d_{2,4} H_2 + d_{5,4} H_5 + d_{12,4} H_{12} - H_4 = 0$$

There are 10 internal nodes in this example, so there are 10 equations and 10 unknowns. Table 11.4 summarises the coefficient matrix for these 10 equations.

Each column in Table 11.4 is labelled with the node number of an internal node and provides the flow balance equation for that node. Each of these equations incorporates the known boundary heads and the unknown internal heads listed in the left hand column of the table. For example at node 10

$$d_{6,10} H_6 + d_{7,10} H_7 + d_{9,10} H_9 - H_{10} + d_{15,10} H_{15} = 0$$

Examination of Table 11.4 shows that there is a maximum of 5 non-zero coefficients for any given equation, represented by a column of coefficients relating to one of the internal nodes. All zero coefficients indicate an absence of direct connection between a pair of nodes. The coefficient matrix for internal heads, in the lower part of Table 11.4, is symmetrical about a leading

Table 11.4 Coefficient matrix for the 10 flow balance equations relating to the 10 internal nodes in Fig. 11.12

	Internal nodes									
Boundary heads ↓	4	5	6	7	9	10	12	13	14	15
H_1	$d_{1,4}$	0	0	0	0	0	0	0	0	0
H_2	$d_{2,4}$	0	0	0	0	0	0	0	0	0
H_3	0	0	$d_{3,6}$	0	0	0	0	0	0	0
H_8	0	0	0	$d_{8,7}$	0	0	0	0	0	0
H_{11}	0	0	0	0	0	0	$d_{11,12}$	0	0	0
H_{16}	0	0	0	0	0	0	0	0	0	$d_{16,15}$
H_{17}	0	0	0	0	0	0	0	$d_{17,13}$	0	0
H_{18}	0	0	0	0	0	0	0	0	$d_{18,14}$	0
Internal heads ↓										
H_4	-1	$d_{4,5}$	0	0	0	0	$d_{4,12}$	0	0	0
H_5	$d_{5,4}$	-1	$d_{5,6}$	0	$d_{5,9}$	0	0	0	0	0
H_6	0	$d_{6,5}$	-1	$d_{6,7}$	0	$d_{6,10}$	0	0	0	0
H_7	0	0	$d_{7,6}$	-1	0	$d_{7,10}$	0	0	0	0
H_9	0	$d_{9,5}$	0	0	-1	$d_{9,10}$	0	$d_{9,13}$	0	0
H_{10}	0	0	$d_{10,6}$	$d_{10,7}$	$d_{10,9}$	-1	0	0	0	$d_{10,15}$
H_{12}	$d_{12,4}$	0	0	0	0	0	-1	0	0	0
H_{13}	0	0	0	0	$d_{13,9}$	0	$d_{13,12}$	-1	$d_{13,14}$	0
H_{14}	0	0	0	0	0	0	0	$d_{14,13}$	-1	$d_{14,15}$
H_{15}	0	0	0	0	0	$d_{15,10}$	0	0	$d_{15,14}$	-1

diagonal of -1s. The non-zero coefficients in this matrix are clustered, or banded, about this leading diagonal. The degree of clustering, and thereby the efficiency of the solution method, is controlled by the way in which the nodes are numbered.

The following recursive algorithm works well for the solution of small to medium sized networks such as the one in this example.

(i) Assign the appropriate boundary heads to all boundary nodes and assign an initial total head of zero to all internal nodes. The heads at these internal nodes will be adjusted as the solution proceeds.

(ii) At the jth internal node, taking the current values of heads at the immediately adjacent nodes, use equation 11.30 to calculate the head H_{jc} that currently applies at this j^{th} internal node.

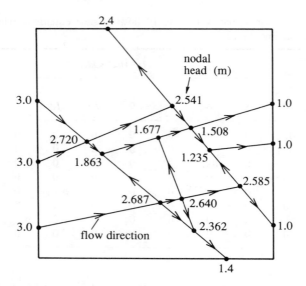

Figure 11.13   Nodal heads and fluid flow directions for Example 11.3.

(iii) If the value of total head from a previous iteration cycle at the jth internal node was H_{jp}, then a new value of total head H_{jn} is calculated as follows:

$$H_{jn} = H_{jp} + F_r(H_{jc} - H_{jp}) \qquad (11.31)$$

where F_r is an 'over-relaxation factor'. Values of F_r in excess of 1.0 (between about 1.1 and 1.5) accelerate the rate of convergence but have no influence on the final solution.

(iv) Repeat steps (ii) and (iii) for each internal node in turn.
(v) Repeat step (iv) until the values of total head at all internal nodes stabilise within a suitable precision.

It is generally more efficient to use values of H_{jn} as soon as they become available, rather than waiting for the end of an iteration cycle before they are brought into the calculations. Initial internal heads can be set at the smallest of the boundary heads, rather than at zero, to give a more rapid convergence. Between 20 and 50 iteration cycles may be required before a stable solution is achieved, depending on the boundary heads, the network geometry and the node numbering system. A short BASIC program was employed in the current example to carry out the iterations, adopting an over-relaxation factor of 1.1. After 40 iteration cycles the nodal heads were changing by less than 0.1 mm at each cycle. The nodal heads determined from 45 iteration cycles are plotted in metres on the network in Figure 11.13. This figure also contains arrows which indicate the direction of flow along each channel; this flow is always towards the node with the lower total head. (Those who read the *International Journal*

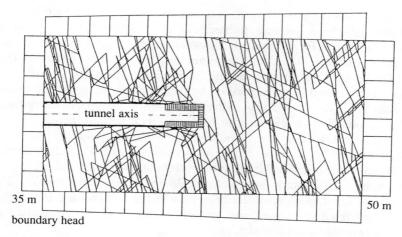

Figure 11.14 Two-dimensional discontinuity realisation for a 20 m length of 2.8 m diameter tunnel through fractured Millstone Grit Series rocks, Derbyshire UK (after Samaniego and Priest, 1984).

of Rock Mechanics and Mining Sciences may recognise this flow network since it forms the front cover of the July 1989 issue of Volume 26.) Table 11.3 lists the head drops and flows for each of the 21 channels in the network. The total flow into the network is given by the sum of the flows in channels 1–4, 2–4 and 3–6, giving 1.102 ml s^{-1} per metre run. The total flow out through the right hand side of the network is given by the summed flows for channels 13–17, 14–18 and 15–16, giving 0.947 ml s^{-1} per metre run. The remaining 0.156 ml s^{-1} disperses laterally along channels 7–8 and 12–11.

Figure 11.13 and Table 11.3 illustrate a number of important principles concerning the flow of fluids through fracture networks. Firstly, although there is a tendency for fluid to flow from the higher boundary head on the left to the lower boundary head on the right, certain fractures conduct fluid across, or even against, the general hydraulic gradient. This flow pattern ensures that a significant quantity of fluid disperses laterally out of the network. Secondly the nodal heads do not change uniformly with distance across the network, indeed the local hydraulic gradients range between 0.03 and 0.83. Finally, it is clear that the flow in a given discontinuity is influenced by the flow in other discontinuities that intersect it. This is graphically illustrated by the fact that three of the discontinuities carry fluid in two opposing directions.

Figure 11.14 shows a two-dimensional realisation, from Samaniego and Priest (1984), for a 20 m length of a 2.8 m diameter tunnel excavated through fractured sandstones, grits and mudstones of the Millstone Grit Series in Derbyshire, England. Samaniego and Priest obtained geometrical and statistical data for the discontinuity network by taking measurements at surface exposures, inspecting the tunnel face and by analysing borehole logs. Permeability data from borehole packer tests at tunnelling level were used to estimate apertures for each of the discontinuity sets, following the methods explained in section 11.4. All of the tunnel, except an approximate 5 m length close to the face was supported with an impermeable concrete lining. This lining was simulated in the realisation by incorporating impermeable elements to within 5 m of the face. The boundary heads on the margins of the realisation were determined from piezometric readings taken in four boreholes within the zone of study. The mean predicted total inflow, based on 10 separate realisations, was found to be 25.5 litres per minute with a standard deviation of 10.6 litres per minute. Actual inflow values at the tunnel face as it passed through the zone of study were between 20 and 80 litres per minute. These results are encouraging, particularly in view of the fact that a complex three-dimensional fracture network and cylindrical tunnel were represented by an idealised two-dimensional model.

11.6   EQUIVALENT PERMEABILITY

A random fracture network and its flow solution provide just one possible flow pattern for a fractured rock mass. In order to provide a more general analysis of mass flow it is desirable to analyse the flow for a large number of random realisations and to average the results in some way. One way of calculating this average flow is to determine an equivalent permeability for each network. In other words, to calculate the permeability of a continuous homogeneous medium that has the same macroscopic flow characteristics as a given network.

The permeability tensor for a continuous medium that is hydraulically equivalent, on the macroscopic scale, to the discontinuous network can be determined by averaging the flow volumes over some specified area covered by the network. The simplest way to do this is to consider the total flows across the boundaries of the network. Introducing the subscripts p = 1, 2 and q = 1, 2 to refer to two orthogonal directions in two dimensions, the macroscopic flow velocity V_p is given by

$$V_p = \frac{Q_p}{A_p}$$

where Q_p is the total flow in the p direction across a boundary of area A_p orientated at right angles to the p direction. The link between flow velocity and equivalent permeability for an anisotropic continuum can be expressed in terms of the generalised form of Darcy's law, in tensor notation, as follows

$$V_p = -K_{pq}\frac{\delta H}{\delta x_q} \tag{11.32}$$

where K_{pq} is the permeability tensor and $\dfrac{\delta H}{\delta x_q}$ is the gradient of total hydraulic head in the q direction. The repeated subscript in equation 11.32 should be taken to imply summation. In other words, this equation should be interpreted as follows for two-dimensional macroscopic flow in direction 1

$$V_1 = -\left[K_{11} \frac{\delta H}{\delta x_1} + K_{12} \frac{\delta H}{\delta x_2} \right]$$

and for macroscopic flow in direction 2

$$V_2 = -\left[K_{21} \frac{\delta H}{\delta x_1} + K_{22} \frac{\delta H}{\delta x_2} \right]$$

The leading diagonal terms K_{11} and K_{22} in the permeability tensor link the flow velocity in one direction to the hydraulic gradient in the same direction. The off diagonal terms K_{12} and K_{21} link the flow velocity in one direction to the hydraulic gradient at right angles to that direction. The negative sign ensures that positive flow occurs in the direction of reducing head. If the flow network is within a square area of side length L, subjected to a constant input boundary head H_n and a constant output boundary head H_o, as shown in Figure 11.12, then regarding left to right as direction 1 gives

$$\frac{\delta H}{\delta x_1} = \frac{(H_o - H_n)}{L} \quad \text{and} \quad \frac{\delta H}{\delta x_2} = 0$$

For unit distance normal to the plane of flow $A_1 = L$, and so

$$K_{11} = \frac{-Q_1}{(H_o - H_n)} \quad \text{and} \quad K_{21} = \frac{-Q_2}{(H_o - H_n)} \qquad (11.33)$$

The other terms K_{22} and K_{12} can be found by applying the hydraulic gradient in direction 2, to give

$$K_{22} = \frac{-Q_2}{(H_o - H_n)} \quad \text{and} \quad K_{12} = \frac{-Q_1}{(H_o - H_n)} \qquad (11.34)$$

It has been assumed above that the conductance of a given channel depends only on its geometrical properties and on the physical properties of the fluid. This assumption means that the conductance does not depend on the rate or the direction of flow and that the principles of reciprocity must apply. Hence $K_{21} = K_{12}$ and the permeability tensor must, in theory, be symmetrical.

Although the above approach to determining the permeability tensor, by summing the flow across a single boundary, is appealing in its simplicity, the results obtained are highly sensitive to the location of the selected boundary (Long, 1983). Indeed, Samaniego and Priest (1984) have noted that boundaries on opposite sides of a network can give equivalent permeabilities that differ by up to two orders of magnitude. This difficulty, caused by the fact that an inhomogeneous flow regime has been used to estimate continuum properties, has been tackled by Cundall (1983). His approach, summarised in the final paragraphs of this section, is based on the flow through, and the location of, each of the inflow and outflow nodes.

In equations 11.33 and 11.34 the boundary flow quantities Q_1 and Q_2 are assumed to be transported the distance L completely across the network. In reality, fluid transport is achieved by fluid entering the network at certain nodes and leaving at others. In Figures 11.12 and 11.13 for example, fluid enters at nodes 1, 2 and 3 and leaves at nodes 8, 11, 16, 17 and 18. The flow quantities along the channels associated with these boundary nodes are listed, together with flow details for the internal channels, in Table 11.3. Clearly, fluid leaving the network laterally through nodes 8 and 11 has not been transported the full distance L = 10 m across the network. Here it is desirable to consider the product of flow rate and distance for each boundary node separately. If the total flow rate through the tth boundary node is Q_t (taking flow into the network as negative and flow out as positive) and if the coordinate of this boundary node in the p direction is x_{pt}, then the aggregated products of flow rate and distance are

$$\sum_{t=1}^{m} x_{pt} Q_t$$

where there are m boundary nodes. This summation represents the true fluid transport condition for the network and can be used to calculate an equivalent boundary flow rate Q'_p as follows

$$Q'_p = \frac{1}{L} \sum_{t=1}^{m} x_{pt} Q_t \qquad (11.35)$$

The computed equivalent boundary flow can be input to equations 11.33 and 11.34 in order to calculate equivalent permeability. The resulting value of K_{11} for the network analysed in Example 11.3 is 1.067×10^{-7} m s^{-1}. This low permeability reflects the fact that fluid is being carried by only three or four narrow fractures across a 10 m wide sample. Although permeabilities calculated in this way give a true reflection of the fluid transport properties of a given network, even a slight change in the geometry of the fractures can have a dramatic effect on the results.

11.7 TRANSIENT FLOW

If the boundary conditions for a particular flow regime are maintained constant then the flow pattern will eventually settle down to a steady state during which all internal heads and flow quantities remain constant. If one of the boundary conditions is changed, however, the network will enter a period of transient flow during which time the internal heads and flow quantities change continuously until they have adjusted to a new steady state that is in balance with the new boundary conditions. In this section we will examine briefly the phenomenon of transient flow and illustrate how it can be analysed by reference to the simple network in Figure 11.11 and Example 11.2.

Node A is in the bed of a shallow creek. We will imagine that the creek dries up, causing the water level to fall in channel AB, but we will keep node A at the falling water surface. The initial flow quantity in channel AB is $Q_{AB} = 0.236$ litres s^{-1} per metre run. For an aperture e_{AB} this gives a flow velocity $V_{AB} = Q_{AB}/e_{AB} = 0.236$ m s^{-1} along the channel. In order to examine the transient nature of the flow we will apply a time step of 10s and then re-analyse the flow under pseudo-static conditions. After 10s the water level will have moved 2.36 m along the channel giving a new effective channel length of 97.64 m and a new channel conductance of 8.373×10^{-6} m s^{-1}. The conductance has increased simply because the channel has become effectively shorter. Since the discontinuity ABCD is inclined at 40°, the total head at A will have reduced to $120 - (2.36 \sin 40°) = 118.48$ m. We will assume that the water level in the reservoir remains constant. Re-analysis of the network under pseudo-static conditions, as in Example 11.2, gives new total heads $H_B = 90.73$ m and $H_C = 86.58$ m, a new flow volume in channel AB of $Q_{AB} = 0.232$ litres s^{-1} per m run and hence a new flow velocity $V_{AB} = 0.232$ m s^{-1}. The flow velocity has decreased because the total head at A has fallen. Analysis of the transient flow continues by applying another 10 second time step and repeating the analysis cycle. After many cycles the flow rate in channel AB will become very small as the network settles towards a new steady state condition. A more precise transient analysis can be achieved by applying a smaller time step; a more rapid convergence to steady state can be achieved by applying a larger time step. These calculations would normally be performed by a computer.

It is not necessary to work through the complete transient analysis to determine the new steady state condition for the above example. If it is assumed that there is no flow into channel AB from the creek then there will be no flow from node A to node B. Hence $H_A = H_B$ and the flow balance equation for node B becomes

$$H_B = \frac{(C_{AB} \times H_B) + (54.50 \times H_C) + (8.829 \times 90)}{C_{AB} + 54.50 + 8.829}$$

where C_{AB} is the conductance of channel AB. Cancelling the $(C_{AB} H_B)$ term gives

$$H_B = 12.547 + 0.861 H_C$$

Equation 11.27 is still applicable to the new boundary conditions, giving $H_A = H_B = 73.98$ m and $H_C = 71.39$ m. The ultimate total head of 73.98 m at node A indicates that the water level in this channel stabilises at about 16 m below the surface of the reservoir. It is worth remarking that under these new boundary conditions the total head at B is now less than that at E; the total flow for channel BE is 0.141 litres s^{-1} per m run from E to B, which indicates leakage from the reservoir out through the spring at node F.

The time-stepping methods introduced in this section are extremely powerful and can be applied to a range of complex networks in which the water levels in several channels are allowed to change simultaneously. In particular the methods are well suited to determining the steady state water table for a rock slope with continuous recharge at a point that is remote from the crest.

11.8 FLOW IN THREE-DIMENSIONAL NETWORKS

Long (1983) and Long et al. (1985) were among the first of an increasing number of researchers to address the problem of modelling fluid flow through a three-dimensional network of fractures. They adopted a geometrical model comprising disc shaped discontinuities distributed through an impermeable rock material. Each set of discontinuities is represented by a group of discs that can be arbitrarily located within the generation volume and can take any desired distribution of orientation, radius, aperture and volumetric density. Figure 6.15a, taken from Long et al. (1985), shows a realisation of orthogonal discs within a cubic sample volume. This figure demonstrates how each discontinuity presents a finite region of two-dimensional flow containing line elements produced by intersections with other discontinuities. The analytical solution for flow in each discontinuity plane is based on the assumption that each line element represents a line of constant head within the two-dimensional flow regime, as shown in Figure 11.15. In general such line elements will represent either a source or a sink for flow and thereby control the distribution of total head in the discontinuity plane. Solving Laplace's equation for flow in this plane gives an expression for the distribution of total head in terms of the total flow into or out of each line element. From this expression, a set of equations can be derived that gives the total flow through a given line element in terms of the average total head at each of the line elements. Such equations are developed for each discontinuity plane. Consequently, for any given line element there will be two values for flow: one where it behaves as a source and another where it behaves as a sink. Constraining this pair of flows to have the same magnitude, and ensuring that the sum of the inflows and outflows for each discontinuity is zero, imposes a mass balance on the flow system which can be solved to give the average head, and hence the total flow, for each line element.

The techniques developed by Long et al. (1985) comprise a mixed analytical/numerical approach. The flow in a given discontinuity is solved analytically by employing image sources and sinks to represent the influence of the boundaries of the finite flow region. When this is done it is possible to

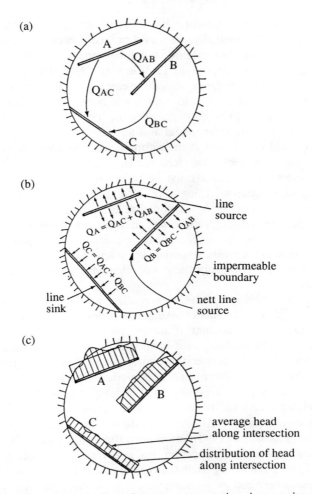

Figure 11.15 Flow through line elements representing intersections on a single circular fracture showing (a) fracture disc intersecting fractures A, B and C, (b) line sources and line sink to achieve flow balance, and (c) assumption of constant head along each line element (after Long *et al.*, 1985).

utilise the standard solution of Laplace's equation for the potential due to a point source in an infinite plane. In this case, since the real sources and sinks are linear elements, giving images that are parts of circular arcs, it is necessary to integrate the solution of Laplace's equation over the length of each real element and its image. Although this integration can be carried out analytically for the simpler element geometries, a more generalised approach requires the adoption of numerical integration methods. When the mass balance equations for the three-dimensional network have been formulated in this way it is necessary to specify the conditions of total head, or flow, at those line elements on the boundaries of the flow volume. A similar approach to that used for two-dimensional analyses is adopted here. When the boundary conditions have been specified, the mass balance equations can be solved numerically to give the steady state values of total head, and hence flow, for each line element.

Long *et al.* (1985) present a number of progressively more complex examples both to validate their model and to demonstrate its capabilities. One criticism that could be levelled at their approach is the adoption of a constant, average total head for each line element. In reality, variations in total head across each discontinuity plane must be reflected as variations in head along the associated line elements. Long *et al.* (1985) sought.to render their model more sensitive to this effect by discretising the line elements into up to 10 segments. In general, although there was an improvement in accuracy for head and flux with increasing discretisation, computational costs also increased. In order to minimise costs while retaining accuracy, Long *et al.* found it to be more efficient to discretise only those line elements on the boundaries of the sample volume.

Strafford *et al.* (1990) describe a three-dimensional fracture-network flow model code NAPSAC. The model assumes that flow is restricted to a network of two-dimensional rectangular fracture planes with spatially-correlated variable aperture. The pressure field is discretised in terms of values which are assumed to vary linearly between network nodes along each fracture inter-section. The flow in each fracture plane is modelled by finite element methods based on a regular grid of typically 4000 triangular elements. Flow through three-dimensional random realisations containing several thousand frac-tures can be modelled by NAPSAC running on the Cray-2 super-computer. Kobayashi and Yamashita (1990) introduce a three-dimensional flow model for fractured rock masses incorporating leakage from the rock material and unsaturated flow. Flow along each fracture is modelled by conventional finite element methods serviced by an automatic three-dimensional mesh generator. Kobayashi and Yamashita (1990) present examples containing only five fractures; it is not clear whether the method has the capacity to handle large numbers of fractures. Jixian and Cojean (1990) describe a numerical model for analysing fluid flow through a three-dimensional network in which flow along each polygonal discontinuity plane is analysed by the boundary element method. They present a number of examples, including a regular network containing 1260 blocks, an irregular network containing 244 blocks and a problem involving the determination of a free water surface.

The work of Long *et al.* (1985) and others to extend the analysis of fluid flow to three-dimensional discontinuity networks represents a major advance in the understanding of fluid flow in rock masses. Since the image theory approach adopted by Long *et al.* (1985) is only applicable to circular dis-continuities there is no immediate need to develop more complex models for discontinuity shape in three-dimensions. The work of Warburton (1980) discussed in Chapter 6 is, however, clearly relevant here since it provides the vital link between the geometrical parameters of circular discs and the statistical properties of the traces produced by their intersections with a planar rock face. Generating the input data for three-dimensional fluid flow models will rely heavily on this link.

EXERCISES FOR CHAPTER 11

11.1

The average mechanical aperture of a horizontal discontinuity with a Joint Roughness Coefficient of 10 was observed to be 0.1 mm. Taking the kinematic viscosity of water to be $1 \times 10^{-6}\, m^2\, s^{-1}$ and the acceleration due to gravity as $9.81\, m\, s^{-2}$, estimate (i) the conductance of a 1 m wide, 3 m channel length of this discontinuity and (ii) the rate of water flow in litres per day along this channel if the hydraulic pressure at one end is 25 kPa and 10 kPa at the other.

11.2

A series of borehole water permeability tests in a jointed slate rock mass gave the following results:

RQD for test zone %	Rock mass permeability $m\, s^{-1} \times 10^{-6}$
35	2.10
50	1.70
65	1.30
80	0.84
95	0.43

Estimate the discontinuity frequency for each test zone and, taking the viscosity of water to be $10^{-3}\, N\, s\, m^{-2}$, estimate the effective discontinuity hydraulic aperture.

11.3

A worked-out open pit mine 130 m deep, 450 m in diameter, with 40° pit walls is to be used for the disposal of tailings and waste water created by the processing of waste dumps. The crest of the open pit is, at its closest point, 1500 m from the banks of a creek that runs at the bottom of a steep gorge. The bed of the creek is at the same elevation as the bottom of the open pit at RL 25 m. The water surface in the creek is consistently at RL 40 m while the proposed ultimate water level in the open pit will be maintained at RL 125 m. The natural ground surface slopes gently at 1:50 down from the crest of the pit to the crest of the creek gorge and then dips steeply to the water's edge.

Site investigation studies reveal that the country rock is a cemented sandstone containing laterally-extensive, open horizontal bedding planes at an average vertical spacing of 0.8 m. A programme of borehole water permeability tests was conducted by isolating 1 m lengths of vertical borehole with a pair of inflatable packers and then pumping water in, under pressure, to determine rock mass permeability. Each test zone was inspected with a borehole TV camera to determine the number of water-conducting bedding planes intersecting the test length. The following results were obtained:

Number of conductive bedding planes in test length	Average apparent rock mass permeability, $m\,s^{-1}$
0	2.72×10^{-12}
1	7.68×10^{-6}
2	1.55×10^{-5}
3	2.36×10^{-5}

Acceleration due to gravity $= 9.81\,m\,s^{-2}$. Density of water $= 1000\,kg\,m^{-3}$. Viscosity of water $= 10^{-3}\,N\,s\,m^{-2}$.

Use the data given above to estimate the effective hydraulic aperture of the bedding planes and hence estimate the total water flow, in litres per year, from the open pit with its water at the ultimate level, into the creek and its gorge.

11.4

The figure shows a vertical cross-section through a 6 m diameter tunnel which is to be excavated in jointed rock beneath the bed of a shallow river. The section shows three discontinuities which strike parallel with the tunnel axis and which are visible in the bed of the river. Tests indicate that these discontinuities have effective hydraulic apertures of (1) 0.4 mm, (2) 0.7 mm and (3) 0.3 mm. Reduced levels of nodes A to F, and the associated channel lengths are tabulated below

Feature	Reduced level, m above sea level		Channel	Channel length m
River surface	51.0		AB	7.3
Tunnel axis	35.0		BC	2.5
A	46.2		BE	4.5
B	40.1		DE	3.6
C	37.9		EF	3.5
D	44.4			
E	41.7			
F	43.0			

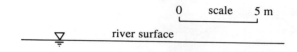

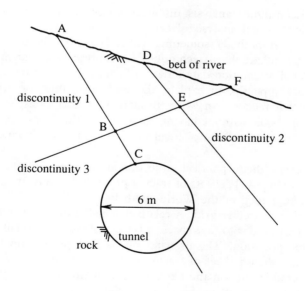

Taking the unit weight and kinematic viscosity of water as $9.81\,\mathrm{kN\,m^{-3}}$ and $1 \times 10^{-6}\,\mathrm{m^2\,s^{-1}}$, respectively, estimate the rate of water inflow in litres per hour that could be expected per metre run of tunnel at this section.

Answers to these exercises are given on page 464.

Appendix A

Hemispherical projection methods

A.1 INTRODUCTION

Aspects of discontinuity analysis discussed in most chapters of this book involve the plotting and analysis of orientation data of various types. Hemispherical projection methods (sometimes called stereographic projection) offer simple and efficient graphical techniques for representing and manipulating three-dimensional orientation data on an ordinary sheet of tracing paper. It is the aim of this appendix to explain the basic principles of hemispherical projection, so that readers can work through the descriptions, examples and exercises of this book without having to refer to other texts. A more comprehensive description of hemispherical projection methods is given by Priest (1985).

The basic tools of hemispherical projection are the circular equal angle net, reproduced in Figure A.1, sheets of tracing paper and a drawing pin. The net looks rather like a map of the World, with lines of 'longitude' and lines of 'latitude' forming a circular grid. A relatively small diameter net will be used in this appendix in order to save space; a larger net would normally be used to provide greater precision. The drawing pin is first pushed up through the centre of the net then a sheet of tracing paper is centralised and impaled on the pin. The graduations on the net can be seen through the tracing paper, which can be rotated about the drawing pin. Before rotating the tracing paper, however, it is necessary to trace off the north point, labelled 'N', which lies at the 12 o'clock position on the net. The perimeter of the net represents the range of trend directions marked in 10° intervals in Figure A.1 from 0° (north) through 90° (east), 180° (south), 270° (west) then round to 360° which also represents north. Many choose to trace off this perimeter, though this is not strictly necessary. The assembly is now ready for use.

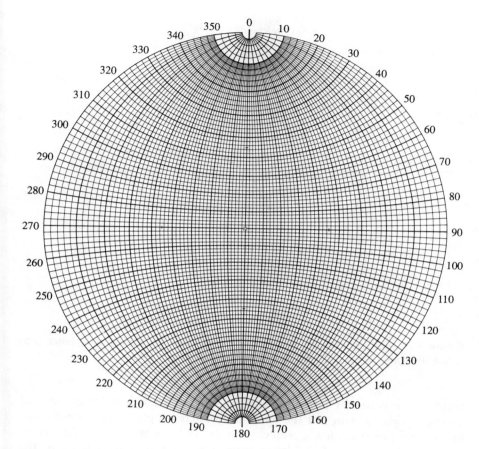

Figure A.1 Equal angle net, printed at reduced size.

Before proceeding with the techniques of hemispherical projection, it is necessary to understand what the curved lines of 'longitude' and 'latitude' on the net mean and how they are constructed. The term 'lower hemisphere projection' refers to the lower hemisphere of an imaginary reference sphere that has the same diameter as the net, and that is positioned with its centre at the centre of the net, as shown in Figure A.2. This reference sphere not only provides the geometrical basis for construction of the net, it also provides a valuable aid to the visualisation of the three-dimensional orientation of features that have been plotted on the projection.

All lines and planes that will be plotted are first notionally translated through space so that they pass through the centre of the reference sphere. A line translated in this way will, however, intersect the sphere at two points

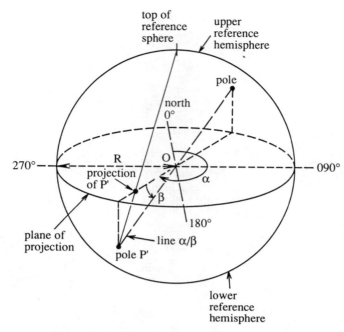

Figure A.2 The reference sphere intersected by a line of trend α and plunge β to define the point (or pole) P′ and its projection (after Priest, 1985).

which are sometimes referred to as 'poles'. To remove this ambiguity we will choose to operate with just the lower hemisphere. A plane will intersect this lower hemisphere to form a semi-circular arc called a great circle. Any given point on the surface of the lower hemisphere can be projected on to the circular net simply by drawing a straight line from the given point to the top of the reference sphere. The projection of the point occurs where this line passes through the plane of the net, as shown in Figure A.2 for the point, or pole, P′ representing a line of trend α and plunge β. This, the simplest form of projection, is commonly referred to as 'equal angle projection' and is the one that we will use here. If we regard a plane as being formed from a large number of radiating coplanar lines, which intersect the lower reference hemisphere to form a locus of points, we can visualise the projection of a great circle simply as the projection of each point along the locus. The lines of 'longitude' on the net are the projections of the great circles of planes that have a north–south strike and that have angles of maximum dip of 0°, 2°, 4° . . . 86°, 88° to the west, through vertical and then angles of maximum dip of 88°, 86° . . . 4°, 2° and 0° to the east. These lines of 'longitude' are also referred to as great circles.

The lines of 'latitude' are formed when a plane with a north–south strike,

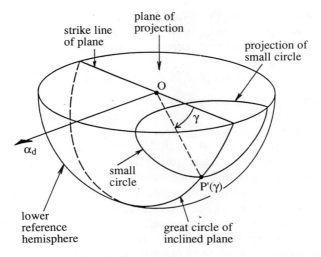

Figure A.3   Construction of a small circle and its projection (after Priest, 1985).

that contains a line with a pitch angle γ, is rotated through 180° about the north–south diameter of the net from a dip of 0° to the west round to a dip of 0° to the east. The line of constant pitch will inscribe a circular arc on the surface of the lower reference hemisphere during this rotation, as shown in Figure A.3. Circular arcs such as this, which will have diameters that are equal to or smaller than the diameter of the net, are called small circles. The lines of 'latitude' are the projections of these small circles for angles of pitch γ in the range 0 to 90° measured in increments of 2° from the southern end and from the northern end of the north–south strike line. These small circles are of particular value when undertaking rotations about axes. In such cases it is necessary to count the rotation angle along a small circle, using the inter-sections with the great circles as graduations every 2°. It is also sometimes necessary to count angles along a great circle; in this case the intersections with the small circles provide the graduations.

A.2 PLOTTING AND UN-PLOTTING LINES

The plotting of a line of some general orientation in three-dimensional space is linked to the definitions of trend and plunge given in Chapter 1 and summarised below:

Plunge, β ($-90° \leq \beta \leq 90°$). This is the acute angle measured in a vertical plane between a given line and the horizontal plane. Positive angles of plunge correspond to lines that are directed downwards; negative angles of plunge correspond to lines that are directed upwards.

Trend, α ($0° \leq \alpha \leq 360°$). This is the geographical azimuth, measured in clockwise rotation from north (0°), of the vertical plane containing the given line. Any vertical plane possesses two geographical azimuth directions, 180° apart; trend is the azimuth that corresponds to the direction of plunge of the line.

The following steps are adopted in the plotting of a line:

1. Push a drawing pin up through the centre of the net. Centralise and impale a fresh sheet of tracing paper on this drawing pin so that it is free to rotate. Align the edge of the tracing paper with the edge of the net then trace off the north point, and, if desired trace off the perimeter of the net. The tracing paper will henceforth be referred to as the **projection**. The projection is said to be at its **home** position when its north point is in exact alignment with the north point on the net.
2. With the projection at its home position, mark its perimeter with a small radial reference line at the geographical azimuth that corresponds to the trend of the line that is being plotted. It is generally helpful to annotate this reference line with the value of trend for future reference.
3. Rotate the projection until the reference line lies at **either** the eastern end **or** the western end of the east–west diameter of the net. It does not matter which end is used.
4. Count in from the perimeter of the net, along the east–west diameter, the angle of plunge for the line that is being plotted. Mark the point on the projection with a small dot and then annotate it with an appropriate label.
5. Return the projection to its home position.

It is often the case that a series of operations produces a point on the projection that represents a line whose orientation (trend/plunge) is required. The process of determining the orientation of a line represented by a point is here referred to as 'un-plotting' and is essentially the reverse of the above process.

The un-plotting of a line:

1. Rotate the projection until the point in question lies exactly on the western★ half of the east–west diameter of the net.
2. Mark, with a small radial reference line, the point on the perimeter of the projection where it is intersected by the western★ end of the east–west diameter of the net.
3. Read off the angle of plunge of the point by counting the angle from the western★ end of the perimeter of the net along the east–west diameter.
4. Return the projection to its home position and then read off the trend indicated by the radial reference line

The following simple example illustrates the process of plotting and un-plotting.

★ Note: it is quite acceptable to use instead the eastern half of the east–west diameter.

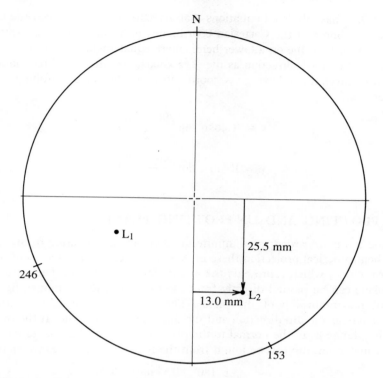

Figure A.4 Plotting and un-plotting lines, Example A.1.

Example A.1 (Figure A.4)

(i) Plot on a lower hemisphere equal angle projection the point that represents the orientation of a line of trend 246° and plunge 37°.

(ii) A point on a lower hemisphere equal angle projection of 90 mm diameter plots 13.0 mm to the east of the north–south diameter of the net, and 25.5 mm south of the east–west diameter, when the projection is at its home position. Un-plot this point to determine the trend and plunge of the line that it represents.

Solution

(i) Figure A.4 shows that the line of trend/plunge 246/37 plots as a point, labelled L_1, in the south west quadrant of the projection.

   (ii) The point labelled L_2 has been plotted at the coordinates given, in the south east quadrant of the projection in Figure A.4. Un-plotting this point reveals that it represents a line that has a trend/plunge of approximately 153/25.

Priest (1985) has tabulated equations that give the relation between the trend/plunge of a line and the Cartesian coordinates of a point that represents the orientation of that line on a lower hemisphere equal angle projection of radius R. Taking the north direction as the +ve x-axis, and the east direction as the +ve y-axis gives the following x,y coordinates for a line of trend/plunge α/β in degrees

$$x = R \cos\alpha \tan\left(\frac{90° - \beta}{2}\right) \tag{A.1}$$

$$y = R \sin\alpha \tan\left(\frac{90° - \beta}{2}\right) \tag{A.2}$$

A.3 PLOTTING AND UN-PLOTTING PLANES

A plane can be regarded as an infinite number of lines radiating from a point. On a hemispherical projection these lines will project to form a locus of points, or great circle, which represents the orientation of the plane. The great circle of a plane can be plotted directly from the trend α_d and the plunge β_d of the line of maximum dip of the plane. These angles are usually referred to respectively as the dip direction and the dip angle of the plane. If the trend α_n and the plunge β_n of the normal to the plane are known, the orientation of the line of maximum dip can be found from the following simple expressions

$$\alpha_d = \alpha_n \pm 180° \quad 0 \leqslant \alpha_d \leqslant 360° \tag{A.3}$$

$$\beta_d = 90° - \beta_n \tag{A.4}$$

In order to plot the great circle of the plane it is first necessary to plot its line of maximum dip by following steps 1 to 4 of the procedure for plotting a line. While the line of maximum dip is still on the east–west diameter of the net, the great circle that is closest to it is traced off and annotated. The great circle is in its **plotting** position when the projection is rotated such that the line of maximum dip of the plane lies on the east–west diameter in this way. If the dip angle is an odd number it will be necessary to trace between a pair of great circles marked on the net. It is generally helpful to represent the line of maximum dip by a small cross so that it is clearly visible on the great circle. The two points where the great circle of a plane intersects the perimeter of the net give the strike directions of the plane when the projection is in its home position. It is often convenient to emphasise these points with small crosses or ticks. The trend and plunge of the normal to the plane can be determined from equations A.3 and A.4 then plotted and labelled in the usual way. Alternatively, the normal can be plotted directly from the line of maximum dip by counting 90° across the east–west diameter of the net as described below and in Example A.2.

It is often the case that a series of operations produces a point on the projection that represents the normal to a plane whose orientation (dip direction/dip angle) is required. The procedure for un-plotting the normal to a plane is as follows:

1. Rotate the projection until the normal lies on the east–west diameter of the net.
2. Count 90° from the normal, along the east–west diameter and through the centre of the net, then plot and label the line of maximum dip of the plane. Although it is not necessary, the great circle of the plane can also be plotted at this stage.
3. Follow steps 1 to 4 of the procedure for un-plotting a line to determine the trend and plunge of the normal and the dip direction/dip angle of the plane.

Example A.2 (Figure A.5)

(i) Plot on a lower hemisphere equal angle projection the line of maximum dip, great circle and the normal to a plane of dip direction/dip angle 328/33.
(ii) The normal to a plane on a lower hemisphere equal angle projection of 90 mm diameter plots 18.0 mm to the east of the north-south diameter of the net, and 23.0 mm north of the east-west diameter, when the projection is at its home position. Un-plot this point to determine the dip direction/dip angle of the plane.

Solution
(i) Figure A.5 shows that the line of maximum dip 328/33 plots as a cross, labelled D_1, at the mid-point of the great circle of the plane in the north-west quadrant of the projection. Application of equations A.3 and A.4 in inverted form gives the trend/plunge of the normal to the plane as 148/57, which plots as a point labelled N_1 in the south-east quadrant. This normal can, alternatively, be plotted directly by counting 90° across the east-west diameter from D_1 with the great circle in its plotting position.

(ii) The normal, labelled N_2, has been plotted at the coordinates given, in the north-east quadrant of the projection in Figure A.5. The projection is first rotated until N_2 lies on the east-west diameter of the net. Counting 90° across this diameter and through the centre of the net gives the line of maximum dip D_2 and the associated great circle of the plane. Un-plotting D_2 reveals that it represents a line that has a trend/plunge of approximately 218/66 which are the dip direction and dip angle of the plane. Unplotting the normal, or the application of equations A.3 and A.4, reveals that the normal to the plane has a trend plunge 038/24.

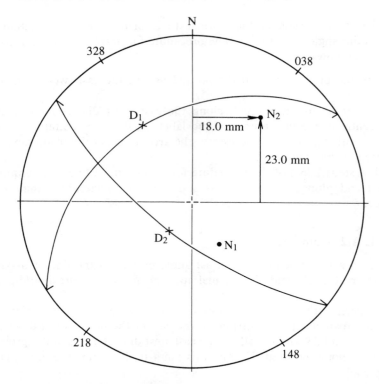

Figure A.5   Plotting and un-plotting planes, Example A.2.

A.4   THE ANGLE BETWEEN LINES

If two lines L_1 and L_2 of trend/plunge α_1/β_1 and α_2/β_2 intersect in three-dimensional space they will define a plane of dip direction/dip angle α_d/β_d. Two supplementary angles θ_a and θ_b ($\leq 180°$) can be measured in this plane between the two lines. The angles α_d, β_d, θ_a and θ_b can be found by applying the vectorial methods in equations 7.1, 7.4 and 7.5 of section 7.2. In particular θ_a and θ_b can be found from the following expressions.

$$\cos \theta_a = (\cos(\alpha_1 - \alpha_2) \cos \beta_1 \cos \beta_2) + (\sin \beta_1 \sin \beta_2) \qquad (A.5)$$

$$\cos \theta_b = -\cos \theta_a \qquad (A.6)$$

The angle θ_a is here termed the 'internal angle' and θ_b the 'external angle' of the supplementary pair. The reason for adopting this terminology can be appreciated by examining how the angles α_d, β_d, θ_a and θ_b can be determined graphically from α_1/β_1 and α_2/β_2 by hemispherical projection methods.

Points representing the orientations of the two lines L_1 and L_2 are plotted

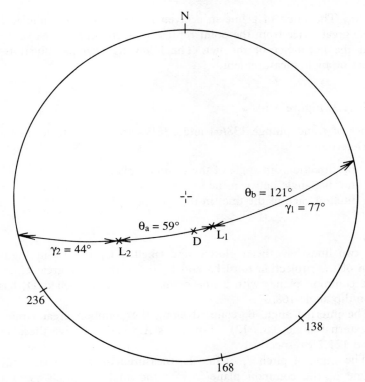

Figure A.6   The angle between a pair of lines, Example A.3.

on the lower hemisphere projection in the usual way. The projection is then rotated until the two points lie on the same great circle, which represents the plane that contains the two lines. The line of maximum dip of the common plane is marked where its great circle crosses the east–west diameter of the net. The dip direction/dip angle of this plane can be determined by following the un-plotting procedures outlined in section A.3.

The internal angle θ_a between the two lines is determined by putting their common great circle back into its plotting position and then counting the direct angle between the two points along this great circle without crossing the perimeter of the net. This internal angle can lie in the range 0 to 180°. The external angle θ_b is counted between the points along their common great circle **via the perimeter of the net**, i.e. count from point L_1 to an exit point on the perimeter of the net, re-enter the net at a point diametrically opposite the exit point, and then complete the measurement along the same great circle from the perimeter of the net to L_2. Of course it is never necessary actually to count an external angle once the internal angle has been measured since $\theta_b =$

$180° - \theta_a$. The pitch of a line in a given plane is the acute angle, counted along the great circle from the point representing the line, to the strike of the plane at the perimeter of the net. The following example illustrates these principles of angle measurement.

Example A.3 (Figure A.6)

Two lines of trend plunge 138/64 and 236/39 are known to lie in the same plane. Determine:

(i)   the dip direction/dip angle of the common plane,
(ii) the internal angle between the two lines, and
(iii) the pitch of each of the lines in the common plane.

Solution

(i) The two lines have been plotted and labelled L_1 and L_2 in Figure A.6. Rotation of the projection until L_1 and L_2 lie on the same great circle shows that the common plane, with a line of maximum dip labelled D, has a dip direction/dip angle 168/67.

   (ii) The internal angle θ_a counted along the common great circle is 59°, so the external angle θ_b is 121°. Equations A.5 and A.6 give these angles as 58.8° and 121.2°, respectively.

   (iii) The angle of pitch γ_1 of line L_1 measured to the eastern 'end' of the strike line of the common plane is 77°; the angle of pitch γ_2 of line L_2 measured to the western 'end' of the strike line is 44°.

The final part of the above example illustrates the importance of recording the 'end' of the strike line to which the angle of pitch has been measured. For this purpose it is generally sufficient to specify the geographical quadrant (east, north-west etc) rather than the exact azimuth of the strike line.

A.5   INTERSECTING PLANES

If two planes intersect they will define a line whose orientation depends on the orientation of both planes. This dependency can be expressed mathematically in the form of a solution to a pair of simultaneous equations that constrain the line of intersection to be simultaneously coplanar with both planes. These equations lead to the following vectorial solution in which the orientation of the line of intersection is given by the vector product of the unit normals to the two intersecting planes. If the trend and plunge of the **normals** to planes 1 and 2 are α_l/β_l and α_m/β_m, respectively, then, adopting the Cartesian co-ordinate system in Figure 1.2, the direction cosines for the two normals are, respectively

$$l_x = \cos \alpha_l \cos \beta_l \quad m_x = \cos \alpha_m \cos \beta_m$$
$$l_y = \sin \alpha_l \cos \beta_l \quad m_y = \sin \alpha_m \cos \beta_m \qquad \text{(A.7)}$$
$$l_z = \sin \beta_l \qquad\qquad m_z = \sin \beta_m$$

The Cartesian components of the line of intersection are given by the vector product as follows

$$i_x = l_y m_z - l_z m_y$$
$$i_y = l_z m_x - l_x m_z \qquad\qquad \text{(A.8)}$$
$$i_z = l_x m_y - l_y m_x$$

The trend and plunge α_i/β_i of the line of intersection can be found from i_x, i_y and i_z as follows

$$\alpha_i = \arctan \left(\frac{i_y}{i_x}\right) + Q \qquad\qquad \text{(A.9)}$$

$$\beta_i = \arctan \left(\frac{i_z}{\sqrt{i_x^2 + i_y^2}}\right) \qquad\qquad \text{(A.10)}$$

The parameter Q is an angle, in degrees that ensures that α_i lies in the correct quadrant and in the range 0 to 360°. This parameter, which depends on the signs of i_x and i_y as listed in Table 1.1 and discussed in section 1.2, is required because the arc tangent function of most computers returns a value in the range $-90°$ to $+90°$.

The line of intersection between two planes plotted on a lower hemisphere projection is given by the point of intersection between their great circles. The trend and plunge of this intersection can be un-plotted in the usual way. It is worth noting that the line of intersection is itself normal to the plane that contains the normals to the two intersecting planes. This geometrical relation can be appreciated by working through the following example.

Example A.4 (Figure A.7)

Two planes of dip direction/dip angle 105/58 and 216/34 are known to intersect. Determine:

(i) the trend/plunge of their line of intersection, and
(ii) the dip direction/dip angle of the plane that contains the normals to the two intersecting planes.

Solution
(i) Figure A.7 shows the great circles, normals and lines of maximum dip of the two intersecting planes. The point of intersection between the two great circles, labelled I_{12}, represents the line of intersection between the two planes and has a trend/plunge of approximately 176/27.

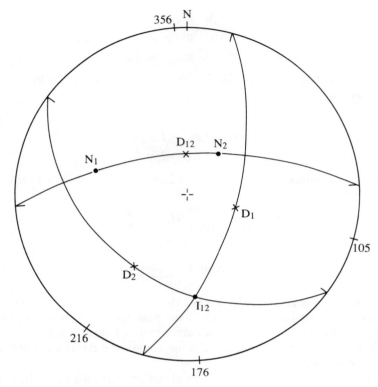

Figure A.7   Intersecting planes, Example A.4.

(ii) The great circle that passes through the normals to the two intersecting planes has a dip direction/dip angle 356/63. This result confirms that I_{12} is itself normal to the plane that contains the normals to the two intersecting planes.

Application of the vectorial methods in equations A.7 to A.10 gives the Cartesian components of the line of intersection $i_x = -0.853$, $i_y = 0.058$ and $i_z = 0.443$, which, by equations A.9 and A.10, has a trend $176.13°$ and plunge $27.37°$.

Appendix B

Statistics and probability density

The aim of this appendix is to explain some of the principles of statistical analysis and probability density distributions. These principles are particularly relevant to the work in Chapters 2, 3, 5 and 6. Although most of the concepts presented in this appendix can be found in standard texts on probability and statistics, such as Krumbein and Graybill (1965), Koch and Link (1971), Larson (1974), Meyer (1970), Till (1974) and Smith (1986), these concepts will here be presented in an abbreviated, and somewhat different, way. In particular, an effort will be made to explain the underlying physical principles by means of examples that are relevant to, and indeed essential for, the work in the main body of the book. I beg the indulgence of statisticians who find my way of explaining things rather different from what they are used to. I must add, however, that the need for an appendix such as this arises from the excessively mathematical and abstract explanations of probability theory found in many texts.

B.1 POPULATIONS, SAMPLES AND STATISTICS

For the purposes of statistical analysis a population can be regarded as any definite group of values from which samples can be taken. The values in a population can be of a continuous nature, such as the spacings between pairs of discontinuities, which are therefore described by real numbers. Alternatively, the values in a population can be of a discrete nature, such as the number of discontinuities intersecting a given length of a scanline, and are therefore represented by integers.

The aim of most site investigation studies is to estimate the properties of a given population of values by determining the properties of a sample taken from the population. For this purpose it is usual to assume that a population possesses an almost limitless supply of values for sampling. A sample from a population can either be taken at random or can be selected in a way that is biased. Sampling systems that rely on personal selection usually suffer from a subtle bias that the operator is unaware of, a bias that is often inconsistent and difficult to quantify. Samples obtained in this way can provide misleading information on the properties of the population. For example, personal selection of discontinuities usually provides a sample that is biased towards the larger, more noticeable features at a given face. Although it can be argued that these larger features are more important in controlling rock stability, there is no simple way of quantifying the bias that a given operator has chosen to impose. To overcome this difficulty it is necessary to obtain an effectively random sample by imposing an objective sampling system in which each value in the population has an equal chance of occurrence. The sampling strategies described in Chapter 2 have been designed to minimise personal bias in this way and to provide representative random samples of discontinuity characteristics. Although these sampling strategies do impose a geometrical bias, this bias is consistent and quantifiable, so its effects on the properties of the sample can be determined and eliminated during analysis, as explained in Chapters 2–6.

   Consider a random sample of n continuous values from a given population. It is assumed that the population is large compared with n so that non-replacement of the sample has a negligible effect on the characteristics of the population. Scanline sampling is non-replacement sampling because a discontinuity that has been sampled at one point along the scanline cannot usually be sampled again. Let X_i be the ith in the sequence of n random values constituting the sample. In this case the values $X_1, X_2 \ldots X_n$ form a sample of the random variable X. The expected value of X in the population, written E(X), is usually termed the mean or average value of X and denoted by μ_X. The best estimate, $\bar{X}$ of μ_X based on the values in the sample is given by

$$\bar{X} = \frac{1}{n} \sum_{i=1}^{n} X_i \qquad (B.1)$$

The expected value of $(X - \mu_X)^2$ written $E[(X - \mu_X)^2]$ is usually termed the variance of the random variable X and denoted by σ_X^2. The best estimate S^2 of σ_X^2 based upon the sample is given by

$$S^2 = \frac{1}{(n - 1)} \sum_{i=1}^{n} (X_i - \bar{X})^2 \qquad (B.2)$$

The standard deviation of the sample is given by $S = \sqrt{S^2}$. The value S^2 is called the variance because it provides a measure of the variability of the sample, and hence the variability of the population. The squared term in equation B.2 ensures that deviations $(X_i - \bar{X})$ from the mean $\bar{X}$ always tend to increase the variance. Most statistical texts provide an argument based on the degrees of freedom in the chi-square distribution as the reason for adopting the term $(n - 1)$ instead of n as the denominator in equation B.2. A more direct appreciation can be obtained by noting that the property of variability does not exist until the sample size exceeds one, so only $(n - 1)$ of the values in the sample contribute to the development of variability.

Variance, which involves raising deviations from the mean to the power 2, is the 2nd moment of the sample about the mean. A more general measure of sample properties is the kth sample moment about $X = 0$. The expected value of $(X)^k$, written $E[(X)^k]$, is termed the kth moment of the random variable X and denoted by m_{Xk}. The best estimate M_{Xk} of m_{Xk} based upon the sample is given by

$$M_{Xk} = \frac{1}{n} \sum_{i=1}^{n} (X_i)^k \qquad (B.3)$$

It can be noted, therefore, that $\bar{X} = M_{X1}$ and, by expansion of equation B.2, that

$$S^2 = \frac{n}{n - 1}[M_{X2} - (M_{X1})^2] \qquad (B.4)$$

The values $\bar{X}$, S^2 and M_{Xk} are collectively termed statistics; their evaluation for a particular random sample provides a basis for inferring the properties of the population from which the sample was taken.

B.2 DISTRIBUTIONS

Although the values of statistics can provide a great deal of information about a population, it can be more instructive also to consider the manner in which the values in a sample are distributed. A visual expression of the distribution of values in a sample can be obtained by selecting an appropriate class interval of, say $\Delta \approx \bar{X}/10$, and then plotting the sampled values on a histogram. Figure B.1 is a histogram of hypothetical total discontinuity spacings x, as defined in Chapter 5. The ordinate axis gives the number of values $N(x)$ that lie within a class interval centred upon a value x on the abscissa. For histograms based on sample sizes n exceeding about 50 it is usually found that $N(x)$ varies continuously as a function of x, this variation becoming smoother and better defined as n becomes larger. It is also often found that different samples from the same population tend to exhibit consistently similar patterns of variation that reflect the distributional properties of the population. The variation of $N(x)$ with x can be plotted on a given histogram by a smooth curve joining the mid-points at the top of each histogram column, as shown in Figure B.1. The distributional characteristics of the sample can then be represented in terms of some appropriate power law or polynomial function

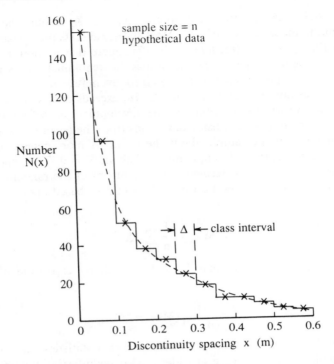

Figure B.1   Histogram of discontinuity spacing values.

that describes the shape of the smooth curve. There are several public domain programs available that contain routines for fitting functions of this type to observed data. The resulting function is, however, of limited general use. To understand why this is so, and to develop a more useful general approach, it is necessary to consider some fundamental ideas concerning probability density distributions of continuous variables.

We return to the continuous function N(x) that has been obtained to represent the shape of a histogram plotted at a class interval Δ for a sample size n. For given values of x and Δ, N(x) will be directly proportional to n. It is desirable, therefore, to define a new function R(x) as follows

$$R(x) = \frac{N(x)}{n} \tag{B.5}$$

where R(x) gives the relative frequency in a class interval centred on x. The relative frequency in a given class interval will, at small values of Δ, be directly proportional to Δ. This is simply because a larger class interval will tend to contain more values. We will, therefore, define another new function f(x) as follows

$$f(x) = \frac{N(x)}{n\,\Delta} \tag{B.6}$$

where $f(x)$ gives the relative frequency per unit width of class interval centred on x. Since $f(x)$ gives the relative frequency per unit width of class interval, it is usually referred to as a probability density function or a **probability density distribution**. The function can be visualised by imagining a single class interval of unit width moving continuously, rather than in increments of Δ, through the full range of x values; equation B.6 gives the relative frequency at any given value of x. A more useful form of equation B.6 gives the numerical frequency $N(x)$ as a function of n, Δ and $f(x)$ as follows

$$N(x) = n\,\Delta\,f(x) \qquad f(x) \geqslant 0 \tag{B.7}$$

The probability density function $f(x)$ represents only the shape of the distribution and is theoretically independent of both the sample size and the class interval. It is the form of $f(x)$ that is important when considering the way in which values are distributed. The function $N(x)$ and the sample size n in equation B.7 are dimensionless numerical values. Consequently, since the class interval Δ has the dimensions of the quantity being considered, the density distribution $f(x)$ must have dimensions that are the reciprocal of this quantity. Also, since relative frequency cannot be negative it is necessary to stipulate that $f(x) \geqslant 0$.

Although it is possible to utilise multi-parameter expressions to represent, almost exactly, the form of $N(x)$ for a given sample and thereby to derive $f(x)$, there is little point in doing so. This is because the precise form of $N(x)$ is influenced by random variability in the sample, particularly when the sample size is small. This variability means that samples taken from the same population could exhibit slightly different probability density distributions. It is preferable instead to select a relatively simple function for $f(x)$ that reflects the underlying physical processes and accept that samples will tend to exhibit random variability about this idealised model. It is also desirable to select functions that have few parameters, ideally only one or two, that can be calculated directly from the values in the sample. Some of the more common functions that have been used as density distributions are listed in Table B.1.

Consider a hypothetical sample containing a large number of values, whose distribution can be represented closely by functions for $N(x)$ and for $f(x)$. Let the histogram class interval Δ become very small, and be represented by the increment dx commencing at x, rather than centred on x. If one further value were selected at random from the population it is reasonable to assume that this value would tend to conform to $N(x)$. Although a single value cannot, of course, have a distribution, it is possible to make exact statements concerning the probability that the value will lie within a specified range. The existing relative frequency of values in the range x to x + dx is given by $R(x) = N(x)/n$ and can be taken to predict empirically the probability, $P(x)$, that a single value selected at random will lie in the range x to x + dx, so

Table B.1 Probability density distributions

Name	Function	Range	Mean	Variance
Negative exponential	$f(x) = \lambda e^{-\lambda x}$	$0 \leqslant x \leqslant \infty$	$\dfrac{1}{\lambda}$	$\dfrac{1}{\lambda^2}$
Uniform	$f(x) = \dfrac{1}{a}$	$0 \leqslant x \leqslant a$	$\dfrac{a}{2}$	$\dfrac{a^2}{12}$
Triangular	$f(x) = \dfrac{2(a-x)}{a^2}$	$0 \leqslant x \leqslant a$	$\dfrac{a}{3}$	$\dfrac{a^2}{18}$
Normal	$f(x) = \dfrac{1}{\sigma\sqrt{2\pi}} e^{-0.5\left(\frac{x-\mu}{\sigma}\right)^2}$	$-\infty \leqslant x \leqslant \infty$	μ	σ^2
Lognormal	$f(x) = \dfrac{1}{x\sigma\sqrt{2\pi}} e^{-0.5\left(\frac{\ln(x)-\mu}{\sigma}\right)^2}$	$0 \leqslant x \leqslant \infty$	$\mu_1 = e^{(\mu + 0.5\sigma^2)}$	$\mu_1^2(e^{\sigma^2} - 1)$

$$P(x) = \frac{N(x)}{n} \qquad 0 \leqslant P(x) \leqslant 1 \qquad (B.8)$$

But, replacing Δ by dx in equation B.7 and rearranging gives

$$\frac{N(x)}{n} = f(x)\,d(x) \qquad (B.9)$$

hence

$$P(x) = f(x)\,d(x) \qquad (B.10)$$

This result is applicable only to continuous variables, such as discontinuity spacing, and does not apply to discrete variables such as the outcomes of throwing an unbiased six-sided die. The probability of throwing a value in the range, say, 3.8 to 4.1 on such a die (in other words the probability of throwing a 4) is 1 in 6 or 0.167, whereas the probability of throwing a value in the range 4.1 to 4.4 is zero. In this case the density function is discontinuous because the variables are discrete.

The probability of selecting a discontinuity spacing within any finite range is defined for all values within the range zero to infinity (or at least some large value). The probability of selecting a spacing value of **exactly**, say, 0.3 m must, however, be zero since the term 'exactly' requires that dx is zero in equation B.10. We can, however, be 100% certain that a given randomly selected spacing value will lie in the range zero to infinity. Taking the sum of the probabilities given by equation B.10 over this range and equating the result to unity gives

$$\int_0^{\infty} f(x)\,dx = 1 \qquad (B.11)$$

All probability density functions must conform to the above equation; although, in general, the lower limit of integration will be $-\infty$.

The probability $F(x)$, that a randomly selected value is less than or equal to x, is found by summing the probabilities from $-\infty$ to x, or from 0 to x in our case since if x is a spacing value it cannot be negative. Here it is necessary to introduce the dummy variable y, giving

$$F(x) = \int_0^x f(y)\,dy \qquad (B.12)$$

If the original density function is integrable, then $F(x)$ will be a continuous function of x, a function that is usually called the **cumulative probability distribution,** or the cumulative distribution function, of x. Conversely, if $F(x)$ is differentiable, the density function $f(x)$ can be obtained by writing down the first derivative of $F(x)$ with respect to x. This valuable result is used in Chapter 6.

B.3   THE MEAN AND OTHER MOMENTS

One way of calculating the mean value of a sample utilises the data derived for plotting a histogram. If it is assumed that the mean of the $N(x_j)$ values, occurring in the jth class interval centred on x_j, is itself close to x_j (a reasonable assumption if the class interval is small), then the sum of the values in this class interval is given by $x_j N(x_j)$. If there are m class intervals, the sum of the values in the sample is given by the following summation, which can be equated to the product of sample size n and the sample mean $\bar{X}$ as follows

$$\sum_{j=1}^{m} x_j N(x_j) = n\bar{X}$$

Dispensing with the subscript and rearranging gives the following expression for the sample mean

$$\bar{X} = \sum \frac{x\, N(x)}{n} \tag{B.13}$$

where the summation is carried out over the full range of class intervals.

If the sample size is sufficiently large, it may be possible to deduce the likely form of the probability density distribution, $f(x)$, for the population. If this can be done, utilising equation B.9, the term $N(x)/n$ in equation B.13 can be replaced by $f(x)\, dx$. When this is done, the sample mean $\bar{X}$ must be replaced by μ_X the theoretical mean for the random variable X in the population, which is assumed to conform to $f(x)$. Hence

$$\mu_X = \sum x\, f(x)\, dx$$

or, replacing the summation by an integration with appropriate limits

$$\mu_X = \int_0^{\infty} x\, f(x)\, dx \tag{B.14}$$

As before, the lower limit of integration would, in general be $-\infty$, depending on the properties of the variable being considered. Equation B.14, which gives the mean value, is in reality the first moment, m_{X1}, of the density function taken about $x = 0$, hence

$$\mu_X = m_{X1}$$

Replacing $f(x)$ by $(x)^0 f(x)$ inside the integration in equation B.11 shows that the zeroth moment of any density function is always unity, i.e. that $m_{X0} = 1$. The second moment, m_{X2}, taken about $x = 0$ is given by

$$m_{X2} = \int_0^{\infty} x^2\, f(x)\, dx \tag{B.15}$$

Again, the lower limit of integration for the evaluation of a moment would usually be $-\infty$.

The variance, σ_X^2, of the random variable X is the second moment of f(x) taken about $x = \mu_X$. The moments of a probability density function are directly analogous to the moments of area of a geometrical shape. In particular, application of the well known parallel axis theorem allows us to write down the following expression for the variance of f(x)

$$\sigma_x^2 = m_{X2} - (\mu_X)^2 \qquad (B.16)$$

If the density distribution function is integrable, it is possible to determine any k^{th} moment m_{Xk}, where in general

$$m_{Xk} = \int_{-\infty}^{+\infty} x^k \, f(x) \, dx \qquad (B.17)$$

Moreover, it is often possible to derive a general moment generating function that gives the kth moment directly. For example, m_{Xk} for the negative exponential distribution in Table B.1 is given by

$$m_{Xk} = \frac{k!}{(\lambda)^k} \qquad (B.18)$$

Although the first and second moments are the most commonly used, the third and fourth moments are also sometimes used in statistical analysis; the third moment is used to compute a quantity termed skewness and the fourth moment to compute kurtosis. The texts by Larson (1974), Meyer (1970) and by Smith (1986) are recommended to those who wish to pursue the topic of probability theory and statistical inference in more depth.

This section concludes with two examples to illustrate the main principles. Results obtained in these examples will be used for the probabilistic analysis of discontinuity characteristics, presented in Chapters 2 to 6.

Example B.1 (Figure B.2)

A random sample comprising 352 total discontinuity spacing values was plotted on a histogram at a class interval of 0.05 m. A linear regression on the mid-points at the top of each histogram column gave a good fit for the following straight line relation

$$N(x) = 73.34 - 152.79x$$

where N(x) is the number of values in a class interval centred on a discontinuity spacing x. Obtain expressions for the probability density distribution and the cumulative probability distribution of discontinuity spacing x based on this sample. Use your results to estimate mean discontinuity spacing and the probability that a randomly selected value of discontinuity spacing will be less than 0.2 m.

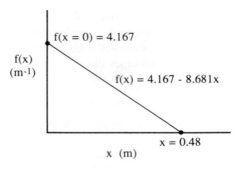

Figure B.2   Triangular probability density distribution, Example B.1.

Solution
In this example the sample size n = 352 and the class interval Δ = 0.05 m.
Applying equation B.6 gives

$$f(x) = \frac{N(x)}{n\,\Delta} = \frac{73.34 - 152.79x}{17.6} = 4.167 - 8.681x \qquad f(x) \geqslant 0$$

The above expression, which is a form of the triangular distribution listed in
Table B.1, is sketched in Figure B.2. Note that $f(x) = 4.167\,\mathrm{m}^{-1}$ when x = 0,
and that $f(x) = 0$ when x = 0.48 m. We must, therefore, stipulate that $f(x) = 0$
when x $\geqslant$ 0.48 m. Utilising equation B.12, and introducing the dummy
variable y, gives the cumulative probability distribution as

$$F(x) = \int_0^x 4.167 - 8.68\mathrm{l}y \, dy$$

or

$$F(x) = \left[4.167y - \frac{8.681y^2}{2} \right]_0^x = 4.167x - 4.341x^2$$

Since the sample size was large, and the linear regression gave a good fit, it will
be assumed that $f(x)$ and $F(x)$ provide an acceptably accurate model of the
distributional properties of the population.
   By equation B.14 the mean value μ_X is given by

$$\mu_X = \int_0^{0.48} x\, f(x)\, dx$$

Note that the upper limit of integration is 0.48 because $f(x) = 0$ when x $\geqslant$
0.48 m.

so

$$\mu_X = \int_0^{0.48} 4.167x - 8.681x^2 \, dx$$

hence

$$\mu_X = \left[\frac{4.167x^2}{2} - \frac{8.681x^3}{3} \right]_0^{0.48} = 0.16\,m$$

The probability, $P\ (\leqslant 0.2)$, that a randomly selected value of discontinuity spacing will be less than or equal to $0.2\,m$ can be found directly from the cumulative probability distribution $F(x)$, derived above, by setting $x = 0.2\,m$. Hence $P\ (\leqslant 0.2) = 0.66$. Note also that $P\ (\leqslant 0.48) = 1.0$.

Example B.2

Evaluate the zeroth, first and second moments, and also the variance, of the negative exponential, uniform and triangular distributions listed in Table B.1

Solution
(i) Negative exponential
   Here the probability density function is given by

$$f(x) = \lambda e^{-\lambda x} \qquad 0 \leqslant x \leqslant \infty$$

By equation B.17, the zeroth moment is given by

$$m_{X0} = \int_0^\infty f(x)\,dx = \lambda \int_0^\infty e^{-\lambda x}\,dx$$

so

$$m_{X0} = \lambda \left[\frac{-e^{-\lambda x}}{\lambda} \right]_0^\infty = 1.0$$

By equation B.14 or B.17 the first moment is given by

$$m_{X1} = \int_0^\infty x\,f(x)\,dx = \lambda \int_0^\infty x\,e^{-\lambda x}\,dx$$

integrating by parts

$$m_{X1} = \lambda \left[\frac{-x\,e^{-\lambda x}}{\lambda} - \frac{e^{-\lambda x}}{\lambda^2} \right]_0^\infty = \frac{1}{\lambda} = \mu_X \qquad (B.19)$$

By equation B.15 or B.17 the second moment is given by

$$m_{X2} = \int_0^\infty x^2\,f(x)\,dx = \lambda \int_0^\infty x^2\,e^{-\lambda x}\,dx$$

Integrating successively by parts

$$m_{X2} = \lambda \left[\frac{-x^2 e^{-\lambda x}}{\lambda} - \frac{2x\,e^{-\lambda x}}{\lambda^2} - \frac{2\,e^{-\lambda x}}{\lambda^3} \right]_0^\infty = \frac{2}{\lambda^2} \qquad (B.20)$$

Note that the above results are consistent with the moment generating function given in equation B.18.

By equation B.16, the variance is given by $\sigma_X^2 = m_{X2} - (\mu_X)^2$. Now $\mu_X = m_{X1} = 1/\lambda$

so

$$\sigma_X^2 = \frac{2}{\lambda^2} - \left[\frac{1}{\lambda}\right]^2 = \frac{1}{\lambda^2}$$

(ii) Uniform

Here the probability density function is given by

$$f(x) = \frac{1}{a} \qquad 0 \leq x \leq a$$

By equation B.17, the zeroth moment is given by

$$m_{X0} = \int_0^a f(x)\,dx = \int_0^a \frac{1}{a}\,dx$$

so

$$m_{X0} = \frac{1}{a}\,[x]_0^a = 1.0$$

By equation B.14 or B.17 the first moment is given by

$$m_{X1} = \int_0^a x\,f(x)\,dx = \frac{1}{a}\int_0^a x\,dx$$

so

$$m_{X1} = \frac{1}{a}\left[\frac{x^2}{2}\right]_0^a = \frac{a}{2} = \mu_X$$

By equation B.15 or B.17 the second moment is given by

$$m_{X2} = \int_0^a x^2\,f(x)\,dx = \frac{1}{a}\int_0^a x^2\,dx$$

so

$$m_{X2} = \frac{1}{a}\left[\frac{x^3}{3}\right]_0^a = \frac{a^2}{3}$$

Again, by equation B.16, the variance is given by $\sigma_X^2 = m_{X2} - (\mu_X)^2$. Here $\mu_X = m_{X1} = a/2$, so

$$\sigma_X^2 = \frac{a^2}{3} - \left[\frac{a}{2}\right]^2 = \frac{a^2}{12}$$

(iii) Triangular

Here the probability density function is given by

$$f(x) = \frac{2(a - x)}{a^2} \qquad 0 \leqslant x \leqslant a$$

By equation B.17, the zeroth moment is given by

$$m_{X0} = \int_0^a f(x)\, dx = \frac{2}{a^2} \int_0^a (a - x)\, dx$$

so

$$m_{X0} = \frac{2}{a^2} \left[ax - \frac{x^2}{2} \right]_0^a = 1.0$$

By equation B.14 or B.17 the first moment is given by

$$m_{X1} = \int_0^a x\, f(x)\, dx = \frac{2}{a^2} \int_0^a (ax - x^2)\, dx$$

so

$$m_{X1} = \frac{2}{a^2} \left[\frac{ax^2}{2} - \frac{x^3}{3} \right]_0^a = \frac{a}{3} = \mu_X$$

By equation B.15 or B.17 the second moment is given by

$$m_{X2} = \int_0^a x^2\, f(x)\, dx = \frac{2}{a^2} \int_0^a (ax^2 - x^3)\, dx$$

so

$$m_{X2} = \frac{2}{a^2} \left[\frac{ax^3}{3} - \frac{x^4}{4} \right]_0^a = \frac{a^2}{6}$$

Finally, by equation B.16, the variance is given by $\sigma_X{}^2 = m_{X2} - (\mu_X)^2$. Here $\mu_X = m_{X1} = a/3$, so

$$\sigma_X{}^2 = \frac{a^2}{6} - \left[\frac{a}{3} \right]^2 = \frac{a^2}{18}$$

B.4 GENERATION OF RANDOM VALUES

The simulation of stochastic systems, such as discontinuity networks, usually requires the generation of random values from a specified distribution. This section contains simple algorithms for generating random values from uniform, negative exponential, normal and Fisher distributions. The generation of random values is rather like the reverse of plotting a histogram. Given a particular probability density distribution the aim is to generate a single value, or a sequence of values, that reflect the properties of the distribution. The important point is that the values in the random sequence must obey any range limits and must reflect the distribution pattern of the parent distribution. This requirement means that if the sequence of random values were compiled into a histogram, it should, for large sample sizes, tend to have the same shape as the parent distribution. Pine (1991) describes a method called the Latin Hypercube sampling method which satisfies this requirement for relatively small sample sizes by imposing a stratified sampling regime without replacement, but with random selection within each stratum.

B.4.1   Uniform distribution

A uniformly distributed variable x within the range 0 to a has the following density

$$f(x) = \frac{1}{a} \quad 0 \leqslant x \leqslant a$$

with a mean value of a/2. We adopt the symbol $R^i_{U,a}$ to represent the ith random value from a uniform distribution in the range 0 to a. This apparently cumbersome use of symbols is necessary in order to represent sequences of random values from different distributions with different controlling parameters. A special case $R^i_{U,1}$ occurs when a = 1.0. In most cases, sequences of random values are generated by computers, which have been specifically designed to give predictable non-random results. The element of randomness can be introduced by obtaining the first value $R^1_{U,1}$, or seed, for a sequence of random values from a uniform distribution in the range 0 to 1.0, by referring to random number tables. For example, the first 8 digits in the first row of the table of Random Sampling Numbers given by Lindley and Miller (1953) are 20174228, which give a seed $R^1_{U,1} = 0.20174228$. A sequence of random values can now be obtained by applying the following simple recursive algorithm

$$R^{i+1}_{U,1} = \text{Decimal part of } (29.0 \; R^i_{U,1})$$

and

$$R^{i+1}_{U,a} = a \; R^{i+1}_{U,1} \tag{B.21}$$

For example, adopting the above seed, gives

$$R^2_{U,1} = 0.85052612 \qquad R^3_{U,1} = 0.66525748$$

and so on. (Note: the superscripted numbers are simply **counters** in this case and have nothing to do with raising to powers). For a uniform distribution, say, in the range 0 to 4.6, a = 4.6 so these three values give random values of 0.928, 3.912 and 3.060 correct to 3 decimal places. It is a relatively simple matter to program this algorithm into a subroutine of a computerised simulation program and generate long sequences of random numbers. Strictly speaking, such a sequence of random numbers should be called pseudo-random since although the values conform to the parent distribution, the sequence is predictable if the seed value is known. This characteristic is a definite advantage since it makes it possible to repeat a particular random sequence by specifying the same seed. The algorithm in equation B.21 can be criticised since it re-cycles after a finite number of values, depending on the seed. For example a seed of 0.10000000 re-cycles the sequence after just 2 values; a seed of 0.12000000 re-cycles the sequence after 10 values. Seeds involving 8 digits, such as the one above, generally take several thousand values to re-cycle.

B.4.2 Negative exponential distribution

A negative exponentially distributed variable x has the following density

$$f(x) = \lambda e^{-\lambda x} \qquad 0 \leqslant x \leqslant \infty$$

with a mean value $1/\lambda$. An algorithm that gives random values $R^i_{E,\lambda}$ from this distribution can be obtained by applying the principle of the integral transform, described in statistical texts such as Meyer (1970). The integral transform is obtained from the cumulative probability distribution $F(x)$ given by equation B.12 as follows

$$F(x) = \int_0^x f(y) \, dy = 1 - e^{-\lambda x}$$

We replace $F(x)$ by the uniform random value $R^i_{U,1}$, replace the variable x by the required random values $R^i_{E,\lambda}$ and then rearrange to give the desired algorithm

$$R^i_{E,\lambda} = \frac{-\ln(1 - R^i_{U,1})}{\lambda} \qquad (B.22)$$

Subtraction of $R^i_{U,1}$ from 1 in the above expression is a consequence of the mathematical development and is not, of course, strictly necessary since $R^i_{U,1}$ and $(1 - R^i_{U,1})$ are both random values from a uniform distribution in the range 0 to 1.0. Taking the value $R^1_{U,1} = 0.20174228$ from the previous section, and, say, adopting $\lambda = 12.5$ gives $R^1_{E,\lambda} = 0.018$ to 3 decimal places.

B.4.3 Normal and lognormal distributions

A normally distributed variable x has the following density

$$f(x) = \frac{1}{\sigma \sqrt{2\pi}} e^{-0.5 \left(\frac{x - \mu}{\sigma} \right)^2} \qquad -\infty \leqslant x \leqslant \infty$$

where μ is the mean and σ is the standard deviation. Random values $R^i_{N,\mu,\sigma}$ from a normal distribution with a mean μ and a standard deviation σ can be generated as follows by utilising triplets of random values $R^i_{U,1}$, $R^{i+1}_{U,1}$ and

$R^{i+2}{}_{U,1}$ previously generated from a uniform distribution in the range 0 to 1.0. The first step is to generate a pair of random values $R^j{}_{N,0,1}$ $R^k{}_{N,0,1}$ from a normal distribution with a mean of zero and a standard deviation of unity as follows

$$R^j{}_{N,0,1} = \cos(2\pi \, R^i{}_{U,1})\sqrt{-2 \, \ln(R^{i+1}{}_{U,1})}$$

and

$$R^k{}_{N,0,1} = \sin(2\pi \, R^i{}_{U,1})\sqrt{-2 \, \ln(R^{i+1}{}_{U,1})} \qquad (B.23)$$

Values such as this are sometimes referred to as standardised normal variables. Either $R^j{}_{N,0,1}$ or $R^k{}_{N,0,1}$ is adopted, by random choice, for determining $R^i{}_{N,\mu,\sigma}$ This choice can be based on the value of $R^{i+2}{}_{U,1}$ as follows

(If $R^{i+2}{}_{U,1} < 0.5$) then $R^i{}_{N,\mu,\sigma}$ takes the value $\sigma \, R^j{}_{N,0,1} + \mu$ (discard $R^k{}_{N,0,1}$)

(If $R^{i+2}{}_{U,1} \geqslant 0.5$) then $R^i{}_{N,\mu,\sigma}$ takes the value $\sigma \, R^k{}_{N,0,1} + \mu$ (discard $R^j{}_{N,0,1}$)
$$\qquad (B.24)$$

Taking the values $R^1{}_{U,1} = 0.20174228$, $R^2{}_{U,1} = 0.85052612$, $R^3{}_{U,1} = 0.66525748$ determined earlier, gives $R^j{}_{N,0,1} = 0.170$ and $R^k{}_{N,0,1} = 0.543$. Although these values are both positive in this case, the trigonometrical function ensures that other values will, on average, be negative 50% of the time. Since $R^3{}_{U,1}$ exceeds 0.5 we select $R^k{}_{N,0,1}$ and discard $R^j{}_{N,0,1}$. For a normal distribution, say, with a mean $\mu = 7.5$ and a standard deviation $\sigma = 1.6$, this result gives $R^1{}_{N,7.5,1.6} = 8.369$ to 3 decimal places.

Random values $R^i{}_{L,\mu,\sigma}$ from a lognormal distribution derived from a normal distribution with a mean of μ and a standard deviation σ are given by

$$R^i{}_{L,\mu,\sigma} = e^{(R^i{}_{N,\mu,\sigma})} \qquad (B.25)$$

The above transformation ensures that $\ln(R^i{}_{L,\mu,\sigma})$ will be normally distributed. The relations between the mean and variance of the lognormal distribution, and μ, σ for the parent normal distribution, are given in Table B.1.

B.4.4   Fisher distribution

A variable θ that obeys the Fisher distribution has the following density (see Chapter 3)

$$f(\theta) = \frac{K \sin \theta \, e^{K\cos\theta}}{e^K - e^{-K}} \qquad 0 < \theta < \pi/2$$

where θ is the angular deviation from the mean, or true, orientation and K is Fisher's constant. Random values $R^i{}_{F,K}$ from this distribution can be obtained from the integral transform. In this case it is convenient to use the approximate expression for the cumulative probability distribution given in equation 3.24 as follows

$$P\ (<\theta) \approx 1 - e^{K(\cos\theta - 1)}$$

As before, we replace $P(<\theta)$ by the uniform random value $R^i_{U,1}$, replace the variable θ by the required random values $R^i_{F,K}$ and then rearrange to give the desired algorithm

$$R^i_{F,K} = \text{Arc } \cos\left(\frac{\ln\ (1 - R^i_{U,1})}{K} + 1\right) \qquad (B.26)$$

For example, taking the value $R^1_{U,1} = 0.20174228$ from the earlier section, and, say, adopting $K = 23.5$ gives $R^1_{F,K} = 7.941°$ to 3 decimal places. It is worth noting that the sequence of random values given by equation B.26 is essentially one-dimensional. These random values can be converted to three-dimensional form by permitting random rotation about the mean axis. This aspect is discussed further in section 6.8.1.

Appendix C

Rock mass classification

This appendix contains an outline summary of the two widely used rock mass classification schemes. Those who wish to learn more about these classification schemes are advised to consult the review text by Bieniawski (1989).

C.1 ROCK MASS RATING SYSTEM FOR GEOMECHANICS CLASSIFICATION

The CSIR Rock Mass Rating (RMR) system described by Bieniawski (1973, 1976 and 1989) is based on assigning a rating to the following six parameters:

uniaxial compressive strength of the rock material,
Rock Quality Designation (RQD),
spacing of discontinuities,
condition of discontinuities,
groundwater conditions, and
orientation of discontinuities.

Ratings for the first five of these parameters are determined from part (a) of Table C.1 drawing on the guidelines in Table C.2 for assessing discontinuity condition (after Bieniawski 1976 and 1989). Figure C.1 (after Laubscher 1977) provides some assistance in determining the rating for discontinuity spacing where there are two or three separate sets. The ten regions in the upper left hand portion of this chart provide the ratings when there are two discontinuity sets (minimum and intermediate spacing) with mean spacings between 0.01 and 10 m. For example two sets with mean spacings of 0.08 and 0.4 m would earn a rating of 11, as shown. If there were a third set with a mean spacing of

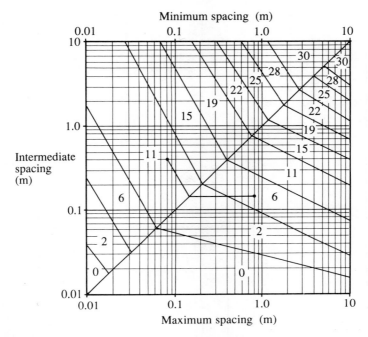

Figure C.1 Ratings for discontinuity spacing where there are two or three sets (after Laubscher, 1977).

0.8 m the rating would be reduced to 6, this value being obtained by moving parallel to the contours as far as the diagonal and then moving horizontally to the (maximum) spacing of 0.8 m as shown. It is, of course, necessary to rank the mean spacings for the sets to use the table in this way. Laubscher (1990) provides a more recent discussion of these and other aspects of rock mass classification.

Rating adjustments for discontinuity orientation are summarised for underground excavations, foundations and slopes in part (b) of Table C.1. A more detailed explanation of these rating adjustments for tunnelling is given in Table C.3, after Wickham *et al.* (1972).

The six separate ratings are summed to give the overall Rock Mass Rating (RMR) out of 100, with a higher rating indicating better quality rock. A summary of the five possible rock mass classifications based on the observed RMR value is given in part (c) of Table C.1. Part (d) of this table presents an interpretation of these five rock mass classes in terms of roof stand-up time, cohesion and the angle of friction for the rock mass. The RMR value forms an important input parameter for the Hoek–Brown empirical rock mass strength criterion, discussed in Chapter 9.

Table C.1 The Rock Mass Rating System for the geomechanics classification of rock masses (after Bieniawski, 1976 and 1989)

a. Classification parameters and their ratings

Parameter		Range of values						
1	Strength of intact rock material — Point-load strength index (MPa)	>10	4–10	2–4	1–2	Uniaxial compressive test is preferred for this low range		
	Uniaxial compressive strength (MPa)	>250	100–250	50–100	25–50	5–25	1–5	<1
	Rating	15	12	7	4	2	1	0
2	Drill core quality RQD (%)	90–100	75–90	50–75	25–50	<25		
	Rating	20	17	13	8	3		
3	Spacing of discontinuities	>2 m	0.6–2 m	200–600 mm	60–200 mm	<60 mm		
	Rating	20	15	10	8	5		
4	Condition of discontinuities	Very rough, Not continuous, No separation, Unweathered wall rock	Slightly rough, Separation <1 mm, Slightly weathered wall rock	Slightly rough, Separation <1 mm, Highly weathered wall rock	Slickensided or Gouge < 5 mm thick or Separation 1–5 mm, Continuous	Soft gouge > 5 mm thick or Separation >5 mm, Continuous		
	Rating	30	25	20	10	0		

5 Groundwater	Inflow per 10 m tunnel length (litres per min)	None or	<10 or	10–25 or	25–125 or	>125 or
	Joint water pressure $\dfrac{\text{Joint water pressure}}{\text{Major principal stress}}$ Ratio	0 or	<0.1 or	0.1–0.2 or	0.2–0.5 or	>0.5 or
	General conditions	Completely dry	Damp	Wet	Dripping	Flowing
	Rating	15	10	7	4	0

b. Rating adjustment for discontinuity orientation

Strike and dip orientations of discontinuities (see Table C.2)		Very favourable	Favourable	Fair	Unfavourable	Very unfavourable
Ratings	Tunnels and mines	0	−2	−5	−10	−12
	Foundations	0	−2	−7	−15	−25
	Slopes	0	−5	−25	−50	−60

Table C.1 *(Continued)*

c. Rock mass classification determined from total ratings

Rating	100 ← 81	80 ← 61	60 ← 41	40 ← 21	<20
Class no.	I	II	III	IV	V
Description	Very good rock	Good rock	Fair rock	Poor rock	Very poor rock

d. Meaning of rock mass classification

Class number	I	II	III	IV	V
Average stand-up time	20 yrs for 15 m span	1 yr for 10 m span	1 wk for 5 m span	10 h for 2.5 m span	30 min for 1 m span
Cohesion of the rock mass (kPa)	>400	300–400	200–300	100–200	<100
Friction angle of the rock mass (deg)	>45	35–45	25–35	15–25	<15

Table C.2   Guidelines for classifying discontinuity condition (after Bieniawski, 1989)

Parameter	Rating Measurement or description				
Discontinuity length, (persistence/continuity) m	6 <1	4 1–3	2 3–10	1 10–20	0 >20
Separation (aperture) mm	6 None	5 <0.1	4 0.1–1.0	1 1–5	0 >5
Roughness	6 Very rough	5 Rough	3 Slight	1 Smooth	0 Slickensided
			Hard filling	Soft filling	
Infilling (gouge) thickness mm	6 None	4 <5	2 >5	2 <5	0 >5
Degree of weathering	6 None	5 Slight	3 Moderate	1 High	0 Decomposed

Note: Some conditions are mutually exclusive. For example, if infilling is present, it is irrelevant what the roughness may be, since its effect will be overshadowed by the influence of the gouge. In such cases, use Table C.1 directly.

Table C.3   Ratings for discontinuity orientations in tunnelling (after Wickham *et al.*, 1972)

Strike perpendicular to tunnel axis			
Drive with dip		*Drive against dip*	
Dip 45–90°	Dip 20–45°	Dip 45–90°	Dip 20–45°
Very favourable	Favourable	Fair	Unfavourable

Strike parallel to tunnel axis		*Irrespective of strike*
Dip 20–45°	Dip 45–90°	Dip 0–20°
Fair	Very unfavourable	Fair

C.2   THE Q-SYSTEM FOR ROCK CLASSIFICATION AND SUPPORT DESIGN

The Q-system was devised by Barton *et al.* (1974) for the purposes of rock mass classification and tunnel support design. The following six parameters, assessed from the extensive descriptions in Table C.4, are combined to determine the rock mass quality Q as follows

$$Q = \frac{RQD}{Jn} \times \frac{Jr}{Ja} \times \frac{Jw}{SRF} \qquad (C.1)$$

where

RQD = Rock Quality Designation,
Jn = joint set number,
Jr = joint roughness number,
Ja = joint alteration number,
Jw = joint water reduction factor, and
SRF = stress reduction factor, as assessed from Table C.4.

The range of possible Q values is approximately 0.001 (exceptionally poor quality rock) to approximately 1000 (exceptionally good quality rock). Barton *et al.* provide a detailed list of recommended support measures for 38 separate support categories identified on the basis of the excavation span, the observed Q value and other parameters.

Table C.4 The Q-System and associated parameters RQD, Jn, Jr, Ja, SRF and Jw (after Barton *et al.*, 1974)

	Rock Quality Designation RQD %	
Very poor	0–25	Note:
Poor	25–50	(i) Where RQD is reported or measured
Fair	50–75	to be <10 a nominal
Good	75–90	value of 10 is used to
Excellent	90–100	evaluate Q in equation C.1
		(ii) Take RQD to the nearest 5%
	Joint Set Number Jn	
Massive, none or few joints	0.5–1.0	Note:
One joint set	2	(i) For intersections use (3.0 × Jn)
One joint set plus random	3	
Two joint sets	4	(ii) For portals use (2.0 × Jn)
Two joint sets plus random	6	
Three joint sets	9	
Three joint sets plus random	12	
Four or more joint sets, random, heavily jointed, 'sugar cube', etc	15	
Crushed rock, earthlike	20	

Table C.4 *(Continued)*

	Joint Roughness Number Jr	
(a) Rock wall contact and		
(b) Rock wall contact before 10 cm shear		
Discontinuous joint	4	Note:
Rough or irregular, undulating	3	(i) Add 1.0 if the mean
Smooth, undulating	2	spacing of the relevant
Slickensided, undulating	1.5	joint set is greater than
Rough or irregular, planar	1.5	3 m
Smooth, planar	1	(ii) Jr = 0.5 can be used
Slickensided, planar	0.5	for planar slickensided joints having lineations, provided the lineations are favourably orientated
(c) No rock wall contact when sheared		
Zone containing clay minerals thick enough to prevent rock wall contact	1	(nominal)
Sandy, gravelly or crushed zone thick enough to prevent rock wall contact	1	(nominal)

	Joint Alteration Number Ja	Approximate residual angle of friction, degrees
(a) Rock wall contact		
A. Tightly healed, hard, non-softening, impermeable filling, i.e. quartz or epidote	0.75	
B. Unaltered joint walls, surface staining only	1	25–35
C. Unaltered joint walls. Non-softening mineral coatings, sandy particles, clay-free disintegrated rock, etc.	2	25–30
D. Silty or sandy clay coatings, small clay fraction (non-softening)	3	20–25
E. Softening or low friction clay mineral coatings, i.e. kaolinite, mica. Also chlorite, talc, gypsum and graphite, etc, and small quantities of swelling clays (discontinuous coatings, 1–2 mm or less in thickness)	4	8–16

Table C.4 *(Continued)*

(b) Rock wall contact before 10 cm shear		
F. Sandy particles, clay free disintegrated rock, etc	4	25–30
G. Strongly over-consolidated, non-softening clay mineral fillings (continuous, <5 mm in thickness)	6	16–24
H. Medium or low over-consolidation, softening, clay mineral fillings (continuous, <5 mm in thickness)	8	12–16
J. Swelling clay fillings, i.e. montmorillonite (continuous, <5 mm in thickness). Value of Ja depends on percentage of swelling clay-sized particles and access to water, etc	8–12	6–12
(c) No rock wall contact when sheared		
K. Zones or bands of disintegrated or crushed rock and clay (see G, H, J for description of clay condition)	6, 8 or 8–12	6–24
L. Zones or bands of silty or sandy clay, small clay fraction (non-softening)	5	
M. Thick, continuous zones or bands of clay (see G, H, J for description of clay condition)	10, 13 or 13–20	6–24

	Joint Water Reduction factor J_w	*Approximate water pressure kPa*
A. Dry excavations or minor inflow, i.e. < 5 litres per min locally	1	<100
B. Medium inflow or pressure occasional outwash of joint fillings	0.66	100–250
C. Large inflow or high pressure in competent rock with unfilled joints	0.5	250–1000
D. Large inflow or high pressure, considerable outwash of joint fillings	0.33	250–1000
E. Exceptionally high inflow or water pressure at blasting, decaying with time	0.2–0.1	>1000
F. Exceptionally high inflow or water pressure continuing without noticeable decay	0.1–0.05	>1000

Table C.4 *(Continued)*

Note:
(i) Factors C–F are crude estimates. Increase Jw if drainage measures are installed

(ii) Special problems caused by ice formation are not considered

	Stress Reduction Factor SRF	
(a) Weakness zones intersecting excavation, which may cause loosening of rock mass when tunnel is excavated		
A. Multiple occurrences of weakness zones containing clay or chemically disintegrated rock, very loose surrounding rock (any depth)	10	Note: (i) Reduce these SRF values by 25–50% if the relevant shear zones only influence but do not intersect the excavation
B. Single weakness zones containing clay or chemically disintegrated rock (depth of excavation <50 m)	5	
C. Single weakness zones containing clay or chemically disintegrated rock (depth of excavation >50 m)	2.5	
D. Multiple shear zones in competent rock (clay free) loose surrounding rock (any depth)	7.5	
E. Single shear zones in competent rock (clay free, depth of excavation <5 m)	5	
F. Single shear zones in competent rock (clay free, depth of excavation >50 m)	2.5	
G. Loose open joints, heavily jointed, or 'sugar cube' etc (any depth)	5	

(b) Competent rock, rock stress problems Strength/stress ratios:	(σ_c/σ_1)	(σ_t/σ_1)	SRF
H. Low stress, near surface	>200	>13	2.5
J. Medium stress	200–10	13–0.66	1

Table C.4 (*Continued*)

	σ_c/σ_1	σ_t/σ_1	SRF	
K. High stress, very tight structure (usually favourable to stability, may be unfavourable to wall stability)	10–5	0.66–0.33	0.5–2.0	(ii) If stress field is strongly anisotropic when $5 < (\sigma_1/\sigma_3) < 10$: reduce σ_c and σ_t to $0.8\,\sigma_c$ and $0.8\,\sigma_t$. When $(\sigma_1/\sigma_3) > 10$: reduce σ_c and σ_t to $0.6\,\sigma_c$ and $0.6\,\sigma_t$. where σ_c = unconfined compressive strength; σ_t = tensile strength; σ_1 = major principal stress; σ_3 = minor principal stress
L. Mild rock burst (massive rock)	5–2.5	0.33–0.16	5–10	
M. Heavy rock burst (massive rock)	<2.5	<0.16	10–20	
(c) *Squeezing rock; plastic flow of incompetent rock under the influence of high rock pressures*				
N. Mild squeezing rock pressure			5–10	
O. Heavy squeezing rock pressure			10–20	
(d) *Swelling rock; chemical swelling activity depending on presence of water*				
P. Mild swelling rock pressure			5–10	(iii) Few case records available where depth of crown below surface is less than span width. Suggest SRF increase from 2.5 to 5 for such cases (see H)
R. Heavy swelling rock pressure			10–15	

Appendix D

Analysis of forces

D.1 VECTORIAL REPRESENTATION OF A FORCE

This appendix is based on the vectorial and hemispherical projection methods for the analysis of forces presented by Priest (1985). Many of the principles adopted in this appendix were also used in Chapter 3 for the vectorial representation of orientation data. The reader is advised to familiarise himself or herself with the basic principles of hemispherical projection, explained in Appendix A, before proceeding.

Although the orientation of force vectors can be represented on a hemispherical projection, as explained in Appendix A, it is generally more convenient to adopt vectorial methods for the analysis of forces. Figure 1.2 shows a right-handed Cartesian coordinate system in which positive x is horizontal to the north (trend 000°), positive y is horizontal to the east (trend 090°) and positive z is vertical down. It is worth reiterating that this coordinate system is slightly different from the left-handed system adopted by Priest (1985) in which x is east and y is north. Conversion from this left-handed system to the current right-handed system can be achieved simply by swopping x and y on the diagrams and in the associated equations.

Any force vector **u** in three-dimensional space can be represented in the Cartesian system of Figure 1.2 by putting the start point of the vector at the origin of the system and then noting the Cartesian coordinates u_x, u_y, u_z of its end point. These coordinates are usually referred to as the Cartesian components of the force. The magnitude of the force is given by

$$|\mathbf{u}| = \sqrt{u_x^2 + u_y^2 + u_z^2} \qquad (D.1)$$

The trend α_u and plunge β_u of a force with Cartesian components u_x, u_y and u_z in the system of axes in Figure 1.2 are given by

$$\alpha_u = \arctan\left(\frac{u_y}{u_x}\right) + Q \tag{D.2}$$

$$\beta_u = \arctan\left(\frac{u_z}{\sqrt{u_x^2 + u_y^2}}\right) \tag{D.3}$$

The parameter Q is an angle, in degrees that ensures that α_u lies in the correct quadrant and in the range 0 to 360°. This parameter, which depends on the signs of u_x and u_y as listed in Table 1.1 and discussed in section 1.2, is required because the arc tangent function of most computers returns a value in the range $-90°$ to $+90°$.

The inverse forms of equations D.2 and D.3 are

$$\begin{aligned}
u_x &= |\mathbf{u}| \cos \alpha_u \cos \beta_u \\
u_y &= |\mathbf{u}| \sin \alpha_u \cos \beta_u \\
u_z &= |\mathbf{u}| \sin \beta_u
\end{aligned} \tag{D.4}$$

D.2 HEMISPHERICAL PROJECTION REPRESENTATION OF A FORCE

Equations D.1 to D.3 allow us to determine the magnitude $|\mathbf{u}|$, the trend α_u and the plunge β_u of a force vector $\mathbf{u}$ that has Cartesian components u_x, u_y, u_z. If the lower hemisphere projection of Appendix A is adopted it is possible to plot directly any force that is directed downwards; i.e. any force that has a positive u_z and therefore a positive angle of plunge β_u. The orientation of the force can be represented by a dot or cross in the usual way, labelled to indicate that it is the force vector $\mathbf{u}$, that it has a magnitude $|\mathbf{u}|$, and that it has a downward sense. Horizontal forces plot on the perimeter of the projection and can, therefore, be taken to have a downward sense.

It is not possible to plot directly on a lower hemisphere projection any force that has an upward sense, i.e. any force that has a negative u_z and therefore a negative angle of plunge β_u. Priest (1985) overcame this problem by plotting instead the orientation of the reverse vector $\mathbf{u}'$ for those forces that were directed upwards. This approach does not change the line of action of the force nor its magnitude; it simply ensures that a positive angle of plunge is generated to allow plotting on the lower hemisphere projection. If α_u and β_u are known, then the force $\mathbf{u}$ has an upward sense if β_u is negative. The trend α'_u and plunge β'_u of the reverse vector $\mathbf{u}'$ are given by

$$\begin{aligned}
\alpha'_u &= \alpha_u \pm 180° \qquad \text{such that } 0 \leqslant \alpha'_u \leqslant 360° \\
\beta'_u &= -\beta_u
\end{aligned} \tag{D.5}$$

The orientation of the reverse vector can now be plotted from α'_u and β'_u on the lower hemisphere projection in the usual way, labelled to indicate that it is the force vector $\mathbf{u}$, that it has a magnitude $|\mathbf{u}|$, and that it has an **upward** sense. If the Cartesian components u_x, u_y, u_z are known, then the force $\mathbf{u}$ has an upward sense if u_z is negative. The Cartesian components u'_x, u'_y, u'_z of the reverse vector $\mathbf{u}'$ are

$$u'_x = -u_x$$
$$u'_y = -u_y$$
$$u'_z = -u_z \tag{D.6}$$

The trend α'_u and plunge β'_u of the reverse vector can be found by substituting the components u'_x, u'_y, u'_z into equations D.2 and D.3, noting that the parameter Q in Table 1.1 is determined from the signs of the reversed components u'_x and u'_y. When the trend and plunge of the reverse vector have been determined, it can be plotted in the manner described above. The following example illustrates the procedures explained above.

Example D.1 (Figure D.1)

Forces $\mathbf{t}$ and $\mathbf{u}$ have trends, plunges and magnitudes as listed below.

1st table for Example D.1

Force	Trend degrees	Plunge degrees	Magnitude kN
t	161	63	126
u	289	−37	215

Forces $\mathbf{v}$ and $\mathbf{w}$ have Cartesian components in the system in Figure 1.2 as listed below.

2nd table for Example D.1

Force	Cartesian components, kN		
	x	y	z
v	6.7	−21.2	49.5
w	21.2	−18.3	−12.4

Plot and label the forces $\mathbf{t}$, $\mathbf{u}$, $\mathbf{v}$ and $\mathbf{w}$ on a lower hemisphere projection.

Solution

Force $\mathbf{t}$ has a positive angle of plunge; it therefore has a downward sense and can be plotted directly, as shown in Figure D.1. Force $\mathbf{u}$ has a negative angle of plunge and therefore has an upward sense. The trend and plunge of the

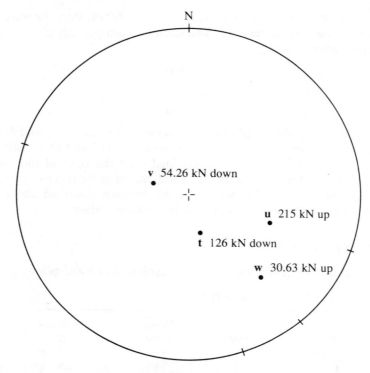

Figure D.1 Representation of forces on a lower hemisphere projection, Example D.1.

reverse vector u' are, from equations D.5, 109° and +37°. This reverse vector has been plotted in Figure D.1, and labelled to indicate that the force acts upwards along the line.

Force v has a positive z component and therefore has a downward sense. Table 1.1 gives Q = 360° for this vector; equations D.1 to D.3 give $|v|$ = 54.26 kN, α_v = 287.5° and β_v = 65.8°, respectively. Force w has a negative z component and therefore has an upward sense. The reverse vector w' has x, y, z components of −21.2, +18.3 and +12.4 kN, respectively. Table 1.1 gives Q = 180° for this reversed vector; equations D.1 to D.3 give $|w|$ = 30.63 kN, α_w = 139.2° and β_w = 23.9°, respectively. Points representing the forces v and w have been plotted and labelled in Figure D.1.

D.3 RESULTANT OF FORCES

The resultant of any number of force vectors can be found simply by summing their x, y and z Cartesian components. If the forces are given in terms of their trends, plunges and magnitudes, determining the resultant will first necessitate the calculation of their separate Cartesian components using equations D.4. The magnitude, trend and plunge of the resultant force can be found from its Cartesian components by applying equations D.1 to D.3. The resultant can then be plotted on a lower hemisphere projection, adopting the approach described in the previous section. This procedure is illustrated in the following example:

Example D.2 (Figure D.2)

The following four forces are known to act at a point

1st table for **Example D.2**

Force	Trend degrees	Plunge degrees	Magnitude kN
g	—	90	649
u	156	−26	124
v	243	−51	187
w	347	15	243

Find the magnitude, trend and plunge of the resultant force at the point and plot it on a lower hemisphere projection.

Solution
The Cartesian components of the four forces, from equations D.4, are as follows:

2nd table for **Example D.2**

Force	Cartesian components, kN		
	x	y	z
g	0	0	649.00
u	−101.82	45.33	−54.36
v	−53.43	−104.86	−145.33
w	228.70	−52.80	62.89
r	73.45	−112.33	512.20

It is worth remarking that in this example the force **g** is vertical, and is presumably the force due to gravity acting on a mass. Simple summation gives the Cartesian components of the resultant force **r** as listed above. Equations

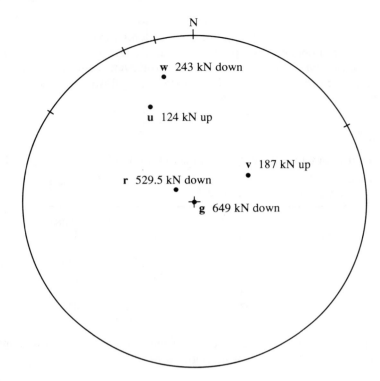

Figure D.2 Resultant of four forces, Example D.2.

D.1 to D.3 give the magnitude, trend and plunge of this resultant as 529.5 kN, 303.2° and 75.3°, respectively. This resultant has a downward sense and has been plotted directly on the lower hemisphere projection in Figure D.2. Of course if this resultant had had an upward sense it would have required reversal prior to plotting.

D.4 DECOMPOSITION OF FORCES

Any given force vector can be decomposed by direct algebraic or graphical methods into up to three non-parallel components in three dimensions. The process of decomposition is the inverse of determining a resultant, in that the components are statically equivalent to the original force. The most common application of decomposition occurs when a given force is split into its components along three orthogonal Cartesian axes by equations such as D.4. The Cartesian axes can have any desired orientation, not necessarily north, east and vertical as in Figure 1.2, so there are clearly an infinite number of feasible decompositions of a given force. For most applications in mechanics and rock engineering the lines of action of the required components are fixed by the geometry of a particular problem, and are not necessarily orthogonal. In such cases, although the solution requires rather more computation than equations D.4, it is unique and involves determining the magnitudes and senses of the component forces along the specified lines of action.

D.4.1 Algebraic method

The direct algebraic method of force decomposition summarised in this section is based on a method presented by Priest (1985). In his method, Priest defined an additional parameter for each force which he referred to as the sense S; this parameter took a value of $+1.0$ for a downward acting force and a value of -1.0 for an upward force. This approach, which serves to formalise the down/up property of a force, will be adopted here.

A known force $\mathbf{r}$ of magnitude $|\mathbf{r}|$ trend α_r and plunge β_r, is to be decomposed into three non-coplanar, non-parallel component forces $\mathbf{u}$, $\mathbf{v}$ and $\mathbf{w}$ subject to the requirement that their trends and plunges are α_u, β_u, α_v, β_v, and α_w, β_w. Since the senses of the component forces are not known at this stage, we will take the **downward directed** line of action for each component force. Such an approach may require the application of equation D.5 to obtain the reverse direction of any orientation that has a negative plunge. Such action is never required when orientations have been plotted and measured from a lower hemisphere projection, since all orientations will have a downward sense in such cases.

The Cartesian components of the force $\mathbf{r}$, which may have a downward or an upward sense (β_r can be $+ve$ or $-ve$), are given by equations D.4 as follows

$$r_x = |\mathbf{r}| \cos \alpha_r \cos \beta_r$$
$$r_y = |\mathbf{r}| \sin \alpha_r \cos \beta_r \qquad \text{(D.7)}$$
$$r_z = |\mathbf{r}| \sin \beta_r$$

The direction cosines of the downward directed ends of each of the lines of action of the component forces are found from equations D.4 by setting the magnitude to 1.0.

The direction cosines of $\mathbf{u}$ are

$$l_x = \cos \alpha_u \cos \beta_u$$
$$l_y = \sin \alpha_u \cos \beta_u \qquad \text{(D.8)}$$
$$l_z = \sin \beta_u$$

the direction cosines of $\mathbf{v}$ are

$$m_x = \cos \alpha_v \cos \beta_v$$
$$m_y = \sin \alpha_v \cos \beta_v \qquad \text{(D.9)}$$
$$m_z = \sin \beta_v$$

and the direction cosines of $\mathbf{w}$ are

$$n_x = \cos \alpha_w \cos \beta_w$$
$$n_y = \sin \alpha_w \cos \beta_w \qquad (D.10)$$
$$n_z = \sin \beta_w$$

Our aim is to determine the unknown senses S_u, S_v, S_w and the unknown magnitudes $|\mathbf{u}|$, $|\mathbf{v}|$, $|\mathbf{w}|$ of the component forces such that $\mathbf{r} = \mathbf{u} + \mathbf{v} + \mathbf{w}$. These unknown senses and magnitudes are represented as follows

$$U = S_u\,|\mathbf{u}|$$
$$V = S_v\,|\mathbf{v}| \qquad (D.11)$$
$$W = S_w\,|\mathbf{w}|$$

The unknown Cartesian components of the forces $\mathbf{u}$, $\mathbf{v}$ and $\mathbf{w}$ are, therefore, given by Ul_x, Ul_y, Ul_z, Vm_x, Vm_y, Vm_z and Wn_x, Wn_y, Wn_z, respectively. These Cartesian components must give the components of the given vector $\mathbf{r}$, by addition as follows

$$r_x = Ul_x + Vm_x + Wn_x$$
$$r_y = Ul_y + Vm_y + Wn_y \qquad (D.12)$$
$$r_z = Ul_z + Vm_z + Wn_z$$

The above three equations contain three unknowns U, V and W. These unknowns can be found from the following application of Cramer's rule. The determinant $|A|$ of the coefficient matrix is given by

$$|A| = l_x(m_y n_z - m_z n_y) + m_x(l_z n_y - l_y n_z) + n_x (l_y m_z - l_z m_y) \quad (D.13)$$

If the determinant $|A|$ is zero then the decomposition cannot be solved. This difficulty occurs when $\mathbf{u}$, $\mathbf{v}$ and $\mathbf{w}$ are all coplanar, or when two or more of the component directions are parallel. If $|A|$ is non-zero the method proceeds with the evaluation of the determinants of the modified coefficient matrices as follows

$$|A_1| = r_x(m_y n_z - m_z n_y) + m_x(r_z n_y - r_y n_z) + n_x(r_y m_z - r_z m_y)$$
$$|A_2| = l_x(r_y n_z - r_z n_y) + r_x(l_z n_y - l_y n_z) + n_x(l_y r_z - l_z r_y) \qquad (D.14)$$
$$|A_3| = l_x(m_y r_z - m_z r_y) + m_x(l_z r_y - l_y r_z) + r_x(l_y m_z - l_z m_y)$$

Finally

$$U = \frac{|A_1|}{|A|} \quad V = \frac{|A_2|}{|A|} \quad \text{and} \quad W = \frac{|A_3|}{|A|} \qquad (D.15)$$

The signs of U, V and W give the senses of the unknown forces $\mathbf{u}$, $\mathbf{v}$ and $\mathbf{w}$, respectively, with a positive sign indicating a downward sense and a negative sign an upward sense. The absolute values of U, V and W give the magnitudes of the unknown forces $|\mathbf{u}|$, $|\mathbf{v}|$ and $|\mathbf{w}|$, respectively. The following example illustrates the application of this algebraic method for the decomposition of forces.

Example D.3 (Figure D.3)

A force $\mathbf{r}$ of magnitude 683 kN, acts along a line of trend 138° and plunge $-27°$. Find the magnitudes and senses of the components of this force that act along lines with trends/plunges of 065/62, 211/35 and 309/76.

Solution
Equation D.7 gives the x, y, z components of $\mathbf{r}$, which has an upward sense, as -452.25, 407.20 and -310.08 kN, respectively, to the nearest 0.01 kN. Labelling the three unknown forces $\mathbf{u}$, $\mathbf{v}$ and $\mathbf{w}$, and applying equations D.8 to D.10, gives the following values for the direction cosines of the downward directed ends of the lines of action:

Table for Example D.3

Force	Direction cosines of lines of action		
	x	y	z
u	0.198	0.425	0.883
v	-0.702	-0.422	0.574
w	0.152	-0.188	0.970

Equation D.13 gives $|A| = 0.4405$; equations D.14 give $|A_1| = 388.50$, $|A_2| = 253.78$ and $|A_3| = -644.31$ kN. Equation D.15 gives $U = 881.98$, $V = 576.15$ and $W = -1462.73$ kN. The force components $\mathbf{u}$ and $\mathbf{v}$ therefore have magnitudes of 881.98 and 576.15 kN, respectively, and both act downwards along the specified lines of action, since both U and V are positive. The force component $\mathbf{w}$ has a magnitude of 1462.73 kN and, since W is negative, must act upwards along the specified line of action for this force. In summary then, the component forces have trends/plunges and magnitudes of $\mathbf{u}$: 065/62, 881.98 kN, $\mathbf{v}$: 211/35, 576.15 kN and $\mathbf{w}$: 129/-76, 1462.73 kN, as plotted in Figure D.3. This solution can be checked by determining the resultant of the component vectors $\mathbf{u}$, $\mathbf{v}$ and $\mathbf{w}$, by applying the methods explained in section D.3.

D.4.2 Graphical method

The graphical method described by Priest (1985) for decomposing a known force utilises lower hemisphere projection techniques for the plotting of force vectors and the measurement of angles. Although this graphical method has

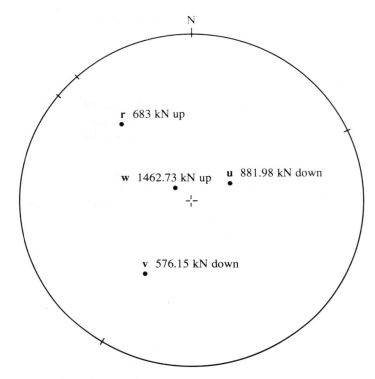

Figure D.3 Algebraic decomposition of forces, Example D.3.

the advantage of simplicity, it is only possible to decompose a given force into two components at any one time. It will be shown later in this section that this restriction does not prove to be serious when analysing the stability of rigid blocks. If the reader has not already done so, he or she is advised to consult Appendix A, which deals with hemispherical projection methods, and in particular to study the techniques for measuring internal and external angles between points that plot on a common great circle.

It is assumed that the magnitude, trend and plunge of a particular force **r** are known and that the task is to determine the magnitudes and senses of the two components **b** and **c** of this force along two lines of action whose trends and plunges are given. It is important to appreciate that since **r** is the resultant of **b** and **c** these three forces **must be coplanar**. When the orientations of the forces are plotted on a lower hemisphere projection they must, therefore, lie on a common great circle. If **r**, **b** and **c** are not coplanar the decomposition cannot proceed.

The first step in the decomposition process is to plot and to label the forces **r**, **b** and **c** on a lower hemisphere projection and to check that they lie on a

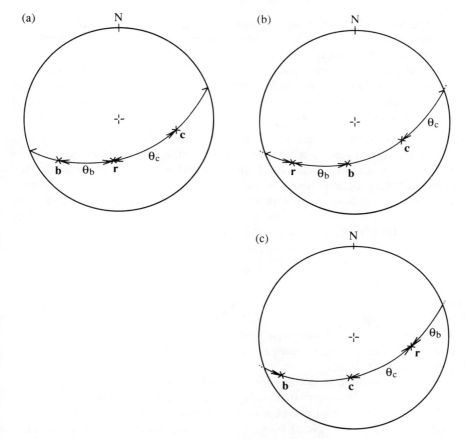

Figure D.4 Measurement of angles for the decomposition of a force into two components (after Priest, 1985).

common great circle. If the forces are coplanar the next step is to measure the angle θ_b $(0 \leqslant \theta_b \leqslant 180°)$ between **b** and **r**, and to measure the angle θ_c $(0 \leqslant \theta_c \leqslant 180°)$ between **c** and **r**, along their common great circle. These angles are measured internally or externally, depending on which force plots between the other two; a force plots between two others if it lies somewhere along their internal angle on the projection. Figure D.4, after Priest (1985) shows the three possible cases that can arise:

(a) If **r** plots between **b** and **c** (Figure D.4a) the angle θ_b is measured internally between **b** and **r**, and the angle θ_c is measured internally between **c** and **r**. The forces **b** and **c** both have the same sense as the force **r**.
(b) If **b** plots between **r** and **c** (Figure D.4b) the angle θ_b is measured

internally between **b** and **r**, but the angle θ_c is measured externally between **c** and **r**. The force **b** has the same sense as the force **r**, but **c** has the opposite sense to **r**.

(c) If **c** plots between **r** and **b** (Figure D.4c) the angle θ_b is measured externally between **b** and **r**, and the angle θ_c is measured internally between **c** and **r**. The force **b** has the opposite sense to the force **r**, but **c** has the same sense as **r**.

Priest (1985) suggested that a simple way to remember the above rules is to ensure that the angles θ_b and θ_c are measured either internally or externally to **r** so that the lines of measurement **do not overlap**. An **internal** angle is then associated with a component that has the **same** sense as **r**, while an **external** angle is associated with a component that has the **opposite** sense to **r**. The magnitudes of **b** and **c** are found by applying the sine rule to the solution of the two-dimensional vector diagram, as follows:

$$|\mathbf{b}| = \frac{|\mathbf{r}| \sin \theta_c}{\sin (\theta_b + \theta_c)} \tag{D.16}$$

$$|\mathbf{c}| = \frac{|\mathbf{r}| \sin \theta_b}{\sin (\theta_b + \theta_c)} \tag{D.17}$$

It is worth noting the somewhat counter intuitive results in equations D.16 and D.17: that $|\mathbf{b}|$ is associated with $\sin \theta_c$ in the numerator while $|\mathbf{c}|$ is associated with $\sin \theta_b$.

It is only possible to decompose a given force into two components by the above methods. However, if the angle between the two component forces is 90°, it is permissible to decompose one of the components into two further components. For example, if **b** and **c** were orthogonal it would be permissible to decompose *either* **b** *or* **c** into two further components. If **b** is selected for further decomposition, such decomposition must occur in a plane that has **c** as its normal; similarly if **c** is selected for further decomposition, this must occur in a plane that has **b** as its normal. Although such conditions may appear to be quite onerous, they occur quite routinely in the analysis of double plane sliding of rigid blocks, as discussed in section 8.4 and illustrated in the following example.

Example D.4 (Figure D.5)

The resultant **r** of gravitational, hydraulic and other forces acting on a given rigid block of rock has a magnitude of 1438 kN, and acts downwards along a line of trend 302° and plunge 74°. The underside of the block is formed by two planar discontinuities that have dip directions/dip angles of (1) 059/64 and (2) 267/53. Determine the components of the resultant force that act along the normal to each of the discontinuity planes and along the line of intersection between the two discontinuities.

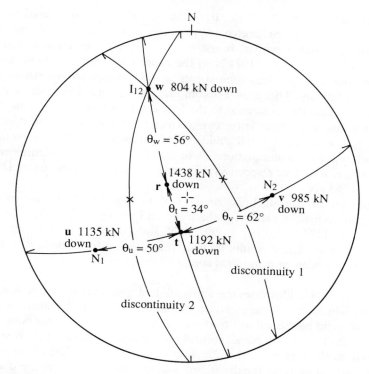

N

I_{12} × w 804 kN down

$\theta_w = 56°$

1438 kN
r • down
—|—
$\theta_t = 34°$ N_2

$\theta_v = 62°$ v 985 kN
down

u 1135 kN
down
←• $\theta_u = 50°$ t   1192 kN
N_1 down

discontinuity 1

discontinuity 2

Figure D.5 Graphical decomposition of a force into three components, Example D.4.

Solution

Figure D.5 is a lower hemisphere projection showing the resultant force **r** together with the great circles and normals to the two discontinuity planes. The three unknown force vectors have been labelled **u** (normal to plane 1, N_1), **v** (normal to plane 2, N_2) and **w** (the line of intersection between planes 1 and 2, I_{12}). These three forces act along lines with trends/plunges of 239/26, 087/37 and 340/21 (approx.), respectively. The great circle passing through N_1 and N_2, and the great circle passing through I_{12} and **r** have been constructed. These two great circles intersect to define the temporary intermediate vector **t**. It is important to note that I_{12} is the normal to the plane represented by the great circle through N_1 and N_2, and so **t**, which lies on this great circle, must be at 90° to **w**. The vectors **r**, **t** and **w** must be coplanar since they lie on the same great circle. The vectors **t**, **u** and **v** are also coplanar.

The geometrical conditions outlined in the previous paragraph make it possible to conduct the decomposition in two stages. In the first stage **r** is decomposed into component **w** acting along I_{12} and into component **t**. In this case **r** plots between **w** and **t** so these latter two vectors must have the same downward sense as r. The angles $\theta_w = 56°$ and $\theta_t = 34°$, measured from the projection to the nearest degree. Application of equations D.16 and D.17, identifying r, t and w with r, b and c respectively in these equations, gives $|w| = 804$ kN and $|t| = 1192$ kN to the nearest kN. In the second stage of decomposition t is split into components u and v which are normal to planes 1 and 2 respectively. This second decomposition is permissible because it takes place in the plane that is normal to the first component w. In this case t plots between u and v so these latter two vectors must have the same downward sense as t. The angles $\theta_u = 50°$ and $\theta_v = 62°$, measured to the nearest degree. A second application of equations D.16 and D.17, this time identifying t, u and v with r, b and c, respectively, in these equations, gives $|u| = 1135$ kN and $|v| = 985$ kN.

Application of the algebraic method of section D.4.1 to this example, adopting more precise values for the trend and plunge of I_{12} (339.94°/21.27°) gave, $|u| = 1134.9$ kN, $|v| = 992.4$ kN and $|w| = 792.7$ kN, all with a downward sense. These results indicate that the graphical methods can offer acceptable precision with minimal computational effort.

The above example illustrates the application of graphical force decomposition methods, which can be applied on a routine basis for the analysis of the stability of rigid blocks subject to double plane sliding. The force components normal to the two sliding planes control the amount of frictional shear strength mobilised on these planes, while the component along the line of intersection gives the activating force for the sliding mechanism. These ideas are discussed further in section 8.4.

Appendix E

Stress analysis

E.1 THREE-DIMENSIONAL STRESS

This appendix contains a brief review of the important fundamental principles and definitions necessary for the analysis of three-dimensional stress. Even those who are fully conversant with these principles may find it helpful to clarify the sign conventions and equations adopted in Chapter 7.

In order to specify a state of stress it is first necessary to define a set of coordinate axes. It is usually convenient to adopt geographical directions as the basis for these axes. For example Figure E.1 (a copy of Figure 1.2) shows a set of orthogonal, or Cartesian, axes in which the positive direction of the x axis is horizontal to the north, the positive y axis is horizontal to the east, and the positive z axis is downwards vertical. This is the same coordinate system adopted elsewhere in the book. It is important to note that the Cartesian coordinate system shown in Figure E.1 is right handed. The 'handedness' of a set of orthogonal axes is governed by the way in which the axes are labelled and has nothing to do with the orientation of these axes. For handedness to exist there must be a recognisable ordering in these labels, for example: x first, y second and z third. The axes in Figure E.1 are taken to be right handed because a right handed screw thread aligned parallel with the third axis will advance in the positive direction of that axis when the screw is rotated from the positive end of the first axis through the 90° angle to the positive end of the second axis. The importance of the ordering of the axes is recognised by authors who prefer to label the axes with subscripted variables such as x_1, x_2, x_3. It is important in stress transformation computations always to work with a consistent handedness of axes; most workers adopt the right

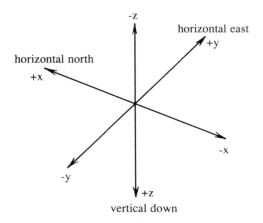

Figure E.1 Three-dimensional right handed Cartesian coordinate system, viewed from above.

handed system (Jaeger and Cook, 1979; Hoek and Brown, 1980; Brady and Brown, 1985).

In continuum mechanics, stress can be regarded as a force distributed over an infinitesimally small area within a continuous solid body. To analyse three-dimensional stress it is convenient to consider the stresses produced by forces acting on the faces of a very small cubic element within the material. It is usual to orientate the edges of the cube so that they are parallel to a system of coordinate axes such as x, y, z in Figure E.1. The force on each face of the cube can be represented in terms of its components in the x, y and z directions. Each force component, when divided by the area of the face on which it acts, gives a stress component for that face. Each face, therefore, carries three stress components — one parallel to each of the coordinate axis directions. Figure E.2 shows the stress components acting on three faces of a small cubic element viewed from above. The three faces visible in Figure E.2, orientated normal to the x, y and z axes, each have a corner at the origin. These three visible faces will, therefore, here be referred to as the origin-x, origin-y and origin-z faces; the three faces that are hidden in Figure E.2 will be referred to as the obverse-x, obverse-y and obverse-z faces.

Before proceeding with the analysis of stress it is necessary to set out clearly the nomenclature and sign convention that will be adopted. Stress, or force per unit area, is conventionally represented by the parameter σ doubly-subscripted to indicate on which plane and in which direction it acts. The first subscript gives the orientation of the normal to the plane on which the stress component acts; the second subscript gives the direction in which the stress component acts. For example σ_{xy} refers to a stress component acting in the y direction on a plane whose normal is in the x direction. The stresses σ_{xx}, σ_{yy} and σ_{zz} act

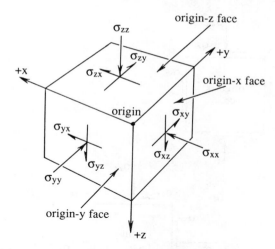

Figure E.2 Positive stress components acting on the origin faces of a small cubic element viewed from above.

along the normal to their respective planes and are referred to as **normal stresses**; the second subscript for normal stresses is sometimes omitted for the sake of brevity. The other stresses such as σ_{xy}, σ_{yz} and σ_{zx} act parallel to their respective planes and are referred to as **shear stresses**; some workers use the parameter τ instead of σ for these shear stresses.

The stresses have been represented by arrows in Figure E.2 to indicate the **positive** stress directions. The negative stress directions are found simply by reversing the arrows in Figure E.2. The following convention has been adopted:

(i) Normal stresses that tend to compress the cubic element are positive. Tensile normal stresses are negative.

(ii) If the positive normal stress on a given face acts in the **positive** direction of its coordinate axis then the positive shear stress components on that face also act in the **positive** direction of their respective coordinate axes. Conversely, if the positive normal stress on a face acts in the **negative** direction of its coordinate axis, then the positive shear stress components on that face also act in the **negative** direction of their respective coordinate axes.

For example, on the origin-x face the positive (compressive) normal stress σ_{xx} acts in the positive direction of the x axis. Consequently the positive shear stress σ_{xy} on this face also acts in the positive direction of the y axis and the positive shear stress σ_{xz} acts in the positive direction of the z axis. The convention that compressive stress is positive has been adopted because stresses in the ground are almost always compressive. Adoption of the more widely used engineering mechanics convention, that tensile stresses are positive,

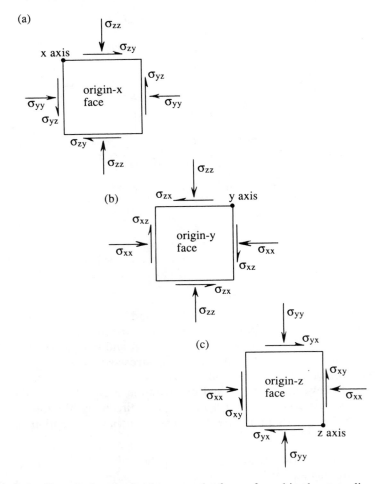

Figure E.3 Shear and normal stresses on the faces of a cubic element adjacent to (a) the origin-x face, (b) the origin-y face and (c) the origin-z face.

would require the repetitive use of negative signs to represent the most common stress state encountered in geomechanics. Adoption of the convention that compressive stresses are positive carries with it the important corollary that positive shear stresses on origin faces of the cubic element act in the positive direction of their coordinate axes. Positive shear stresses on obverse faces of the cubic element act in the negative direction of their coordinate axes.

The cubic element has six faces so it is possible to draw in 18 stress components. These components comprise three pairs of compressive normal stresses and three groups of four shear stresses. These groups of normal and shear stresses are illustrated in Figure E.3 which shows the three origin faces of the cubic element viewed along the positive direction of each coordinate axis. For example Figure E.3a shows a view along the x axis with the normal stresses σ_{zz} and shear stresses σ_{zy} acting on the adjacent horizontal faces and the normal stresses σ_{yy} and shear stresses σ_{yz} acting on the adjacent vertical faces; the stresses on the origin-x face itself are omitted.

It is implicit in the nomenclature, and necessary for static equilibrium, that the 9 stress components σ_{xx}, σ_{yy}, σ_{zz}, σ_{xy}, σ_{yx}, σ_{yz}, σ_{zy}, σ_{xz} and σ_{zx} on the origin faces are equal to those with the same labels on the obverse faces. The 18 stress components therefore comprise 9 separate terms, which are often written in matrix form as follows:

$$[\sigma] = \begin{bmatrix} \sigma_{xx} & \sigma_{xy} & \sigma_{xz} \\ \sigma_{yx} & \sigma_{yy} & \sigma_{yz} \\ \sigma_{zx} & \sigma_{zy} & \sigma_{zz} \end{bmatrix} \tag{E.1}$$

where $[\sigma]$ is the stress matrix.

In order to maintain rotational equilibrium of the elements depicted in Figure E.3 it is necessary to stipulate that in Figure E.3a $\sigma_{yz} = \sigma_{zy}$, in Figure E.3b $\sigma_{xz} = \sigma_{zx}$, and in Figure E.3c $\sigma_{xy} = \sigma_{yx}$. These equalities mean that the stress matrix is symmetrical and that there are only 6 independent stress values required to define completely the three-dimensional state of stress.

E.2 STRESS TRANSFORMATION

In order to achieve a transformation of stresses it is necessary to define a second set of coordinate axes, right handed like the one in Figure E.1 but at a different orientation and labelled in a different way. The labels l, m and n will be adopted here to define the first, second and third axes respectively of the rotated system. The l, m, n axes may be selected according to the orientation of some mine opening or major geological feature. For example the l axis may be the strike of a planar shear zone, m its line of maximum dip and n its normal. The n axis must be directed either upwards or downwards to ensure the definition of a right handed coordinate system.

The geometrical relation between the x, y, z coordinate system and the l, m, n system can be expressed in terms of the cosine of the angle δ ($0 \leqslant \delta \leqslant 180°$) between the positive ends of pairs of axes. These values, termed direction cosines, are here represented by subscripted variables. For example if δ_{lx} is the direction angle between the positive ends of the l axis and the x axis then the direction cosine is given by

$$l_x = \cos \delta_{lx}$$

The complete geometrical relation between the two sets of axes can be summarised in terms of a 3 by 3 matrix, usually called the rotation matrix $[\mathbf{R}]$ as follows

$$[\mathbf{R}] = \begin{bmatrix} l_x & l_y & l_z \\ m_x & m_y & m_z \\ n_x & n_y & n_z \end{bmatrix} \qquad (E.2)$$

The state of stress previously represented in the x, y, z system can, instead, be expressed in terms of the l, m, n system. The resulting rotated stress matrix $[\sigma^*]$ is as follows

$$[\sigma^*] = \begin{bmatrix} \sigma_{ll} & \sigma_{lm} & \sigma_{ln} \\ \sigma_{ml} & \sigma_{mm} & \sigma_{mn} \\ \sigma_{nl} & \sigma_{nm} & \sigma_{nn} \end{bmatrix} \qquad (E.3)$$

It is important to appreciate that $[\sigma]$ and $[\sigma^*]$ describe the **same state of stress**, all that has changed is the orientation of the coordinate axes. Most standard rock mechanics texts containing sections on stress analysis, such as Brady and Brown (1985), show that there is a simple relation between $[\sigma]$ and $[\sigma^*]$ as follows

$$[\sigma^*] = [\mathbf{R}] \, [\sigma] \, [\mathbf{R}]^T \qquad (E.4)$$

where

$$[\mathbf{R}]^T = \begin{bmatrix} l_x & m_x & n_x \\ l_y & m_y & n_y \\ l_z & m_z & n_z \end{bmatrix} \qquad (E.5)$$

Equation E.4 is the fundamental equation for the three-dimensional transformation of stress. The form of this equation shows that, from a mathematical point of view, stress behaves as a second order tensor in transformation. From a practical point of view it is helpful to perform the matrix multiplication in equation E.4 and to write down the results for the 6 independent stress components. Although any one of these equations can be used to generate the other five by cyclic lmn permutation, all six are presented here for completeness.

$\sigma_{ll} = \sigma_{xx}l_xl_x + \sigma_{yy}l_yl_y + \sigma_{zz}l_zl_z + \sigma_{xy}(l_xl_y + l_yl_x) + \sigma_{yz}(l_yl_z + l_zl_y) + \sigma_{zx}(l_zl_x + l_xl_z)$

$\sigma_{mm} = \sigma_{xx}m_xm_x + \sigma_{yy}m_ym_y + \sigma_{zz}m_zm_z + \sigma_{xy}(m_xm_y + m_ym_x)$
$\qquad + \sigma_{yz}(m_ym_z + m_zm_y) + \sigma_{zx}(m_zm_x + m_xm_z)$

$\sigma_{nn} = \sigma_{xx}n_xn_x + \sigma_{yy}n_yn_y + \sigma_{zz}n_zn_z + \sigma_{xy}(n_xn_y + n_yn_x) + \sigma_{yz}(n_yn_z + n_zn_y)$
$\qquad + \sigma_{zx}(n_zn_x + n_xn_z)$

$\sigma_{lm} = \sigma_{xx}l_xm_x + \sigma_{yy}l_ym_y + \sigma_{zz}l_zm_z + \sigma_{xy}(l_xm_y + l_ym_x) + \sigma_{yz}(l_ym_z + l_zm_y)$
$\qquad + \sigma_{zx}(l_zm_x + l_xm_z)$

$\sigma_{mn} = \sigma_{xx}m_xn_x + \sigma_{yy}m_yn_y + \sigma_{zz}m_zn_z + \sigma_{xy}(m_xn_y + m_yn_x)$
$\qquad + \sigma_{yz}(m_yn_z + m_zn_y) + \sigma_{zx}(m_zn_x + m_xn_z)$

$\sigma_{nl} = \sigma_{xx}n_xl_x + \sigma_{yy}n_yl_y + \sigma_{zz}n_zl_z + \sigma_{xy}(n_xl_y + n_yl_x)$
$\qquad + \sigma_{yz}(n_yl_z + n_zl_y) + \sigma_{zx}(n_zl_x + n_xl_z)$

$$\qquad (E.6)$$

It is a relatively simple matter to program equations E.6 on to a calculator or as a subroutine in a larger program.

E.3 PRINCIPAL STRESSES

It is possible to select the orientation of the l, m, n axes such that all the shear stress components, σ_{lm} etc, vanish. In this unique orientation the normal stresses are principal stresses, labelled $\sigma_1 \geqslant \sigma_2 \geqslant \sigma_3$ and referred to as the major, intermediate and minor principal stresses respectively. The following algorithm can be applied for determining these principal stresses and their orientations, termed the principal axes. The algorithm is based on determining solutions for the well known characteristic equation

$$(\sigma_p)^3 - I_1(\sigma_p)^2 + I_2\sigma_p - I_3 = 0 \qquad (E.7)$$

where I_1, I_2 and I_3 are the invariants of stress, which, for the xyz system are as follows

$$I_1 = \sigma_{xx} + \sigma_{yy} + \sigma_{zz} \qquad (E.8)$$

$$I_2 = \sigma_{xx}\sigma_{yy} + \sigma_{yy}\sigma_{zz} + \sigma_{zz}\sigma_{xx} - (\sigma_{xy})^2 - (\sigma_{yz})^2 - (\sigma_{zx})^2 \qquad (E.9)$$

$$I_3 = \sigma_{xx}\sigma_{yy}\sigma_{zz} + 2\sigma_{xy}\sigma_{yz}\sigma_{zx} - \sigma_{xx}(\sigma_{yz})^2 - \sigma_{yy}(\sigma_{zx})^2 - \sigma_{zz}(\sigma_{xy})^2 \qquad (E.10)$$

The terms I_1, I_2 and I_3 in equations E.8 to E.10 are termed 'invariants' because they depend only on the state of stress and not on the choice of axes; the same values for I_1, I_2 and I_3 would be obtained for this state of stress if it were expressed relative to the $l$mn coordinate system.

Five further intermediate parameters are defined as follows

$$J_1 = (I_1)^2 - 3(I_2) \qquad (E.11)$$

$$J_2 = (I_1)^3 - 4.5(I_1I_2) + 13.5(I_3) \qquad (E.12)$$

$$J_3 = \sqrt{|(J_1)^3 - (J_2)^2|} \qquad (E.13)$$

$$J_4 = \sqrt{J_1} \qquad (E.14)$$

$$\theta = \frac{\arctan(J_3/J_2)}{3} \qquad 0 \leqslant \theta \leqslant \pi \qquad (E.15)$$

Although the absolute value sign in equation E.13 is not strictly necessary, it does make the algorithm more robust when implemented in a computer program. The principal stresses are as follows

$$\sigma_p = \frac{I_1 + 2J_4 \cos(\theta - T)}{3} \qquad (E.16)$$

In equation E.16, and in subsequent equations, the parameter p is used to indicate quantities associated with the major (p = 1), intermediate (p = 2) and minor (p = 3) principal stresses. These three principal stresses are generated by setting the parameter T equal to 0, $2\pi/3$ and $4\pi/3$ in turn in equation E.16.

Particular values of T are not associated with any particular principal stress; for example T = 0 does not necessarily give the major principal stress. In view of this it is necessary to rank the three principal stresses to determine the major, intermediate and minor values according to $\sigma_1 \geqslant \sigma_2 \geqslant \sigma_3$.

The direction cosines p_x, p_y and p_z in the x, y, z system for the three principal axes can be found by solving the following set of equations in matrix form

$$\begin{bmatrix} (\sigma_{xx} - \sigma_p) & \sigma_{xy} & \sigma_{xz} \\ \sigma_{yx} & (\sigma_{yy} - \sigma_p) & \sigma_{yz} \\ \sigma_{zx} & \sigma_{zy} & (\sigma_{zz} - \sigma_p) \end{bmatrix} \begin{bmatrix} p_x \\ p_y \\ p_z \end{bmatrix} = 0 \qquad (E.17)$$

One approach to the solution of these equations adopted by Obert and Duvall (1967) is to take co-factors and obtain the direction ratios A_p, B_p and C_p of the principal axis p. For example taking co-factors for rows 2 and 3 of equation E.17 gives

$$\begin{aligned} A_p &= (\sigma_{yy} - \sigma_p)(\sigma_{zz} - \sigma_p) - \sigma_{yz}\sigma_{zy} \\ B_p &= \sigma_{yz}\sigma_{zx} - \sigma_{yx}(\sigma_{zz} - \sigma_p) \\ C_p &= \sigma_{yx}\sigma_{zy} - \sigma_{zx}(\sigma_{yy} - \sigma_p) \end{aligned} \qquad (E.18)$$

Noting that the magnitude M_p of the above vector $(A_p\ B_p\ C_p)$ is given by

$$M_p = \sqrt{(A_p)^2 + (B_p)^2 + (C_p)^2} \qquad (E.19)$$

gives the required direction cosines as follows

$$p_x = \frac{A_p}{M_p} \quad p_y = \frac{B_p}{M_p} \quad p_z = \frac{C_p}{M_p} \qquad (E.20)$$

Substitution of $\sigma_p = \sigma_1(p = 1)$, $\sigma_p = \sigma_2(p = 2)$ and $\sigma_p = \sigma_3(p = 3)$ in turn in equations E.18 to E.20 yields the direction cosines in the xyz system for the three orthogonal principal axes a_1, a_2 and a_3, respectively. It must be noted that equations E.18 are not entirely foolproof. For example if $\sigma_{xx} = \sigma_1 > \sigma_{yy} = \sigma_{zz} = \sigma_2 = \sigma_3$ then some of the shear stresses are zero, M_p is also zero and the direction cosines are not defined. In this case the stress state in the yz plane is hydrostatic so that all directions in this plane are principal axes. If these equations are to be programmed on a computer it is advisable to introduce checks to detect and warn of plane hydrostatic stress states such as this. Although equations E.20 always generate direction cosines for the orthogonal principal axes, these axes are not necessarily right handed if the ordering a_1, a_2, a_3 is adopted. If a right handed system for this ordering is required it is permissible to reverse the direction of one of the principal axes, by changing the sign of its three direction cosines, since there are no associated shear stresses.

References

Amadei, B. (1983) *Rock anisotropy and the theory of stress measurements, Lecture notes in Engineering,* C. A. Brebbia and S. A. Orszag (eds), Springer-Verlag, Berlin.

Amadei, B. (1988) Strength of a regularly jointed rock mass under biaxial and axisymmetric loading conditions. *International Journal of Rock Mechanics and Mining Sciences and Geomechanics Abstracts,* **25,** No. 1, 3–13.

Amadei, B. and Goodman, R. E. (1981a) A 3-D constitutive relation for fractured rock masses. *Proceedings of the International Symposium on the Mechanical Behavior of Structured Media,* A. P. S. Selvadurai (ed.), Ottawa, Part B, 249–68.

Amadei, B. and Goodman, R. E. (1981b) Formulation of complete plane strain problems for regularly jointed rocks. *Proceedings of the 22nd Symposium on Rock Mechanics,* MIT, 245–51.

Amadei, B. and Saeb, S. (1990) Constitutive models of rock joints. *Proceedings of the International Symposium on Rock Joints, Loen, Norway,* N. Barton and O. Stephansson (eds), Balkema, Rotterdam, 581–94.

Andersson, J., Shapiro, A. M. and Bear, J. (1984) A stochastic model of a fractured rock conditioned by measured information. *Water Resources Research,* **20,** No. 1, 79–88.

Archambault, G., Fortin, M., Gill, D. E., Aubertin, M. and Ladanyi, B. (1990) Experimental investigations for an algorithm simulating the effect of variable normal stiffness on discontinuities shear strength. *Proceedings of the International Symposium on Rock Joints, Loen, Norway,* N. Barton and O. Stephansson (eds), Balkema, Rotterdam, 141–8.

Aswegen, G. van (1990) Fault stability in South African gold mines. *Proceedings of the International Conference on Mechanics of Jointed and Faulted Rock,* Vienna, Austria, H. P. Rossmanith (ed.), Balkema, Rotterdam, 171–25.

Attewell, P. B. and Farmer, I. W. (1976) *Principles of Engineering Geology,* Chapman & Hall, London.

Attewell, P. B. and Sandford, M. R. (1974) Intrinsic shear strength of a brittle, anisotropic rock — I experimental and mechanical interpretation. *International Journal of Rock Mechanics and Mining Sciences and Geomechanics Abstracts*, **11**, 423–30.

Attewell, P. B. and Woodman, J. P. (1971) Stability of discontinuous rock masses under polyaxial stress systems. In *13th Symposium on Rock Mechanics, Stability of Rock Slopes*, ASCE, New York, 665–83.

Baecher, G. B. (1980) Progressively censored sampling of rock joint traces. *Journal of Mathematical Geology*, **12**, No. 1, 33–40.

Baecher, G. B. (1983) Statistical analysis of rock mass fracturing. *Journal of Mathematical Geology*, **15**, No. 2, 329–47.

Baecher, G. B. and Lanney, N. A. (1978) Trace length biases in joint surveys. *Proceedings of 19th US Symposium on Rock Mechanics*, **1**, 56–65.

Baecher, G. B., Lanney, N. A. and Einstein, H. H. (1977) Statistical description of rock properties and sampling. *Proceedings of 18th US Symposium on Rock Mechanics*, 5C1-1 to 5C1-8.

Bandis, S. C. (1990) Mechanical properties of rock joints. *Proceedings of the International Symposium on Rock Joints, Loen, Norway*, N. Barton and O. Stephansson (eds), Balkema, Rotterdam, 125–40.

Bandis, S. C., Lumsden, A. C. and Barton, N. R. (1981) Experimental studies of scale effects on the shear behaviour of rock joints. *International Journal of Rock Mechanics and Mining Sciences and Geomechanics Abstracts*, **18**, 1–21.

Bandis, S. C., Lumsden, A. C. and Barton, N. R. (1983) Fundamentals of rock joint deformation. *International Journal of Rock Mechanics and Mining Sciences and Geomechanics Abstracts*, **20**, No. 6, 249–68.

Barr, M. V. and Hocking, G. (1976) Borehole structural logging employing a pneumatically inflatable impression packer. *Proceedings of Symposium on Exploration for Rock Engineering*, Johannesburg, Balkema, Rotterdam, 29–34.

Barton, N. (1976) The shear strength of rock and rock joints. *International Journal of Rock Mechanics and Mining Sciences and Geomechanics Abstracts Rock Mechanics Review*, **13**, 255–79.

Barton, N. and Bandis, S. C. (1990) Review of predictive capabilities of JRC-JCS model in engineering practice. *Proceedings of the International Symposium on Rock Joints, Loen, Norway*, N. Barton and O. Stephansson (eds), Balkema, Rotterdam, 603–10.

Barton, N. and Choubey, V. (1977) The shear strength of rock joints in theory and practice. *Rock Mechanics*, **10**, 1–54.

Barton, N., Lien, R. and Lunde, J. (1974) Engineering classification of rock masses for the design of tunnel support. *Rock Mechanics*, **6**, 183–236.

Barton, N., Bandis, S. C. and Bakhtar, K. (1985) Strength, deformation and conductivity of rock joints. *International Journal of Rock Mechanics and Mining Sciences and Geomechanics Abstracts*, **22**, No. 3, 121–40.

Beasley, A. J. (1981) A computer program for printing geometrically accurate structural fabric diagrams. *Computers and Geosciences*, **7**, 215–27.

Bieniawski, Z. T. (1973) Engineering classification of jointed rock masses. *Transactions of the South African Institution of Civil Engineers*, **15**, 335–44.

Bieniawski, Z. T. (1976) Rock mass classifications in rock engineering. In *Exploration for Rock Engineering*, Z. T. Bieniawski (ed.) A. A. Balkema, Cape Town, **1**, 97–106.

Bieniawski, Z. T. (1989) *Engineering Rock Mass Classifications*, Wiley, Chichester.

Blyth, F. G. H. and de Freitas, M. H. (1974) *A Geology for Engineers*, 6th edition, Edward Arnold, London.

Brady, B. H. G. and Brown, E. T. (1985) *Rock Mechanics for Underground Mining*, George Allen & Unwin, London.

Bray, J. W. (1984) Personal communication.

Bray, J. W. and Brown, E. T. (1976) A short solution for the stability of a rock slope containing a tetrahedral wedge. *International Journal of Rock Mechanics and Mining Sciences and Geomechanics Abstracts*, Technical Note, **13**, 227–9.

Bridges, M. C. (1975) Presentation of fracture data for rock mechanics. *Proceedings of the 2nd Australia — New Zealand Conference on Geomechanics, Brisbane*. Institution of Engineers, Australia.

Bridges, M. C. (1990) Identification and characterisation of sets of fractures and faults in rock. *Proceedings of the International Symposium on Rock Joints, Loen, Norway*, N. Barton and O. Stephansson (eds), Balkema, Rotterdam, 19–26.

Brown, E. T. (1970) Strength of models of rock with intermittent joints. *Journal of the Soil Mechanics and Foundations Division, Proceedings of the American Society of Civil Engineers*, **96**, No. SM6, 685–704.

Brown, E. T. and Hudson, J. A. (1972) Progressive collapse of simple block jointed systems. *Australian Geomechanics Journal*, **G2**, No. 1, 49–54.

Brown, E. T. and Trollope, D. H. (1970) Strength of a model of jointed rock. *Journal of the Soil Mechanics and Foundations Division, Proceedings of the American Society of Civil Engineers*, **96**, No. SM2, 685–704.

Brown, E. T., Richards, L. R. and Barr, M. V. (1977) Shear strength characteristics of Delabole slates. *Proceedings of Conference on Rock Engineering*, Newcastle-upon-Tyne, 33–51.

Casinader, R. J. and Stapledon, D. H. (1979) The effect of geology on the treatment of the dam foundation interface at Sugarloaf dam. *13th International Congress on Large Dams*, New Delhi, Q. 48, R. 32, 591–619.

Cawsey, D. C. (1977) The measurement of fracture patterns in the Chalk of southern England. *Engineering Geology*, **11**, 210–15.

Cheeney, R. F. (1983) *Statistical Methods in Geology*, George Allen & Unwin, London.

Chelidze, T. and Gueguen, Y. (1990) Evidence of fractal fracture. *International Journal of Rock Mechanics and Mining Sciences and Geomechanics Abstracts*, Technical Note, **27**, No. 3, 223–5.

Chen, E. P. (1989) A constitutive model for jointed rock mass with orthogonal sets of joints. *Journal of Applied Mechanics, ASME*, **56**, 25–32.

Choi, S. K. and Coulthard, M. A. (1990) Modelling of jointed rock masses using the distinct element method. *Proceedings of the International Conference on Mechanics of Jointed and Faulted Rock*, Vienna, Austria, H. P. Rossmanith (ed.), Balkema, Rotterdam, 65–71.

Chryssanthakis, P. and Barton, N. (1990) Joint roughness (JRC_n) characterization of a rock joint replica at 1 m scale. *Proceedings of the International Symposium on Rock Joints, Loen, Norway*, N. Barton and O. Stephansson (eds), Balkema, Rotterdam, 471–7.

Clark, I. (1979) *Practical Geostatistics*, Applied Science, London.

Clerici, A., Griffini, L. and Pozzi, R. (1990) Procedure for the execution of detailed geomechanical structural surveys on rock masses with a rigid behavior. *Proceedings of* the *International Conference on Mechanics of Jointed and Faulted Rock*, Vienna, Austria, H. P. Rossmanith (ed.), Balkema, Rotterdam, 87–94.

Colback, P. S. B. and Wiid, B. L. (1965) The influence of moisture content on the compressive strength of rocks. *Proceedings of the 3rd Canadian Symposium on Rock Mechanics*, Toronto, 65–83.

Cruden, D. M. (1977) Describing the size of discontinuities. *International Journal of Rock Mechanics and Mining Sciences and Geomechanics Abstracts*, **14**, 133–37.

Cundall, P. A. (1971) A computer model for simulating progressive large scale movements in blocky rock systems. *Proceedings of the International Symposium on Rock Fracture*, ISRM, Nancy, Paper II-8.

Cundall, P. A. (1983) Numerical modelling of water flow in rock masses. *Geognosis*, DOE (UK) Report No. DOE/RW/83.059.

Cundall, P. A. (1987) Distinct element models of rock and soil structure. *Analytical and Computational Methods in Engineering Rock Mechanics*, E. T. Brown (ed.), George Allen & Unwin, London, 129–63.

Cundall, P. A. (1988) Formulation of a three-dimensional distinct element model — Part I. A scheme to detect and represent contacts in a system composed of many polyhedral blocks. *International Journal of Rock Mechanics and Mining Sciences and Geomechanics Abstracts*, **25**, No. 3, 107–16.

Deere, D. U. (1964) Technical description of rock cores for engineering purposes. *Rock Mechanics and Rock Engineering*, **1**, 17–22.

Donath, F. A. (1972) Strength variations and deformational behaviour in anisotropic rock. In *State of Stress in the Earth's Crust*, W. R. Judd (ed.), Elsevier, New York, 281–97.

Duncan, A. C. (1981) A review of Cartesian coordinate construction from a sphere, for generation of two-dimensional geological net projections. *Computers and Geosciences*, **7**, No. 4, 367–85.

Duncan, J. M. and Chang, C. Y. (1970) Non-linear analysis of stress and strain in soils. *Journal of the Soil Mechanics and Foundation Division of the American Society for Civil Engineers*, **96**, SM5, 1629–55.

Einstein, H. H. and Baecher, G. B. (1983) Probabilistic and statistical methods in engineering geology, specific methods and examples, part 1: exploration. *Rock Mechanics and Rock Engineering*, **16**, 39–72.

Eshwaraiah, H. V. and Upadhyaya, V. S. (1990) Influence of rock joints in the performance of major civil engineering structures. *Proceedings of the International Conference on Mechanics of Jointed and Faulted Rock*, Vienna, Austria, H. P. Rossmanith (ed.), Balkema, Rotterdam, 951–9.

Ewan, V. J. and West, G. (1981) *Reproducibility of Joint Orientation Measurements in Rock*, Department of The Environment Department of Transport, TRRL Report SR 702. Transport and Road Research Laboratory, Crowthorne.

Fisher, R. (1953) Dispersion on a sphere. *Proceedings of the Royal Society of London*, **A217**, 295–305.

Fookes, P. G. and Denness, B. (1969) Observational studies on fissure patterns in Cretaceous sediments of South-East England. *Geotechnique*, **19**, No. 4, 453–77.

Fookes, P. G. and Parrish, D. G. (1969) Observations on small-scale structural discontinuities in the London Clay and their relationship to regional geology. *Quarterly Journal of Engineering Geology*, **1**, 217–40.

Fortin, M., Archambault, G., Aubertin, M. and Gill, D. E. (1988) An algorithm for predicting the effect of a variable normal stiffness on shear strength of discontinuities. *Proceedings of the 15th Canadian Rock Mechanics Symposium, Toronto,* 109–17.

Fortin, M., Gill, D. E., Ladanyi, B., Aubertin, M. and Archambault, G. (1990) Simulating the effect of a variable normal stiffness on shear behavior of discontinuities. *Proceedings of the International Conference on Mechanics of Jointed and Faulted Rock,* Vienna, Austria, H. P. Rossmanith (ed.), Balkema, Rotterdam, 381–8.

Fossum, A. F. (1985) Effective elastic properties for a randomly jointed rock mass. *International Journal of Rock Mechanics and Mining Sciences and Geomechanics Abstracts,* Technical Note, **22**, No. 6, 467–70.

Fourmaintraux, D. (1975) Quantification des discontinuites des roches et des massifs rocheux. *Rock Mechanics,* **7**, 83–100.

Gabrielsen, R. H. (1990) Characteristics of joints and faults. *Proceedings of the International Symposium on Rock Joints, Loen, Norway,* N. Barton and O. Stephansson (eds), Balkema, Rotterdam, 11–17.

Gale, J. (1990) Hydraulic behaviour of rock joints. *Proceedings of the International Symposium on Rock Joints, Loen, Norway,* N. Barton and O. Stephansson (eds), Balkema, Rotterdam, 351–62.

Geological Society (1970) The logging of rock cores for engineering purposes. Geological Society Engineering Group Working Party Report. *Quarterly Journal of Engineering Geology,* **3**, 1–24.

Gerrard, C. (1982) Elastic models of rock masses having one, two, and three sets of joints. *International Journal of Rock Mechanics and Mining Sciences and Geomechanics Abstracts,* **19**, 15–23.

Gerrard, C. (1986) Shear failure of rock joints: appropriate constraints for empirical relations. *International Journal of Rock Mechanics and Mining Sciences and Geomechanics Abstracts,* **23**, No. 6, 421–29.

Gerrard, C. (1991) The equivalent elastic properties of stratified and jointed rock masses. *Proceedings of the International Conference on Computer Methods and Advances in Geomechanics, Cairns,* G. Beer, J. R. Booker and J. P Carter (eds), Balkema, Rotterdam, 333–7.

Goldberg, D. E. and Kuo, C. H. (1987) Genetic algorithms in pipeline optimization. *Journal of Computing in Civil Engineering,* ASCE, **1**, No. 2, 128–41.

Goodman, R. E. (1976) *Methods of Geological Engineering in Discontinuous Rocks,* West, St Paul.

Goodman, R. E. (1980) *Introduction to Rock Mechanics,* Wiley, New York.

Goodman, R. E. and Duncan, J. M. (1971) The role of structure and solid mechanics in the design of surface and underground excavations in rock. *Proceedings of International Symposium on Structure, Solid Mechanics and Engineering Design,* Part 2, Paper 105, Wiley, New York, 1379–1404.

Goodman, R. E. and Shi, G. (1985) *Block Theory and its Application to Rock Engineering,* Prentice-Hall, New Jersey.

Hart, R., Cundall, P. A. and Lemos, J. (1988) Formulation of a three-dimensional distinct element model — Part II. Mechanical calculations for motion and interaction of a system composed of many polyhedral blocks. *International Journal of Rock Mechanics and Mining Sciences and Geomechanics Abstracts,* **25**, No. 3, 117–25.

Heliot, D. (1988) Generating a blocky rock mass. *International Journal of Rock*

Mechanics and Mining Sciences and Geomechanics Abstracts, **25**, No. 3, 127–38.

Hobbs, B. E., Means, W. D. and Williams, P. F. (1976) *An Outline of Structural Geology.* Wiley, New York.

Hoek, E. (1983) Strength of jointed rock masses. *Geotechnique*, **33**, No. 3, 187–223.

Hoek, E. and Bray, J. W. (1977 and 1981) *Rock Slope Engineering*, 2nd and 3rd editions, Institution of Mining and Metallurgy, London.

Hoek, E. and Brown, E. T. (1980a) *Underground Excavations in Rock*, Institution of Mining and Metallurgy, London.

Hoek, E. and Brown, E. T. (1980b) Empirical strength criterion for rock masses. *Journal of the Geotechnical Engineering Division, Proceedings of the American Society of Civil Engineers*, **106**, No. GT9, 1013–35.

Hoek, E. and Brown, E. T. (1988) The Hoek–Brown failure criterion — a 1988 update. *Proceedings of the 15th Canadian Rock Mechanics Symposium, Rock Engineering for Underground Excavations*, Toronto, 31–8.

Huang, T. H. and Doong, Y. S. (1990) Anisotropic shear strength of rock joints. *Proceedings of the International Symposium on Rock Joints, Loen, Norway*, N. Barton and O. Stephansson (eds), Balkema, Rotterdam, 211–18.

Hudson, J. A. and La Pointe (1980) Printed circuits for studying rock mass permeability. *International Journal of Rock Mechanics and Mining Sciences and Geomechanics Abstracts*, Technical Note, **17**, No. 5, 297–301.

Hudson, J. A. and Priest, S. D. (1979) Discontinuities and rock mass geometry. *International Journal of Rock Mechanics and Mining Sciences and Geomechanics Abstracts*, **16**, 339–62.

Hudson, J. A. and Priest, S. D. (1983) Discontinuity frequency in rock masses. *International Journal of Rock Mechanics and Mining Sciences and Geomechanics Abstracts*, **20**, 73–89.

Hutson, R. W. and Dowding, C. H. (1990) Joint asperity degradation during cyclic shear. *International Journal of Rock Mechanics and Mining Sciences and Geomechanics Abstracts*, **27**, No. 2, 109–19.

Hyett, A. J. and Hudson, J. A. (1990) A photoelastic investigation of the stress state close to rock joints. *Proceedings of the International Symposium on Rock Joints, Loen, Norway*, N. Barton and O. Stephansson (eds), Balkema, Rotterdam, 227–33.

ISRM (1978) International Society for Rock Mechanics, Commission on Standardization of Laboratory and Field Tests. Suggested methods for the quantitative description of discontinuities in rock masses. *International Journal of Rock Mechanics and Mining Sciences and Geomechanics Abstracts*, **15**, 319–68.

Jaeger, J. C. (1960) Shear failure of anisotropic rocks. *Geological Magazine*, **97**, 65–72.

Jaeger, J. C. (1971) Friction of rocks and the stability of rock slopes, Rankine Lecture. *Geotechnique*, **21**, 97–134.

Jaeger, J. C. and Cook, N. G. W. (1979) *Fundamentals of Rock Mechanics*, 3rd edition, Chapman & Hall, London.

Jixian, X. Z. and Cojean, R. (1990) A numerical model for fluid flow in the block interface network of three dimensional rock block system. *Proceedings of the International Conference on Mechanics of Jointed and Faulted Rock, Vienna, Austria*, H. P. Rossmanith (ed.), Balkema, Rotterdam, 627–33.

Journel, A. G. and Huijbregts, C. J. (1978) *Mining Geostatistics*, Academic Press, London.

Kalkani, E. C. (1990) Formation of joints and faults in the south-eastern Aegean.

Proceedings of the International Conference on Mechanics of Jointed and Faulted Rock, Vienna, Austria, H. P. Rossmanith (ed.), Balkema, Rotterdam, 163–70.

Kalkani, E. C. and von Frese, R. R. B. (1979) An efficient construction of equal area fabric diagrams. *Computers and Geosciences,* 5, No. 3/4, 301–11.

Kamewada, S., Gi, H. S., Taniguchi, S. and Yoneda, H. (1990) Application of borehole image processing system to survey of tunnel. *Proceedings of the International Symposium on Rock Joints, Loen, Norway,* N. Barton and O. Stephansson (eds), Balkema, Rotterdam, 51–8.

Kaneko, K. and Shiba, T. (1990) Equivalent volume defect model for estimation of deformation behavior of jointed rock. *Proceedings of the International Conference on Mechanics of Jointed and Faulted Rock, Vienna, Austria,* H. P. Rossmanith (ed.), Balkema, Rotterdam, 277–84.

Karzulovic, A. and Goodman, R. E. (1985) Determination of principal joint frequencies. *International Journal of Rock Mechanics and Mining Sciences and Geomechanics Abstracts,* Technical Note, 22, No. 6, 471–3.

Kelker, D. and Langenberg, C. W. A. (1976) Mathematical model for orientation data from macroscopic cylindrical folds. *Journal of Mathematical Geology,* 8, No. 5, 549–59.

Kersten, R. W. O. (1990) The stress distribution required for fault and joint development. *Proceedings of the International Conference on Mechanics of Jointed and Faulted Rock, Vienna, Austria,* H. P. Rossmanith (ed.), Balkema, Rotterdam, 251–6.

Kobayashi, A. and Yamashita, R. (1990) Three dimensional flow model in fractured rock mass. *Proceedings of the International Symposium on Rock Joints, Loen, Norway,* N. Barton and O. Stephansson (eds), Balkema, Rotterdam, 639–46.

Koch, G. S. and Link, R. F. (1971) *Statistical Analysis of Geological Data,* Volume 2, Wiley, New York.

Kojima, K., Tosaka, H., Otsuka, Y., Itoh, K. and Kondoh, T. (1990) Hydraulic characterization of jointed rock masses using the 'Pulsation test'. *Proceedings of the International Symposium on Rock Joints, Loen, Norway,* N. Barton and O. Stephansson (eds), Balkema, Rotterdam, 391–6.

Krahn, J. and Morgenstern, N. R. (1979) The ultimate frictional resistance of rock discontinuities. *International Journal of Rock Mechanics and Mining Sciences and Geomechanics Abstracts,* 16, No. 2, 127–33.

Krumbein, W. C. and Graybill, F. A. (1965) *An Introduction to Statistical Methods in Geology,* McGraw-Hill, New York.

Kulatilake, P. H. S. W. and Wu, T. H. (1984a) Estimation of mean trace length of discontinuities. *Rock Mechanics and Rock Engineering,* 17, 215–32.

Kulatilake, P. H. S. W. and Wu, T. H. (1984b) Sampling bias on orientation of discontinuities. *Rock Mechanics and Rock Engineering,* 17, 243–53.

Kulatilake, P. H. S. W. and Wu, T. H. (1984c) The density of discontinuity traces in sampling windows. *International Journal of Rock Mechanics and Mining Sciences and Geomechanics Abstracts,* Technical Note, 21, No. 6, 345–7.

Kulatilake, P. H. S., Wathugala, D. N. and Stephansson, O. (1990a) Three dimensional stochastic joint geometry modelling including a verification: a case study. *Proceedings of the International Symposium on Rock Joints, Loen, Norway,* N. Barton and O. Stephansson (eds), Balkema, Rotterdam, 67–74.

Kulatilake, P. H. S., Wathugala, D. N. and Stephansson, O. (1990b) Analysis of structural homogeneity of rock mass around ventilation drift Stripa mine. *Proceedings of the International Symposium on Rock Joints, Loen, Norway*, N. Barton and O. Stephansson (eds), Balkema, Rotterdam, 75–82.

Kulhawy, F. H. (1975) Stress-deformation properties of rock and rock discontinuities. *Engineering Geology*, **8**, 327–50.

Kulhawy, F. H. (1978) Geomechanical model for rock foundation settlement. *Geotechnical Engineering Division*, ASCE, **104**, GT2, 211–27.

Kulhawy, F. H. and Goodman, R. E. (1980) Design of foundations on discontinuous rock. *International Conference on Structural Foundations on Rock*, P. J. N. Pells (ed.), Balkema, Rotterdam, 209–20.

Ladanyi, B. and Archambault, G. (1970) Simulation of shear behaviour of a jointed rock mass. *Proceedings of the 11th Symposium on Rock Mechanics*, AIME, New York, 105–25.

Lamas, L. M. N. (1986) *Statistical Analysis of the Stability of Rock Faces*, MSc Thesis, Imperial College, University of London.

La Pointe, P. R. and Hudson, J. A. (1985) Characterisation and interpretation of rock mass jointing patterns. *Geological Society of America*, Special Paper 199, 1–37.

Larson, H. J. (1974) *Introduction to Probability Theory and Statistical Inference*, 2nd edition, Wiley, New York.

Laslett, G. M. (1982) Censoring and edge effects in areal and line transect sampling of rock joint traces. *Journal of Mathematical Geology*, **14**, No. 2, 125–40.

Laubscher, D. H. (1977) Geomechanics classification of jointed rock masses — mining applications. *Transactions of the Institution of Mining and Metallurgy*, **86**, A1–8.

Laubscher, D. H. (1984) Design aspects and effectiveness of support systems in different mining situations. *Transactions of the Institution of Mining and Metallurgy*, **93**, A70–81.

Laubscher, D. H. (1990) A geomechanics classification system for the rating of rock mass in mine design. *Journal of the South African Institute of Mining and Metallurgy*, **90**, No. 10, 257–73.

Lee, Y. H., Carr, J. R., Barr, D. J. and Haas, C. J. (1990) The fractal dimension as a measure of the roughness of rock discontinuity profiles. *International Journal of Rock Mechanics and Mining Sciences and Geomechanics Abstracts*, **27**, No. 6, 453–64.

Leichnitz, W. (1985) Mechanical properties of rock joints. *International Journal of Rock Mechanics and Mining Sciences and Geomechanics Abstracts*, **22**, No. 5, 313–21.

Lemos, J. V., Hart, R. D. and Cundall, P. A. (1985) A generalised distinct element program for modelling jointed rock messes. *Proceedings of the International Symposium on Fundamentals of Rock Joints*, O. Stephansson (ed.). Centak Publishers, Lulea, 335–43.

Lin, D., Fairhurst, C. and Starfield, A. M. (1987) Geometrical identification of three-dimensional rock block systems using topological techniques. *International Journal of Rock Mechanics and Mining Sciences and Geomechanics Abstracts*, **24**, No. 6, 331–8.

Lin, D. and Fairhurst, C. (1988) Static analysis of the stability of three-dimensional blocky systems around excavations in rock. *International Journal of Rock Mechanics and Mining Sciences and Geomechanics Abstracts*, **25**, No. 3, 139–47.

Lindley, D. V. and Miller, J. C. P. (1953) *Cambridge Elementary Statistical Tables*, The University Press, Cambridge.

Long, J. C. S. (1983) *Investigation of Equivalent Porous Medium Permeability in Networks of Discontinuous Fractures*, PhD thesis, University of California, Berkeley.

Long, J. C. S., Gilmour, P. and Witherspoon, P. A. (1985) A model for steady fluid flow in random three-dimensional networks of disc-shaped fractures. *Water Resources Research*, **21**, No. 8, 1105–15.

Lorig, L. J., Brady, B. H. G. and Cundall, P. A. (1986) Hybrid distinct element–boundary element analysis of jointed rock. *International Journal of Rock Mechanics and Mining Sciences and Geomechanics Abstracts*, **23**, No. 4, 303–12.

Louis, C. (1969) *A Study of the Groundwater Flow in Jointed Rock and its influence on the Stability of Rock Masses*. Rock Mechanics Research Report No. 10, Imperial College, London.

Louis, C. (1974) *Rock Hydraulics in Rock Mechanics*, L. Muller (ed.), Springer-Verlag, Vienna.

Maerz, N. H., Franklin, J. A. and Bennett, C. P. (1990) Joint roughness measurement using shadow profilometry. *International Journal of Rock Mechanics and Mining Sciences and Geomechanics Abstracts*, **27**, No. 5, 329–432.

Mahtab, M. A. and Yegulalp, T. M. (1982) A rejection criterion for definition of clusters in orientation data. In *Issues in Rock Mechanics, Proceedings of the 22nd Symposium on Rock Mechanics, Berkeley*. R. E. Goodman and F. E. Heuze (eds), American Institute of Mining Metallurgy and Petroleum. Engineers, New York, 116–23.

Maini, Y. N. T. (1971) *In Situ Hydraulic Parameters in Jointed Rock — Fluid Measurements and Interpretation*, PhD Thesis, Imperial College, University of London.

Makiyama, J. (1979) *Tectonomechanics, an Introduction to Structural Analysis of Folded Oil-field Rocks*. Tokai University Press, Tokyo.

Makurat, A., Barton, N., Vik, G., Chryssanthakis, P. and Monsen, K. (1990) Jointed rock mass modelling. *Proceedings of the International Symposium on Rock Joints, Loen, Norway*, N. Barton and O. Stephansson (eds), Balkema, Rotterdam, 647–56.

Mardia, K. W. (1972) *Statistics of Directional Data*, Academic Press, London.

Martin, C. D., Davison, C. C. and Kozak, E. T. (1990) Characterizing normal stiffness and hydraulic conductivity of a major shear zone in granite. *Proceedings of the International Symposium on Rock Joints, Loen, Norway*, N. Barton and O. Stephansson (eds), Balkema, Rotterdam, 549–56.

Mauldon, M. (1990) Probability aspects of the removability and rotatability of tetrahedral blocks. *International Journal of Rock Mechanics and Mining Sciences and Geomechanics Abstracts*, Technical Note, **27**, No. 4, 303–7.

Mauldon, M. and Goodman, R. (1990) Rotational kinematics and equilibrium of blocks in a rock mass, *International Journal of Rock Mechanics and Mining Sciences and Geomechanics Abstracts*, **27**, No. 4, 291–301.

McLamore, R. and Gray, K. E. (1967) The mechanical behaviour of anisotropic sedimentary rocks. *Journal of Engineering for Industry, Transactions of the American Society of Mechanical Engineers*. Ser. B, **89**, 62–73.

McWilliams, P. C., Kerkering, J. C. and Miller, S. M. (1990) Fractal characterization of rock fracture roughness for estimating shear strength. *Proceedings of the International Conference on Mechanics of Jointed and Faulted Rock, Vienna, Austria*, H. P. Rossmanith (ed.), Balkema, Rotterdam, 331–6.

Meyer, P. L. (1970) *Introductory Probability and Statistical Applications*, Addison-Wesley, Amsterdam.

Meyers, A. G. (1992) *Determination of Rock Mass Strength for Engineering Design*, PhD Thesis, University of Adelaide (in preparation).

Meyers, A. G. and Priest, S. D. (1992a) A micro-processor controlled pump for triaxial cell pressure control, *International Journal of Rock Mechanics and Mining Sciences and Geomechanics Abstracts*, Technical Note, in press.

Meyers, A. G. and Priest, S. D. (1992b) A technique for moulding cylindrical discontinuous models, *Rock Mechanics and Rock Engineering*, in press.

Miller, S. M. (1979) Geostatistical analysis for evaluating spatial dependence in fracture set characteristics. *Proceedings of the 16th Symposium on the Application of Computers and Operations Research in the Mineral Industry*, T. J. O'Neil (ed.) American Institute of Mining, Metallurgical and Petroleum Engineers, 537–44.

Obert, L. E. and Duvall, W. I. (1967) *Rock Mechanics and The Design of Structures in Rock*, Wiley, New York.

Ord, A. and Cheung, C. C. (1991) Image analysis techniques for determining the fractal dimensions of rock joint and fragment size distributions. *Proceedings of the International Conference on Computer Methods and Advances in Geomechanics, Cairns*. G. Beer, J. R. Booker and J. P Carter (eds), Balkema, Rotterdam, 87–91.

Pahl, P. J. (1981) Estimating the mean length of discontinuity traces. *International Journal of Rock Mechanics and Mining Sciences and Geomechanics Abstracts*, **18**, 221–8.

Papaliangas, T., Lumsden, A. C., Hencher, S. R. and Manolopoulou, S. (1990) Shear strength of modelled filled rock joints. *Proceedings of the International Symposium on Rock Joints, Loen, Norway*, N. Barton and O. Stephansson (eds), Balkema, Rotterdam, 275–82.

Paterson, B. R., Ramsay, G. and Jennings, D. N. (1988) Design and construction of the Maniototo Scheme Paerau Diversion, *Proceedings of 5th Australia — New Zealand Conference on Geomechanics*, The Institution of Engineers Australia, Sydney, 591–7.

Paterson, M. S. (1978) *Experimental Rock Deformation — the Brittle Field*, Springer-Verlag, Berlin.

Patton, F. D. (1966) Multiple modes of shear failure in rock. *Proceedings of the 1st International Congress of Rock Mechanics*, **1**, Lisbon, 509–13.

Pereira, J. P. (1990) Shear strength of filled discontinuities. *Proceedings of the International Symposium on Rock Joints, Loen, Norway*, N. Barton and O. Stephansson (eds), Balkema, Rotterdam, 283–7.

Petit, J.-P. and Barquins, M. (1990) Fault propagation in Mode II conditions: comparison between experimental and mathematical models, applications and natural features. *Proceedings of the International Conference on Mechanics of Jointed and Faulted Rock, Vienna, Austria*, H. P. Rossmanith (ed.), Balkema, Rotterdam, 213–20.

Phien-wej, N., Shrestha, U. B. and Rantucci, G. (1990) Effect of infill thickness on shear behavior of rock joints. *Proceedings of the International Symposium on Rock Joints, Loen, Norway*, N. Barton and O. Stephansson (eds), Balkema, Rotterdam, 289–94.

Phillips, F. C. (1971) *The Use of Stereographic Projection in Structural Geology*, 3rd Edition, Edward Arnold, London.

Pine, R. J. (1991) *Risk analysis design applications in mining*. Research Applications in the Mining Industry, University of Nottingham, October 1991.

Piteau, D. R. (1970) Geological factors significant to the stability of slopes cut in rock. In *Symposium on Planning Open Pit Mines*, South African Institute of Mining and

Metallurgy, Johannesburg, 33–53.

Piteau, D. R. (1973) Characterizing and extrapolating rock joint properties in engineering practice. *Rock Mechanics Supplement*, **2**, 5–31.

Price, N. J. (1966) *Fault and Joint Development in Brittle and Semi-Brittle Rock*, Pergamon, Oxford.

Priest, S. D. (1975) *Geotechnical Aspects of Tunnelling in Discontinuous Rock with Particular Reference to the Lower Chalk*, PhD thesis, University of Durham, Durham, UK.

Priest, S. D. (1976) Ground movements caused by tunnelling in chalk. *Proceedings of the Institution of Civil Engineers*, **61**, Part 2, 23–39.

Priest, S. D. (1980) The use of inclined hemisphere projection methods for the determination of kinematic feasibility, slide direction and volume of rock blocks. *International Journal of Rock Mechanics and Mining Sciences and Geomechanics Abstracts*, **17**, 1–23.

Priest, S. D. (1983) Computer generation of inclined hemisphere projections. *International Journal of Rock Mechanics and Mining Sciences and Geomechanics Abstracts*, Technical Note, **20**, 43–7.

Priest, S. D. (1985) *Hemispherical Projection Methods in Rock Mechanics*, George Allen and Unwin, London.

Priest, S. D. and Brown, E. T. (1983) Probabilistic stability analysis of variable rock slopes., *Transactions of the Institution of Mining and Metallurgy*, **92**, A1–12.

Priest, S. D. and Hudson, J. A. (1976) Discontinuity spacings in rock. *International Journal of Rock Mechanics and Mining Sciences and Geomechanics Abstracts*, **13**, 135–48.

Priest, S. D. and Hudson, J. A. (1981) Estimation of discontinuity spacing and trace length using scanline surveys. *International Journal of Rock Mechanics and Mining Sciences and Geomechanics Abstracts*, **18**, 183–97.

Priest, S. D. and Samaniego, J. A. (1983) A model for the analysis of discontinuity characteristics in two dimensions. *Proceedings of 5th ISRM Congress*, ISRM, Melbourne, F199–F207.

Priest, S. D. and Samaniego, J. A. (1988) The statistical analysis of rigid block stability in jointed rock masses. *Proceedings of 5th Australia–New Zealand Conference on Geomechanics*, The Institution of Engineers Australia, Sydney, 398–403.

Ragan, D. M. (1985) *Structural Geology, an Introduction to Geometrical Techniques*, 3rd Edition, Wiley, Chichester.

Ramsay, J. G. (1967) *Folding and Fracturing of Rocks*. McGraw-Hill, New York.

Reeves, M. J. (1985) Rock surface roughness and frictional strength. *International Journal of Rock Mechanics and Mining Sciences and Geomechanics Abstracts*, **22**, No. 6, 429–42.

Regan, W. M. and Read, J. R. L. (1980) Geological aspects of the design and construction of reservoir inlet and draw-off channels, Sugarloaf Reservoir Project. *Proceedings of 3rd Australia–New Zealand Conference on Geomechanics*, The New Zealand Institution of Engineers, Wellington, 2.15–2.20.

Reik, G. and Zacas, M. (1978) Strength and deformation characteristics of jointed media in true triaxial compression. *International Journal of Rock Mechanics and Mining Sciences and Geomechanics Abstracts*, **15**, 295–305.

Rissler, P. (1978) *Determination of the Water Permeability of Jointed Rock*. English Edition of Volume 5, Institute for Foundation Engineering Mechanics, Rock

Mechanics and Waterways Construction, RWTH University, Aachen.

Roberds, W. J., Iwano, M. and Einstein, H. H. (1990) Probabilistic mapping of rock joint surfaces. *Proceedings of the International Symposium on Rock Joints, Loen, Norway*, N. Barton and O. Stephansson (eds), Balkema, Rotterdam, 681–91.

Romero, S. U. (1968) *In situ* direct shear tests on irregular surface joints filled with clayey material. *Proceedings of the International Symposium on Rock Mechanics*, ISRM, Madrid, **1**, 189–94.

Rosengren, K. J. (1970) Diamond drilling for structural purposes at Mount Isa. *Industrial Diamond Review*, **30**, No. 359, 388–95.

Ross-Brown, D. M. and Walton, G. (1975) A portable shear box for testing rock joints. *Rock Mechanics*, **7**, 129–53.

Rouleau, A. and Gale, J. E. (1985) Statistical characterisation of the fracture system in the Stripa Granite, Sweden. *International Journal of Rock Mechanics and Mining Sciences and Geomechanics Abstracts*, **22**, No. 6, 353–67.

Sadagah, B. H., Sen, Z. and De Freitas, M. H. (1990) A mathematical representation of jointed rock masses and its application. *Proceedings of the International Conference on Mechanics of Jointed and Faulted Rock, Vienna, Austria*, H. P. Rossmanith (ed.), Balkema, Rotterdam, 65–70.

Sagar, B. and Runchal, A. (1982) Permeability of fractured rock: effect of fracture size and data uncertainties. *Water Resources Research*, **18**, 266–74.

Samaniego, J. A. (1985) *Fluid Flow through Discontinuous Rock Masses: a Probabilistic Approach*, PhD Thesis, Imperial College, University of London.

Samaniego, J. A. and Priest, S. D. (1984) The prediction of water flows through discontinuity networks into underground excavations. *Proceedings of Symposium on the Design and Performance of Underground Excavations*, Cambridge, International Society for Rock Mechanics, 157–64.

Sattarov, S. S., Veksler, Y. U. A. and Shesnokov, S. A. (1990) Holographic methods in evaluating rock mass structure. *Proceedings of the International Conference on Mechanics of Jointed and Faulted Rock, Vienna, Austria*, H. P. Rossmanith (ed.), Balkema, Rotterdam, 323–7.

Schaeben, H. (1984) A new cluster algorithm for orientation data. *Journal of Mathematical Geology*, **16**, No. 2, 139–53.

Sen, Z. (1990) RQP, RQR and fracture spacing. *International Journal of Rock Mechanics and Mining Sciences and Geomechanics Abstracts*, Technical Note, **27**, No. 2, 135–7.

Sen, Z. and Kazi, A. (1984) Discontinuity spacing and RQD estimates from finite length scanlines. *International Journal of Rock Mechanics and Mining Sciences and Geomechanics Abstracts*, **21**, No. 4, 203–12.

Shamir, G., Zoback, M. D. and Cornet, F. H. (1990) Fracture-induced stress heterogeneity: examples from the Cajon Pass scientific drillhole near the San Andreas Fault, California. *Proceedings of the International Symposium on Rock Joints, Loen, Norway*, N. Barton and O. Stephansson (eds), Balkema, Rotterdam, 719–24.

Shanley, R. J. and Mahtab, M. A. (1976) Delineation and analysis of clusters in orientation data. *Journal of Mathematical Geology* **8**, No. 3, 9–23.

Sharp, J. C. (1970) *Flow through Fissured Media*, PhD Thesis, Imperial College, University of London.

Sharp, J. C. and Maini, Y. N. T. (1972) Fundamental considerations on the hydraulic characteristics of joints in rock. *Proceedings Symposium on Percolation through Fissured*

Rock, Stuttgart, International Society for Rock Mechanics, T1F, 1–15.

Skinas, C. A., Bandis, S. C. and Demiris, C. A. (1990) Experimental investigations and modelling of rock joint behaviour under constant stiffness. *Proceedings of the International Symposium on Rock Joints, Loen, Norway*, N. Barton and O. Stephansson (eds), Balkema, Rotterdam, 301–8.

Smith, G. N. (1986) *Probability and Statistics in Civil Engineering*, Collins, London.

Snow, D. T. (1968) Rock fracture spacings, openings and porosities. *Journal of Soil Mechanics and Foundations, Division of the American Society for Civil Engineers*, 94, SM1, 73–91.

Snow, D. T. (1970) The frequency and apertures of fractures in rock. *International Journal of Rock Mechanics and Mining Sciences and Geomechanics Abstracts*, 7, 23–40.

Spencer, E. W. (1969) *Introduction to the Structure of the Earth*, McGraw-Hill, New York.

Strafford, R. G., Herbert, A. W. and Jackson, C. P. (1990) A parameter study of the influence of aperture variation on fracture flow and the consequences in a fracture network. *Proceedings of the International Symposium on Rock Joints, Loen, Norway*, N. Barton and O. Stephansson (eds), Balkema, Rotterdam, 413–22.

Sun, Z., Gerrard, C. and Stephansson, O. (1985) Rock joint compliance tests for compression and shear loads. *International Journal of Rock Mechanics and Mining Sciences and Geomechanics Abstracts*, 22, No. 4, 197–213.

Swan, G. and Zongqi, S. (1985) Prediction of shear behaviour of joints using profiles. *Rock Mechanics and Rock Engineering*, 18, 183–212.

Terzaghi, R. D. (1965) Sources of error in joint surveys. *Geotechnique*, 15, 287–304.

Till, R. (1974) *Statistical Methods for the Earth Scientist: an Introduction*, Macmillan, London.

Tsang, Y. W. and Tsang, C. F. (1990) Hydraulic characterization of variable-aperture fractures. *Proceedings of the International Symposium on Rock Joints, Loen, Norway*, N. Barton and O. Stephansson (eds), Balkema, Rotterdam, 423–31.

Tse, R. and Cruden, D. M. (1979) Estimating joint roughness coefficients. *International Journal of Rock Mechanics and Mining Sciences and Geomechanics Abstracts*, 16, 303–7.

Tsoutrelis, C. E., Exadactylos, G. E. and Kapenis, A. P. (1990) Study of the rock mass discontinuity system using photoanalysis. *Proceedings of the International Conference on Mechanics of Jointed and Faulted Rock, Vienna, Austria*, H. P. Rossmanith (ed.), Balkema, Rotterdam, 103–12.

Underwood, E. E. (1967) Quantitative evaluation of sectional material. *Proceedings 22nd International Congress for Stereology*, Chicago, 49–60.

Villaescusa, E. (1991) *A Three Dimensional Model of Rock Jointing*, PhD Thesis, University of Queensland.

Villaescusa, E. and Brown, E. T. (1990) Characterizing joint spatial correlation using geostatistical methods. *Proceedings of the International Symposium on Rock Joints, Loen, Norway*, N. Barton and O. Stephansson (eds), Balkema, Rotterdam, 115–22.

Wallis, P. F. and King, M. S. (1980) Discontinuity spacings in a crystalline rock. *International Journal of Rock Mechanics and Mining Sciences and Geomechanics Abstracts*, 17, 63–6.

Warburton, P. M. (1980a) A stereological interpretation of joint trace data. *International Journal of Rock Mechanics and Mining Sciences and Geomechanics*

Abstracts, **17**, 181–90.

Warburton, P. M. (1980b) Stereological interpretation of joint trace data: influence of joint shape and implications for geological surveys. *International Journal of Rock Mechanics and Mining Sciences and Geomechanics Abstracts*, **17**, 305–16.

Warburton, P. M. (1981) Vector stability analysis of an arbitrary polyhedral rock block with any number of free faces. *International Journal of Rock Mechanics and Mining Sciences and Geomechanics Abstracts*, **18**, 415–27.

Warburton, P. M. (1983) Applications of a new computer model for reconstructing blocky rock geometry — analysing single block stability, and identifying keystones. *Proceedings of 5th International Congress on Rock Mechanics*, ISRM, Melbourne, F225–F230.

Warburton, P.M. (1985) A computer program for reconstructing blocky rock geometry and analysing single block stability. *Computers and Geosciences*, **11**, 707–12.

Warburton, P. M. (1987) Implications of keystone action for rock bolt support and block theory. *International Journal of Rock Mechanics and Mining Sciences and Geomechanics Abstracts*, **24**, No. 5, 283–90.

Warburton, P.M. (1990) Laboratory test of a computer model for blocky rock. *International Journal of Rock Mechanics and Mining Sciences and Geomechanics Abstracts*, Technical Note, **27**, No. 5, 445–52.

Watson, G. S. (1966) The statistics of orientation data. *Journal of Geology*, **74**, 786–97.

Whitten, D. G. A. and Brooks, J. R. V. (1972) *A Dictionary of Geology*, Penguin, Harmondsworth.

Whitten, E. H. T. (1966) *Structural Geology of Folded Rocks*. Rand McNally and Co., Chicago.

Wickham, G. E., Tiedemann, H. R. and Skinner, E. H. (1972) Support determinations based on geologic predictions. *Proceedings 1st North American Rapid Excavation and Tunneling Conference*, AIME, New York, **1**, Chapter 7, 43–64.

Wicksell, S. D. (1925) The corpuscle problem I: a mathematical study of a biometric problem. *Biometrika* **17**, 84–99.

Wicksell, S. D. (1926) The corpuscle problem II: a case of ellipsoid corpuscles. *Biometrika* **18**, 151–72.

Witherspoon, P. A., Wang, J. S. Y., Iwai, K. and Gale, J. E. (1980) Validity of cubic law for fluid flow in a deformable rock fracture. *Water Resources Research*, **16**, No. 6, 1016–24.

Xiurun, G. and Shuren, F. (1991) Model of regularly jointed rock mass with consideration of the influence of couple stresses. *Proceedings of the International Conference on Computer Methods and advances in Geomechanics, Cairns*, G. Beer, J. R. Booker and J. P Carter (eds), Balkema, Rotterdam, 327–32.

Yoshinaka, R. and Yamabe, T. (1986) Joint stiffness and the deformation behaviour of discontinuous rock. *International Journal of Rock Mechanics and Mining Sciences and Geomechanics Abstracts*, **23**, No. 1, 19–28.

Yow, J. L. (1987) Blind zones in the acquisition of discontinuity orientation data. *International Journal of Rock Mechanics and Mining Sciences and Geomechanics Abstracts*, Technical Note, **24**, No. 5, 317–8.

Yu, X. and Vayssade, B. (1990) Joint profiles and their roughness parameters. *Proceedings of the International Symposium on Rock Joints, Loen, Norway*, N. Barton and O. Stephansson (eds), Balkema, Rotterdam, 781–5.

Zhang Xing and Liao Guohua (1990) Estimation of confidence bounds for mean trace length of discontinuities using scanline surveys. *International Journal of Rock Mechanics and Mining Sciences and Geomechanics Abstracts*, Technical Note, **27**, No. 3, 207–12.

Zimmerman, R. W., Chen, D. W. and Long, J. C. S. (1990) Hydromechanical coupling between stress, stiffness and hydraulic conductivity of rock joints and fractures. *Proceedings of the International Symposium on Rock Joints, Loen, Norway*, N. Barton and O. Stephansson (eds), Balkema, Rotterdam, 571–7.

Zongqi, S. and Xu, F. (1990) Study of rock joint surface feature and its classification. *Proceedings of the International Symposium on Rock Joints, Loen, Norway*, N. Barton and O. Stephansson (eds), Balkema, Rotterdam, 101–7.

Answers to exercises

Note: In order to facilitate checking and to minimise round-off errors, some of these answers have been quoted to more significant figures than the geological nature of the input data would normally warrant. Extreme caution should be exercised when claiming particular levels of precision in the results of discontinuity analysis for rock engineering.

1.1 Trend/plunge of normal are 337/28. Strike of plane is 067°.

1.2 (i) magnitude = 1.0, trend/plunge = 108/74
    (ii) magnitude = 2.0, trend/plunge = 249/−38

1.3 (i) 0.229, 0.797, −0.559
    (ii) 0.495, −0.142, 0.857

1.4 The angle between the lines is 40°.

1.5 Trend/plunge of the line of intersection is 263/52.

2.1 Sample size $N = 100$, class interval $\Delta = 0.05\,\text{m}$, discontinuity frequency $\lambda = 9.96\,\text{m}^{-1}$.

Mid-point of class, x m	Observed frequency in class	Theoretical frequency $N\Delta\lambda e^{-\lambda x}$
0.025	41	38.8
0.075	27	23.6
0.125	12	14.3
0.175	8	8.7
0.225	5	5.3
0.275	2	3.2
0.325	1	2.0
0.375	2	1.2
0.425	0	0.7
0.475	2	0.4

2.2 Termination index is approximately 28%.

2.3

Mid-point of 1 m range m	Observed number of discontinuities in range
0.5	8
1.5	13
2.5	7
3.5	12
4.5	8
5.5	5
6.5	8
7.5	9
8.5	12
9.5	16

For $h = 1.0\,m$, $\gamma(h) = 8.11\,m^{-2}$. For $h = 2.0\,m$, $\gamma(h) = 8.31\,m^{-2}$.

2.4 The Rock Mass Rating is approximately 40 ± 10 depending on the interpretation of the descriptive data.

3.1 The x,y coordinates for points representing the normals are, respectively, (i) -2.75, $-9.59\,mm$ and (ii) -18.18, $25.02\,mm$.

3.2 (i) At a cone angle of $5°$, $c = 0.0038$ and the smallest value of t for which $P(>t, c) \leqslant 0.0038$ is 5, when $P(>t, c) = 0.0018$, hence $t_{crit} = 5$. (ii) At a cone angle of $10°$, $c = 0.0152$ and the smallest value of t for which $P (>t, c) \leqslant 0.0158$ is 10, when $P (>t, c) = 0.0134$, hence $t_{crit} = 10$.

3.3 (i) The normalised weighting factors are 0.997, 1.143, 1.753, 0.887, 0.650 and 0.570 for the six discontinuities, (ii) Fisher's constant is 22.5 and (iii) the dip direction/dip angle of the mean plane are approximately 220/48. Note: calculations are performed on the discontinuity normals.

3.4 (i) Fisher's constant for the set is 15.765 by equation 3.20, (ii) the expected number of discontinuity normals that should lie within $5°$ and $10°$ of the true normal are 3.96 and 14.48, respectively, by equation 3.24 and (iii) the angular radii for the zones of 80% and 95% confidence are $3.24°$ and $4.43°$, respectively, by equation 3.29.

4.1 The expected total number of discontinuity intersections is approximately 84.

4.2 (i) Total discontinuity frequency along a vertical sampling line is $7.08\,m^{-1}$, (ii) global minimum frequency is $2.26\,m^{-1}$ along the line of intersection between sets 1 and 4 of trend $168.2°$, plunge $24.9°$ and (iii) global maximum frequency is $7.32\,m^{-1}$ along a line of trend $041.0°$, plunge $74.9°$.

4.3

Inter-cusp zone	Digit strings: negative sign indicates that the normal is reversed
(i)	1,2,3,4 and −1,−2,−3,−4
(ii)	−1,2,3,4 and 1,−2,−3,−4
(iii)	1,−2,3,4 and −1,2,−3,−4
(iv)	1,2,−3,4 and −1,−2,3,−4
(v)	1,2,3,−4 and −1,−2,−3,4
(vi)	1,2,−3,−4 and −1,−2,3,4
(vii)	1,−2,−3,4 and −1,2,3,−4

4.4 Discontinuity frequency is approximately $4.1\,m^{-1}$.

5.1 (i) Discontinuity frequency is $12.5\,m^{-1}$, (ii) for 80% confidence, RQD range is 59.7 to 68.2%; for 90% confidence the range is 57.0 to 70.0% and (iii) approximately 54 pieces are longer than 0.1 m; approximately 15 pieces are longer than 0.2 m.

5.2 (i) Ignoring drilling breaks and discontinuities of uncertain origin, the band-widths are 0.096 to 0.116 m for 90% confidence, and 0.094 to 0.118 m for 95% confidence, (ii) the required sample size is 600 so a further 34 m of borehole is required and (iii) taking a discontinuity frequency of $10\,m^{-1}$, approximately 46% of the 1 m lengths will contain either 9, 10, 11 or 12 discontinuities.

5.3 There is an approximately 20% probability that the rock will be classified as 'very good'.

5.4 Expected RQD is 88.6%. (i) Approximately 172 additional discontinuities; (ii) approximately 14 of the 86 runs will contain less than 8 discontinuities.

6.1 $F(a) = \dfrac{4}{s_m\sqrt{\pi}}\left(\sqrt{a} - \dfrac{a}{s_m\sqrt{\pi}}\right)$ $j(a) = \dfrac{4}{s_m\sqrt{\pi}}\left(\dfrac{1}{2\sqrt{a}} - \dfrac{1}{s_m\sqrt{\pi}}\right)$

When $s_m = 10\,m$ and $a = 20\,m^2$, $F(a) = 0.755$ so there is 75.5% probability that $a \leqslant 20\,m^2$.

6.2 Estimated values of μ_L are (i) negative exponential 2.4 m, (ii) uniform 3.6 m, and (iii) triangular 3.2 m.

6.3 Same answers as Exercise 6.2.

6.4 Estimated values of mean trace length μ_L are: negative exponential 5.88 m, uniform 5.17 m, and triangular 5.30 m.

6.5 Estimated values of μ_L are (i) negative exponential 3.70 m, (ii) uniform 6.23 m, and (iii) triangular 5.30 m. The large number of trace lengths observed to be shorter than 8.5 m has produced the smaller estimate for μ_L based on the negative exponential distribution. Approximately 91 traces shorter than 8.5 m would have given the same result as the previous exercise for this distribution. The converse applies for the uniform distribution; approximately 115 traces shorter than 8.5 m would have given the same result as the previous exercise for this distribution.

6.6 Assuming that the trace length distribution is the same along the dip direction of the inclined joints, and ignoring intersections with the top of the slope, the probabilities that none of the n joints extend the 38 m to the next fault are 0.85, 0.72 and 0.61 for n = 1, 2 and 3, respectively.

7.1 The trends, plunges of the specified axes are l: 344.6°, −25.7°, m: 267.4°, 24.7° and n: 215.0°, −53.0°. Note that the l and n axes each have an upward sense.

7.2 Rotated stresses for the l, m, n system are $\sigma_{ll} = 14.92$, $\sigma_{mm} = 13.47$, $\sigma_{nn} = 12.41$, $\sigma_{lm} = -0.72$, $\sigma_{mn} = 2.68$, and $\sigma_{nl} = -3.53$ MPa.

7.3 (i) Normal stress = 9.07 MPa, (ii) shear stress along line of maximum dip = -1.60 MPa, shear stress along strike = 6.62 MPa and (iii) peak shear stress = 6.81 MPa along a line of trend/plunge 177/12. The shear strength is 5.24 MPa so slip will occur.

7.4 (i) Principal stresses are 32.15, 15.54 and 0.00 MPa, (ii) normal stress = 10.04 MPa, shear stress along line of maximum dip = 5.17 MPa, shear stress along strike = -5.35 MPa, (iii) peak shear stress = 7.44 MPa (along a line of trend/plunge 101/17) and (iv) factor of safety against localised bedding plane slip = 1.13.

7.5 The region of the discontinuity at distances d between 0.572 and 1.710 m down dip from point A will be unable to sustain the continuum stress distribution predicted by the Kirsch equations.

8.1 (i) Block weight is 1199 kN (ii) shear capacity is 677 kN (iii) factor of safety is 1.11 (note: $r_w = 0.4165$).

8.2 (i) Block weight is 1107 kN (ii) effective normal stress is 67 kPa (iii) factor of safety is 1.36.

8.3 Collapse pressure is 242 kPa.

8.4

Block	Potential failure mechanism	Sliding direction if unstable trend/plunge
1,2,3	Falling vertically	—
1,2,4	Sliding on plane 1	024/46
1,2,5	Sliding on plane 1	024/46
1,3,4	Insignificant block	—
1,3,5	Sliding on plane 5	325/52
1,4,5	Sliding on planes 1 and 5	006/44
2,3,4	Falling vertically	—
2,3,5	Falling vertically	—
2,4,5	Inclined upwards	—
3,4,5	Sliding on plane 5	325/52

8.5 (i) Resultant force: trend/plunge 283/72, 1556 kN downwards, (ii) predicted to slide on discontinuities 1 and 2 and (iii) factor of safety for this mechanism is 1.62.

9.1 (i) JRC = 6.8 (ii) predicted shear strength = 289 kPa.

9.2 Predicted axial major principal stress for failure of the rock material = 29.43 MPa. Predicted axial major principal stresses for slip along discontinuities 1, 2, 3 and 4 are 43.66, 54.53, 20.79 and 27.68 MPa, respectively. The specimen is predicted to fail by slip along discontinuity 3 at an axial stress of 20.79 MPa.

9.3 Taking m_i = 10, and applying the computed uniaxial compressive strength for the intact rock to each specimen separately, gives R_m = 0.17 and s = 0.004.

9.4 The uniaxial compressive strength of the rock material is 66.28 MPa. The uniaxial compressive strength of the rock mass is, by the Hoek–Brown criterion, predicted to be 16.53 MPa so local yield is likely to occur. Minimum support pressure (σ_3) required to prevent yield is 0.2 MPa.

10.1 Initial aperture e_i ≈ 0.476 mm, initial tangent normal stress stiffness $k_{ni,tan}$ ≈ 6.15 MPa mm^{-1}, maximum normal displacement Δv_{max} ≈ 0.58. At a normal displacement Δv of 0.2 mm, normal stress σ_n ≈ 2.015 MPa and tangent stiffness $k_{n,tan}$ ≈ 16.48 MPa mm^{-1}. The secant stiffness is given by $\sigma_n/\Delta v$ ≈ 10.07 MPa mm^{-1}.

10.2 The shear strength τ_f = 1.274 MPa, the stiffness number k_j = 2.11 MPa mm^{-1} and the initial tangent shear stiffness $k_{si,tan}$ = 2.873 MPa mm^{-1}. The predicted relative shear displacements at shear stresses of 0.4, 0.8 and 1.2 MPa are 0.185, 0.548 and 1.591 mm, respectively.

10.3 (i) The equivalent Young's modulus E_e along the normal to a set of parallel discontinuities is 3.134 GPa; (ii) the equivalent Young's modulus E_e for randomly orientated discontinuities is 16.93 GPa.

10.4

Discon	θ Deg	σ_n MPa	τ MPa	τ_f MPa	Δv_{max} mm	$k_{ni,tan}$ MPa mm^{-1}	Δv mm	$k_{si,tan}$ MPa mm^{-1}	Δu mm
P	40	12.56	8.86	10.22	0.195	13.73	0.161	93.93	0.294
Q	25	16.79	6.89	13.92	0.222	17.10	0.181	216.2	0.052
R	10	19.46	3.08	14.51	0.170	12.52	0.153	57.14	0.065

The vertical components of displacement on discontinuities P,Q and R are 0.312, 0.186 and 0.162 mm, respectively. Vertical compression of the rock material is 0.19 mm. Total vertical compression of the discontinuous specimen is 0.850 mm. The equivalent Young's modulus for the discontinuous specimen is approximately 6.7 GPa.

11.1 (i) Conductance is $8.62 \times 10^{-9} \, m^2 \, s^{-1}$ and (ii) estimated flow is 1.14 litres per day.

11.2 Discontinuity frequencies are 20.5, 16.4, 12.3, 8.3 and $4.2 \, m^{-1}$. Effective hydraulic aperture is consistently approximately 50 microns.

11.3 Average effective hydraulic aperture is 212 microns. Total water flow into the creek and its gorge is approximately 294 Ml per year.

11.4 Rate of water inflow that could be expected at this section is approximately 356 litres per hour per metre run of tunnel.

Index

Page numbers given in italic refer to tables, those given in bold refer to figures